A

D1154009

WESTERN AND CENTRAL EUROPE
A Regional Geography

WESTERN AND CENTRAL EUROPE

A Regional Geography

BY

E. W. SHANAHAN, M.A., D.Sc.(Econ.)

MACMILLAN

London · Melbourne · Toronto

ST MARTIN'S PRESS

New York

1965

MACMILLAN AND COMPANY LIMITED
Little Essex Street London WC2
also Bombay Calcutta Madras Melbourne

THE MACMILLAN COMPANY OF CANADA LIMITED
70 Bond Street Toronto 2

ST MARTIN'S PRESS INC
175 Fifth Avenue New York NY 10010

PRINTED IN GREAT BRITAIN

PREFACE

THIS book is arranged in two parts each on a similar regional basis. A line through and joining the Alps and the Pyrenees marks off the western Mediterranean area from North-Western and Central Europe but for a small extension of the former in south-eastern France. These two major sub-divisions of Peninsular Europe differ broadly not only in their climatic conditions and physical resources, but also in the origins and character of their peoples; and for this and other reasons they are treated as separate units, though the inter-relationships are noted as occasion arises.

North-Western and Central Europe comprises a group of countries the peoples of which have much in common in their geographical milieux and external relations, their economic and political development and their heritage of civilisation. Though this group covers less than a third of the area of the continent, it contains upwards of half the population. Its main geographical interest lies in the intensive utilisation by its active peoples of varied, but relatively limited productive resources, supplemented by world-wide trade connections; and inasmuch as these characteristics are most pronounced in the peoples of North-Western Europe and of Germany and Switzerland in Central Europe, their lands and their economic development are treated here in greater detail than those of the inner borderlands, Finland, western Poland, Bohemia-Moravia and Austria. The contributions which the former have made to the material progress and cultural enlightenment of the world have been great in proportion to their number. Their marked individualism as nations, which may have assisted their creative powers, though now weakening under economic pressures, is still strong enough to justify the treatment of their countries each as a distinct entity.

The earlier development in the western Mediterranean lands of advanced civilisations, inherited largely from sources farther east, was followed by relative stagnation in modern times. The scanty fuel and power resources of the Iberian Peninsula and Italy, other than the recently developed hydro-electric of the Alpine ranges, hindered the growth of industry in them during the period of great expansion

based on coal in North-Western and Central Europe. The peoples of
these lands have accordingly had to depend in the main on various
forms of cultivation for their livelihoods, as they still do over large
parts. In these pursuits however, they are subject in a peculiar
measure to a variety of physical controls which are in consequence of
special significance in the human geography; more than in the regions
north of the Alpine system the purely controlling conditions constitute the major themes of geographical interest in the Mediterranean
lands.

In the course of the following general and regional chapters in each
Part, attempts have been made to present in understandable forms the
structural bases of the existing complex physical settings and the
relationships between them and the agricultural, industrial and urban
development of the areas as wholes and of the several countries. Where
the spatial element of location or areal differentiation seems important,
the descriptive matter has been illustrated by maps and diagrams, in a
number of which use has been made of the abundant statistical and
similar data available for recent years, to add quantitative precision to
the mapping of areal distributions; nearly all the large coalfields,
for example, are further defined by the worked areas, those of active
collieries; and the distribution of crops and live-stock as well as of
populations, is often indicated on a proportionate percentage basis. In
view of current changes, particularly in economic conditions, the
numerical data used in illustrations, and the statistical and the related
descriptive matter embodied in the text, have been selected and
brought as near up to date as possible, almost all within the period
1956–60. Little except incidental reference is made to air transport,
for the routes are commonly independent of surface features, and the
development of services is consequent upon, rather than contributory
to, the growth of particular urban centres.

Features and topics covering the entire areas are treated in the early
chapters in each Part. In the following regional accounts also the
larger geographical units are first surveyed comprehensively and then
described according to their natural or political sub-divisions. This
form of arrangement has appeared logical and desirable to indicate at
the outset how the various parts of those larger and more complex
areas fit together, even though this has involved some risk of occasional repetition between the general and the particular.

The whole has been framed to meet the requirements of more advanced scholars, especially those oversea, as well as for others who may

wish to have reasonably up-to-date information on the geographical-
economic shape of this highly significant part of the world. The
British Isles, forming, as they do, an integral part of North-Western
Europe, are treated accordingly in the general chapters, and at least as
fully in the regional chapters as comparable continental countries.

In the preparation of this survey much useful material has been
obtained from United Nations and numerous other official publications and reports, as well as from the works of various leading British,
American and European continental writers, selections of which are
given in the appended bibliography. I have been especially indebted
to the Map Department of the Royal Geographical Society, to the
National Coal Board and to the Information branches of British and
West European Government Offices in London for access to primary
material, and also to Mr. J. C. Larkinson of Wallington Grammar
School for much valuable, critical constructive help.

1964   E.W.S.

CONTENTS

Part I

North-Western and Central Europe

Part II

The Western Mediterranean:
The Iberian Peninsula and Italy

LIST OF DIAGRAMS AND MAPS

Part I

NORTH-WESTERN AND
CENTRAL EUROPE

Chapter 1

THE LAND: ITS RESOURCES AND PEOPLES

THE continent of Europe falls into three major parts readily distinguishable from one another. Its main framework consists of Russia and the adjoining lands westward to the Vistula and southward to the lower Danube. In the remaining peninsular parts the Mediterranean lands form a definite geographical entity, leaving a north-western broken triangular area most of which drains into the Atlantic and its marginal seas. Ready access to the sea from this section of the continent, and the predominant Atlantic influence upon its climate as far east as central Germany, give it a measure of geographical distinctiveness. These features, together with its varied natural resources, have contributed to the development of external connections and the economic advancement of its peoples, who for several centuries were notable for their maritime activities and their oversea trade and colonisation.

As trade returns and other statistical data are commonly available only by countries, it is convenient to follow political boundaries where possible in determining the landward limits of the area as a whole. A line through the Gulf of Bothnia, thence along the Oder-Neisse and the highland boundaries of Germany with Bohemia and south-west into the Alps, marks off the outer parts of North-Western and Central Europe comprising the British Isles, France, Switzerland, the Benelux countries, West and East Germany and the Scandinavian countries, from the inner borderlands, namely Finland, western Poland, Bohemia-Moravia and Austria. The former, having numerous external connections and being generally more advanced, are of chief importance; the latter, transitional in their situations and their political and economic relations between outer maritime Europe and the eastern continental block, have for these and other reasons been somewhat hampered in development. These two groups cover the whole of North-Western Europe as usually understood, and most, if not all, of Central Europe.[1]

[1] What constitutes Central Europe has been debated, depending on the basis of demarcation. West and East Germany, German Switzerland, Austria, Bohemia-Moravia

In addition to special aptitudes for maritime pursuits, the peoples of this northern part of peninsular Europe have developed other traits in common that distinguish them in particular from the inhabitants of Eastern Europe. A significant factor has been that in earlier times they had much closer contacts with the Mediterranean lands, which were the cradle of European civilisation. Roman institutions and culture spread with the expansion of the Empire northwards into Britain and eastwards to the Rhine and the upper Danube. Though much of this civilisation was later submerged, the Roman Catholic Church, with its insistence upon Latin, and its organisation centralised on Rome, was instrumental in fostering a revival of Roman traditions and Mediterranean civilisation throughout Western and much of Central Europe.

This cultural heritage rendered the peoples of these lands receptive to the great mental stimulus born of the Renaissance, reinforced by the opening up of the world in the Age of Discovery; whereas the people of Eastern Europe, acknowledging the Greek Orthodox Church, long remained secluded and backward. Profiting by these advantages arising from their situation, Western Europeans developed early in the modern age active, enquiring minds, freed from the fetters of tradition, that enabled them to give a lead in material progress and social organisation, by scientific discoveries and by regard for individual freedom. The backthrust of these advances into the Mediterranean lands has been relatively weak, at all events on the material side, owing largely to their poverty in fuel resources, and to the scarcity of productive land to support increasing populations.

The area comprising North-Western and Central Europe together with the inner transitional lands covers less than one-third of the continent, about 1 million sq. miles, although it contains upwards of half the total population. It consists of a patchwork of sixteen political units and parts of such, twelve in the outer group and four inner ones. This extraordinary fragmentation has originated mainly from a marked regional and ethnographical differentiation; it has been reinforced by the persistent desire for independence of each group of people (or peoples), moulded together by their geographical environment, united by a common historical tradition, and thereby distinguished from neighbouring groups. Thus identified each national group has hitherto preferred to go its own way, to work out its own cultural and

and western Poland are to be included by general consent. Definitions of Central Europe by various authorities are examined at some length by K. A. Sinnhuber in *I.B.G. Transactions*, 1954.

economic development, whatever the material advantages of political union with another or other states might be.

Successive waves of human migration have pushed into this section of Europe northwards by land and sea from the western Mediterranean, and westwards from the Anatolian-Caspian region, both in prehistoric times and since. These have contributed to a broad differentiation in the present-day population between the descendants of the three main ancestral types — the tall, fair Nordic longheads, the dark Alpine roundheads, and the normally short and dark Mediterranean longheads. Extensive long-continued intermixture, however, especially on the northern side of the Alpine ethnic wedge, has resulted in a wide variety among individuals in many parts, and also in a mixture of racial characteristics in the same persons. The mid-European mainly lowland zone has for millenia been a melting-pot of peoples of diverse origins entering it in successive streams of migration. There the process of fusion is well advanced, especially in the western lands, France and Britain; though even there 'islands' of autochthonous population have survived from early migrations in relatively inaccessible and uninviting parts such as the central Welsh Highlands and the Basque country of the western Pyrenees.

Regional differentiation has, however, been superimposed upon this general process of racial fusion, operating in a contrary direction. North-Western and West Central Europe contain within their relatively small area an unusual variety of geographical environments, many of which have stamped their inhabitants with distinct characteristics of speech and personality. As the French writer H. Taine has remarked, 'Le sol forme le type'. In rural areas especially, this differentiation tends to persist, supported by a kind of local patriotism; and this in spite of fluidity of movement that has come in the recent age of highly developed transport. Industrialisation, it is true, tends to break down the conservative separatism of the inhabitants of distinctive local areas (equivalent to the French *pays* or German *Gau*) by draining off the younger and more adventurous to the cities. Nevertheless, such groups as remain in comparative isolation remote from the main nerve centres of their respective countries, for example the Bretons of France, the Lapps of Scandinavia, the Highlanders of Scotland, preserve their separate identities, the products of ethnic heritage as moulded by environmental conditions. Significantly, migrants from such parts to others are conscious for long of being uprooted.

The rich pattern of geographical milieux in this North Atlantic section of Europe has contributed much to the vigour and adaptability of its peoples. Continuous internal movement has prevented stagnation. Interchange of ideas has furthered material and intellectual progress, outstanding not only in the larger countries, France, Britain and Germany, where both ethnic and environmental integration is far advanced, but also in the smaller countries, Sweden, the Netherlands and Switzerland among others, that have had numerous external contacts.

Further stimulating impulses have come from maritime connections. These have been favoured by the inter-penetrating marginal seas in the north and by the Mediterranean in the south, and by the many tidal-estuary harbours at the mouths of the Atlantic rivers, notably the Rhine and Elbe, themselves commonly navigable upstream for some distance. As no part of Western and West Central Europe is distant or cut off from the open seas, except for some inland mountain valleys, its peoples have long been conscious of, and have answered a call to the outer world. Utilising first their abundant supplies of oak timber, and later their generous endowments of iron ore and smelting fuels, they have for at least four centuries led the world in shipbuilding and in sea-borne trade. This leadership in navigation, engineering and commerce enabled a number of them to build up large colonial empires, and to spread their form of civilisation over several continents; and though West European overseas domination is dwindling, its civilisation remains a vital force in the non-European world, and itself draws stimulating impulses from without through manifold external contacts and intermovement of people.

PRODUCTIVE RESOURCES

Mingling of racial stocks and favourable conditions for maritime expansion would by themselves have been a slender basis for the growth of an advanced civilisation in Western Europe. The essential foundations have been the wealth of natural resources in fertile land, forests and minerals, the comparative ease of movement by land routes, the reliably moderate precipitation, and the generally equable temperatures, free from extremes that tend to enforce seasonal interruptions in production, yet sufficiently cool and varied in seasonal rhythm to stimulate the human organism to the exercise of foresight and full output of energy.

In the early stages of the development of a civilisation, productive agricultural land, encouraging permanent settlement and yielding some surplus above mere subsistence, sets the train of progress in motion. It enables people to live together in groups in which new ideas may spread by human contacts, where material resources can be accumulated, and where technical discoveries and improvements can take root and grow. The peoples of North-Western and Central Europe have been favoured by nature in that the large extent of lowlands between the Caledonian and the Alpine highlands contains a considerable proportion of fertile soils, and is well suited in its climatic conditions for raising a wide variety of crops and farm animals.

The source of many West European food and fodder plants, other than potatoes and maize (both from the New World), was apparently the Aral-Caspian region, though some are believed to have originated in Iran and in Abyssinia. These, especially the grains and roots, have been adapted, in their westward transference via Central Europe or the Mediterranean lands, to the more humid and milder climate of the Atlantic borderlands. They have also, both en route and since, been greatly improved as food producers by selective breeding. It is noteworthy that Western Europe has been the leading source of most of the varieties of field crops and strains of domestic animals introduced into the extensive temperate lands of North America and the Southern Hemisphere.

The generally dense deciduous and mixed forests, which originally covered much of the now fully settled parts of North-Western Europe, long held man at bay. The main track of early westward movement and settlement lay north of the central highland blocks along the unforested or only lightly forested stretches of the loess belt leading to the likewise relatively open chalk uplands in the west. The forests on either side were avoided, and were cleared only very gradually. In the modern age the remaining forests have been valuable sources of fuel for metallurgical industries and of timbers for all kinds of constructional purposes including shipbuilding; and though charcoal has been displaced by coke for smelting ores, and timber by steel in the construction of ships, the demand for wood is greater than ever, owing to the enormously increased consumption of paper and other pulp products. But inasmuch as forests and farmland are mutually exclusive, the continued growth of population in Western Europe as a whole has given rise to competition in the demands for food and for timber for the use of the available land. This competition would have been much sharper in Western Europe than it has been, had not large imported supplies of timber and timber products been available, especially from North America. As a result, forests, whether indigenous, replanted after cutting, or newly planted by afforestation, have been relegated to lands of low agricultural value. The relative proportions of land devoted to forests and to farms tend to fluctuate in the long run (less so in the short run) in keeping with the economic principle of equi-marginal returns from these two alternative uses.

North-Western and Central Europe has been endowed with a wealth of mineral resources, great in comparison with areas of similar size in other continents. Its relative poverty in precious metals is outweighed by large deposits of iron ore, common salt, potash salts, and kaolin, in addition to extensive supplies of coal, lignite and waterpower. It has also had significant deposits of copper, tin, zinc and lead ores, though these, except the copper ores in the Baltic region,[1] have been largely worked out after over two thousand years of exploitation. The key minerals have been and are iron ore and coking coal. These have been Nature's greatest contribution which, combined with the West European genius for scientific discovery and mechanical invention, have given rise to an extraordinary technical development in the last couple of centuries, greater than any before in human history. Once iron and steel could be cheaply produced, as they were first in Western Europe with Britain in the lead, machines of many kinds could be made and engines to work them. Thenceforward a cumulative process of material progress was set in motion. For the human energy released by machines from manual toil was in part employed in devising further technical advances, in building up capital assets in the form of equipment embodying these advances, and in establishing world-wide trade relations based on cheap bulk transport by land and sea. Large-scale specialised industry, assisted in its development by the transport system which it created, arose in that part of Europe a couple of centuries ago. Though still vigorous enough, it is now rivalled by its North American offshoot endowed with greater natural resources.

UNIFYING GEOGRAPHICAL FRAMEWORK

Though this segment of Europe comprises an unusual variety of distinctive regions and developed resources, yet nature has given its million square miles a basic geographical unity. Inter-communication throughout is physically easy, by systems of transport now fully de-

[1] See pp. 313–14.

veloped. Variety of terrain, of interlocking lands and seas, of high-lands and lowlands and contrasted geological formations compacted together, has facilitated rather than hindered internal movement. Between the broken Caledonian highland system in the extreme north-west and the Alpine chains in the south, likewise interrupted (at the Gulf of Lions), no mountains high and continuous enough to be uninhabitable intervene to hamper communications at all seriously or to bar the penetration of Atlantic air masses into the heart of the continent. Such highlands as do interrupt the surface of the central plains are the much-worn wreckage of the Armorican-Hercynian chains, now broken into fragments and surviving as denuded horsts; they are intersected in places by the valleys of rivers antecedent to the secondary uplift of these horsts in the Alpine orogenesis. Thus navigation on the longer continental rivers is little impeded by rapids; nor is it interrupted by winter freezing except on rare occasions.

Much of North-Western and Central Europe consists, in fact, of lowlands sloping gently towards, and draining into the chain of seas from the mouth of the English Channel to the Inner Baltic, the result of submergence in geologically recent time. This basin-form lie of the land in relation to the sea corridor contributes to the comparatively small difference in winter temperatures between, for example, southern Germany and southern Finland, some 15° farther north. For these seas, containing considerable bodies of water, not only themselves exert a modifying influence upon extremes of temperature, but also induce the passage of depressions and their associated warm sectors over the adjoining lands. Moreover, since bulk transport of goods is more economical by waterways than by land, these seas serve as an arterial commercial highway, inter-connecting by longitudinal and transverse shipping routes all the lands that adjoin them. They, as much as the lie of the land relief, give an element of unity to Western and Central Europe. In this respect they are paralleled by the Mediter-ranean, over which, however, they have the advantage that inland movement from their generally low shores is much easier.

INTERNAL AND EXTERNAL TRADE RELATIONS

The broad similarity in climate over North-Western and West Central Europe precludes any considerable inter-state trade in *diverse* agricultural products. Apart from the long-established export trade in wines from France to the northern countries, there is nothing to parallel the large movements of produce from south to north in the eastern United States, for example. Population, in 1963 totalling some 270 million, has increased in each of the sixteen countries to such numbers that their *net* agricultural surplus is, with the exceptions of Denmark and the Irish Republic, either small or negative. The erstwhile Baltic trade in grain has ceased. The major classes of food products still exported are the dairy-farm group and beef cattle, the former from Denmark and the Netherlands,[1] the latter from the Irish Republic, in each case as the result of specialisation in response to a combination of physical and economic conditions.

In mineral and power resources on the other hand, and also in the manufactures developed on the basis of these resources, the countries of North-Western and Central Europe contain considerable diversity. Minerals give rise to extensive commerce between surplus and deficiency countries within the area, especially in coal, iron ore and natural salts. But a greater engine of trade is specialisation in manufactures, based upon natural advantages where these exist, or even in their apparent absence in some places, according to the varieties of industrial skills and techniques inherent in, or developed by the peoples of the various countries and regions.

The full possibilities of the potentially rich pattern of internal trade in this section of Europe have hitherto been far from realised. It may be that the individualist economic policies commonly followed by most West European countries arise from the fact that diversity in productive capacities among them owes more to human factors than to natural resources. However, the pressure of external developments is forcing the abandonment of nationalist economic practices in Western Europe. Neither customs barriers nor political separatism seem likely to be as obstructive to trade between the member countries as they have been in the past. The Organisation for European Economic Co-operation (O.E.E.C.) was set up in 1948 to develop economic co-operation between member countries, the Council of Europe with headquarters in Strasbourg in 1949, and the European Payments Union (E.P.U.) in 1950, these three including almost all West European countries. Further steps towards economic federation have been taken by the formation in 1947 of the Benelux Customs Union (comprising Belgium, the Netherlands and Luxembourg), and

---

[1] The large Danish and Dutch exports of dairy produce etc. to countries of similar climates such as Britain and Germany, which have also extensive dairy industries, are mainly the outcome of specialised human factors, and in this and other ways resemble manufactured products. See Chapters 19, 23.

by the establishment in 1952 of the European Coal and Steel Community (E.C.S.C.) covering France, Western Germany and Italy together with the Benelux group. These co-operative arrangements were followed by the decision of the E.C.S.C. countries to establish a Common Market by mutual reduction of tariffs from January 1959. It is true to say that some progress in the same direction was made in 1961–3 during the unsuccessful negotiations of the United Kingdom to join the Common Market group, negotiations which involved the interests of other countries in the European Free Trade Association. These economic associations, and others for defence, may be forerunners of political federation at some future time, towards which the Council of Europe gave some promise, but it has yet no binding authority over its members.

INDUSTRY AND AGRICULTURE

An outstanding feature of the economies of the majority of the countries of North-Western and Central Europe is the development of manufactures. Those even that have only scanty or negligible power resources — the Irish Republic, Denmark and Luxembourg — have managed with the help of imported fuels to establish manufactures which supply part of their domestic requirements and some specialised products for export. In Denmark, for example, just over 28% of the working population were employed in industry in 1953 and only 23% in farming; in Luxembourg 39% and 26% respectively, and both these countries export significant quantities of manufactured goods; from the Netherlands, often thought of as a country of farmers and horticulturists, the exports of manufactured products are nearly equal in value to those of the farming and horticultural industries combined. Alone among the dozen or so countries of North-Western Europe, the Irish Republic has a much higher proportion of the active population occupied in farming than in industry — still over twice as great — though industry has expanded rapidly in recent years.

The apparent loss of farm workers to industry in these countries of Europe does not mean that agriculture is declining; on the contrary, agricultural output has increased in all of them since 1940. What has happened there is merely an illustration of the general economic trend in all the more advanced countries of the world. Agricultural production per man-hour has risen through developments such as mechanisation, pest control, and the increased supplies and the more effective use of fertilisers; moreover some forms of the processing of agricultural products have been transferred from the farms to the factories.

In order to maintain the relatively high standard of living enjoyed by the peoples of Western Europe, large quantities of foodstuffs, fodders, raw materials and oil fuels need to be imported from other parts of the world. Their cost is in the main offset by the value of the services rendered by the human factors incorporated in the manufactured products exported. North-Western Europe is the chief focus of world trade. Broadly speaking, its peoples depend for their livelihoods upon selling the products of their factories in exchange for raw materials and foodstuffs from the non-European parts of the world. Factories require adequate and reliable supplies of fuel and power; and though this area of Europe has come to depend increasingly upon imported petroleum for industrial and transport purposes, as a whole it provides the great bulk of its fuel and power requirements from its own resources of solid fuels and hydro-electricity.

Iron ore and salt are key minerals in modern industry as the bases, the former of steel manufacture and engineering of all kinds, the latter of the chemical group of industries. North-Western and Central Europe has extensive deposits and large outputs of both these minerals, though its great iron, steel, shipbuilding and engineering industries require supplementary supplies of iron ore from external sources. For detailed figures of production of these basic minerals and also of sources of fuel and power, see Tables pp. 26, 27.

The long-established agricultural industry is practised in its several branches wherever possible throughout these lands (see chapter 5), generally by intensive methods and up to the margins of cultivation.[1] The area of productive land per head of the population is definitely too small to provide food enough in the climate of North-West Europe, and at the standard of living realised by its peoples. The deficiency is most marked in cereals such as wheat, in fats and oils, and in concentrated fodders such as maize. Great Britain is least able among West European countries to meet its food and fodder requirements, but even those countries that export large quantities of dairy and allied products, import from overseas sources much wheat for

[1] The proportions of *arable* land to total land area expressed as percentages are as follows—Denmark 64·3, West Germany 38·7, France 38·6, Belgium 34·4, Netherlands 33·0, United Kingdom 30·0, Austria 21·1, Irish Republic 17·8, Switzerland 11·1, Sweden 9·2, Finland 8·2, Norway 2·53. Some countries, in particular the United Kingdom, the Irish Republic and France, have in addition large areas of meadow land and rough grazings.

human consumption, and fodders for cattle, pigs and poultry. Among continental countries those most dependent upon imported supplies to supplement those from domestic farms are West Germany, Norway, Belgium, Sweden and Switzerland.

In textile fibres, hides and skins and similar raw materials of agricultural origin, these countries are deficient in varying degrees, due allowance being made for the exports of finished products containing these materials. All the cotton and jute, most of the raw silk, much of the flax and large quantities of wool, hides and skins are obtained from external sources. The production of food crops has the first claim upon the relatively scarce fertile agricultural land. It is not even economical to grow on the farms all the fodder requirements of their live-stock complements.

In the economies of these European countries, as elsewhere in the world, but more significantly in them, manufacturing industry assists the agricultural in a kind of partnership; by securing additional imported supplies of fodders and fertilisers for use by farmers, in exchange for its exported industrial products; by preparing, or releasing as by-products, large quantities of artificial fertilisers essential to the highly intensive farming; by producing a variety of labour-saving agricultural machinery and appliances, as well as transport equipment. Were it not for all this contribution from the industrial group, the agricultural industries of Western and West Central Europe would be unable to provide the major part of the food requirements of 270 million people.

The overall unbalance between industry and agriculture in this area causes its inhabitants to depend directly or indirectly upon foreign trade, in order to maintain essential supplies of foodstuffs and other consumer goods, more than those of any comparable area in the world. Almost all the fodders and considerable proportions of the fibres and metals imported are used as materials in producing goods retained for consumption within the area; similarly much of the large imports of petroleum is consumed in internal transport. Payment for all these requirements, for imported materials embodied in exports of manufactures and also for various imported industrial products must be met largely by the visible items of exports. All this inward and outward movement of goods results in an unusually large foreign trade per capita; world peace is all the more essential for the prosperity of the West European peoples.

Chapter 2

THE PHYSICAL FRAMEWORK

In physical build North-Western and Central Europe is a complex area composed of a skeleton of mountain systems and peneplains of various ages, with lowland connections of which the larger parts fall away into the marginal seas on the continental shelf. On the north-west margin bordering the Atlantic, the Caledonian highlands extend from northern Norway to western Ireland with breaks in the Atlantic approaches to the North and Irish Seas. These have been thrust up in Scandinavia on the western border of the ancient Baltic Shield, which extends eastwards into north-west Russia. In the medial zone between these elements and the new-folded Alpine chains in the south, the broken remnants of the Armorican-Hercynian highlands lie scattered at intervals from south-west Ireland through France, Belgium and Germany to Bohemia, and appear also as elevated massifs within the Alpine system (see pp. 16, 427).

The complex disposition of relief features in this segment of Europe is the heritage of an extremely long and varied geological history, successive episodes in which have contributed structural elements from Pre-Cambrian to late Quaternary. The framework of the area is largely the product of post-Cambrian orogenic and epeirogenic movements[1] combined with the ceaseless processes of erosion. Some of the features produced by earlier movements of this kind have survived and the more distinctive features of later ones have become inter-twined in complex pattern with them. In the central and north-western parts of the continent ancient highlands, after being reduced by prolonged erosion to base level, have been re-elevated, and thus been given a new lease of existence.

In early Pre-Cambrian[2] times folded mountains were elevated in the region of the Baltic Shield in a geosyncline which was situated off the eastern margin of the former North Atlantic continent known as

---

[1] Orogenic movements (orogeneses) result in extensive mountain building, epeirogenic movements in widespread uplift or depression.

[2] See p. 19 for general outline of the geological sequence.

Atlantis. The mountains were peneplaned by subsequent prolonged erosion, and the area was later repeatedly re-elevated and peneplaned. Composed, therefore, of ancient highly resistant crystalline and metamorphic rocks comprising granite, gneiss and schists, it has remained a relatively stable shield area. In the middle Palaeozoic era a further orogenesis raised the so-called Caledonides with a NE.–SW. alignment, out of a geosyncline between the Baltic Shield and Atlantis. These, like the Baltic Shield, were reduced by erosion, but survived as re-elevated masses, highest where they have been partially overthrust on older land-masses in Scandinavia and Scotland, of lower elevation and in places broken into scattered residual mountain blocks, as in north-west Ireland. Other related highlands lie south-west of this main Caledonian system in the British Isles, at intervals round the Irish Sea, among them the Southern Uplands, the Mourne Mountains and the Welsh and Wicklow massifs.

The close of the Carboniferous period witnessed yet another phase of intense folding, which resulted in the elevation of great mountain ranges out of the geosyncline that lay in a broad belt from south-west Ireland through France and central Germany to Bohemia. The mountains so formed constituted the Armorican-Hercynian system. Most of these were reduced during the Mesozoic era almost to peneplanes, but under the stresses of the Alpine orogenesis were rent by numerous faults, and broken into a series of upthrust blocks known as horsts, separated by down-faulted troughs. Volcanic activity accompanied this process of piecemeal elevation in many places, e.g. in Auvergne and in the Taunus-Vogelsberg region of Germany; and this together with active sub-aerial erosion during and subsequent to re-elevation has given many parts of the Hercynian highlands a broken relief with deeply incised river valleys.

The composite name Armorican-Hercynian denotes the two distinct axes of late Carboniferous folding in the once extensive mountain system, which, at its widest from the Sauerland in Germany to the Central Plateau of France inclusive, occupied a zone over 500 miles from north to south. In the south-west peninsulas of Ireland and England, in south Wales and Brittany, the axes of the anticlines and synclines follow a general E.–W. trend, the term Armorican being adopted from the Roman name for Brittany. Thence eastwards the trend lines turn south-east across the River Loire into the northern parts of the Central Plateau, where they meet the NE.–SW. Hercynian axes more or less at right angles. These, called after the Roman epithet Hercynia applied to the forests on the highlands east of the Rhine, appear in the north-eastern part of the Massif Central, in the Ardennes and the plateaux adjoining the Rhine, and in other uplands of central Germany.

The relatively recent Alpine upheaval of mid-Tertiary age developed in Europe in the extensive geosynclinal trough, then situated between the already consolidated Europe to the north and the massive African continental block to the south. This trough was occupied by a sea called Tethys, a wider and larger predecessor of the present Mediterranean. The Alpine system shows evidence of intense pressures from the south, exerted by the pincers movement of the African continent against the stable, though relatively less resistant elements of older Europe. Overthrusts with multiple recumbent folds developed on a stupendous scale, notably in the Swiss-Italian Alps, incorporating Hercynian remnants such as those of the Mt. Blanc and St. Gotthard massifs; while the rocks of the floor of Tethys in the root zone, squeezed vertically upwards under the immense pressures, became plastic and metamorphic, and now form together with the Hercynian remnants the extended high crystalline belt which is the main watershed of the Alps (Fig. 55). A similar crystalline belt appears in the eastern Pyrenees.

Though the main forces of the great Alpine earth-storm were expended in a zone round and just north of the present Mediterranean Sea, their associated swell spread north-west over Western Europe and beyond its present limits. Not only were the peneplaned Hercynian remnants much disturbed by differential vertical movements, but the former Atlantis that lay between the Caledonian front and Greenland, became shattered and eventually foundered except for a few island remnants. These displacements, like those in the Hercynian zone, were accompanied by volcanic activity with outpourings of basalt lava, as in Antrim and western Scotland, to which also the island remnants such as Iceland, the Faeroes and Rockall owe their existence. The extensive Jurassic and Cretaceous sediments laid down in a wide zone north-west of the Hercynian system were also disturbed, being flexed by compression into a series of wave-like structures carved later by subsequent streams into scarplands, e.g. in the Paris Basin and the Weald.

Thus the present land-forms of Western Europe are largely the product of the Alpine upheavals and dislocations. Except perhaps for the Caledonides in the north-west, the highlands and uplands owe their existence by folding and compression, by faulting and re-elevation, to this Alpine revolution; and to this also parts of the plains, e.g. the inner London and Paris Basins, indirectly owe their existence as dry land, having escaped submergence by reason of their cover of late Tertiary sediments formed from the waste of those newly created or recreated highlands. The pattern of the drainage system has likewise been set by the Alpine orogenesis. The larger mainland rivers flow in general on north-westerly courses either from the new folded

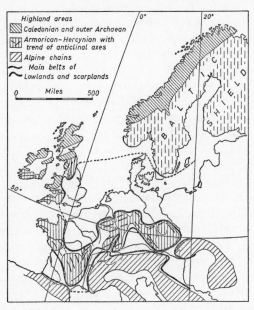

Fig. 1. The major structural elements of Western and Central Europe (generalised).

chains themselves, as do the Rhine and the Garonne, or from the intermediate highlands and uplands elevated by the forces that produced those chains, as do the Elbe, the Weser and the Seine. Even the Rhône and the Danube, which escape in reverse direction through the Alpine girdle, derive most of their waters from the Alps.

In accordance with the tectonic development of the whole area, its major relief elements are arranged in zones, aligned roughly parallel with the Alpine system (Fig. 1). The outermost consists of the Caledonian highlands and the Baltic Shield; the innermost of the Alpine chains, the youngest, thrust up against the belt of Hercynian blocks

B

and disposed in a curve from south-western France through the Rhine Highlands to Bohemia. These Hercynian highlands are separated from the outer Caledonian-Baltic Shield zone by a depression, occupied partly by the North European Plain and its extensions into the Paris Basin and eastern England, and partly by the shallow North Sea and Baltic Sea. In Jurassic and Cretaceous times this depression was lower in elevation, so that the uppermost bedded rocks of much of the existing dry land consist of chalk and sandstone of the Cretaceous period, when seas reached from Britain eastwards into Russia; though in the central parts of the London and Paris Basins, still covered by arms of the sea into the early Tertiary period, the Cretaceous beds are overlaid with clays, sands and gravels.

The underlying series of rocks, in which limestones are common, outcrop as escarpments and platforms inland from the chalk escarpments in the Paris Basin in horse-shoe pattern and also in a diagonal belt through England. Beyond them, sandstones and other rocks of the earlier Triassic period appear at the surface in parts of north-central England, of Lorraine in France and of central Germany. The accumulation of all these stratified deposits in the West European lowlands from the Triassic period onwards is evidence that their present elongated basin form dates from far back in the past.

South of the Armorican-Hercynian massifs sedimentary rocks from Jurassic to Tertiary were also laid down in a zone extending from southern France through Germany and the Alpine Foreland into Austria. This southern intermediate belt widens out in the Aquitaine Basin and in south Germany, but is constricted at intervals into narrow passages by the pressures that raised the Alpine system of mountains against the Hercynian blocks, as at the Carcassonne gateway between the Pyrenees and the Massif Central, the narrow passages between the Jura and the Vosges-Black Forest horsts, and the Danube gorge above Vienna. Alpine pressures, greatest in the central area, contributed also to the elevation of the Swiss and Upper Bavarian plateaux, the surfaces of which were covered with thick deposits of sandstone (molasse) formed from the waste of the rising Alps, and later by loads of morainic debris left by the ice-sheets of the repeated Alpine glaciations.

Distinctive Features and Forms of Utilisation

The physical build of any inhabited part of the earth's surface, together with the climate and the capacities of the people, forms the

THE GEOLOGICAL SEQUENCE

Estimated time past (millions of years)[1]	Periods		Orogeneses	Characteristic rocks
70		Quaternary (Recent)	} Alpine {	Alluvium, clays, sands
		Tertiary		Partly consolidated beds of above and soft limestones
	Mesozoic	Cretaceous		Chalk and soft sandstones
		Jurassic		Limestones
		Triassic		Sandstones, often with beds of salt and gypsum
270	Palaeozoic	Permian	} Hercynian	Reddish sandstones and conglomerates
		Carboniferous		Limestones, sandstones and coal measures
400		Devonian (Old Red Sandstone)	} Caledonian	Coloured sandstones and marble limestones
		Silurian		Slates, schists, quartzite and
500		Ordovician		other mainly metamorphic
		Cambrian		rocks
600 to 2000 +		Pre-Cambrian	Charnian and at least three earlier	Granite, gneiss and highly metamorphic sedimentary rocks

Note. Intrusive granites and other igneous rocks, as well as mineralised veins, occur in the stratified rocks of all periods from Pre-Cambrian to Tertiary.

essential basis of possible developments in agriculture, exploitation of minerals, industry and commerce; it provides the framework within which economic activities may function. With incidental references to such inter-relationships, selected structural elements with their associated resources and forms of utilisation are described in the following sections.

(a) General features of the lowlands and their human occupation

The main lowland zone of Peninsular Europe is but the western continuation, partly dismembered by seas, of the Polish-Russian plains

[1] Based on *A Revised Geological Time-scale*, Arthur Holmes, Transactions Edinburgh Geological Society 17 (1960).

east of the Oder River, which, incidentally, because of their extent, cause Europe to have the lowest average elevation (under 1,000 feet) of all the continents. Western and Central Europe has a considerably greater average height; over one-third of the total area exceeds 1,200 feet in elevation and contains considerable tracts of uninhabitable mountain country both above that height in the north-west, and above 3,000 feet in the south.

The remaining two-thirds or more of the whole area is for the greater part agriculturally productive and habitable. It comprises numerous detached portions of lowlands, inland basins and valleys and highland slopes, in addition to, and on either side of the medial lowland arc. Besides those north of the Alpine mountain system, others of some importance by reason of size and population are the Scottish lowlands and the Central Irish Plain in the British Isles, and the Elbe Plain in Bohemia. All of these are bordered by scantily populated highlands on two or more sides, which as regions of dispersion restrict inter-communication, and have in the past tended to induce a separatist spirit in the peoples of the somewhat isolated lowlands. However, some of the continental inter-mont lowlands, in particular those of the Rhine Rift Valley, the lower Rhône and the middle Danube, have from early times been thoroughfares of conquest, travel and trade; and thus their inhabitants, exposed to multipatterned contacts, have never been able to slide into self-contained inertia. Similarly also, the people of the Swiss Plateau, though secluded enough to preserve their independence, have been kept alert and vigorous by age-long external contacts arising from their situation on important routes via the Alpine passes between Mediterranean and Northern Europe.

The main lowland belt from eastern England and northern France to the Polish Plain is itself far from level. It has, in fact, a great variety of low to moderate relief. In the western section the outer waves of the Alpine upheaval have caused rocks of varying resistance to appear at the surface; these have been attacked selectively by the forces of erosion with resulting accentuation of relief in the form of scarplands. In the eastern and larger section from the Low Countries eastwards, uniformity of relief is broken by a series of ridges consisting of terminal moraines averaging several hundred feet in height, and also, especially towards the southern borders, by outliers and projecting limbs of the Hercynian highlands. Thus in both the western and eastern parts of these lowlands, incidents in relief are related to differences in the nature of the surface rocks or surface deposits; and these two structural elements have either singly or in combination contributed to a great variety of local landscapes — in slope and drainage, in soils and agricultural utilisation, and in density of settlement. A good example of this variety in a relatively small area is seen in the Weald of south-east England.

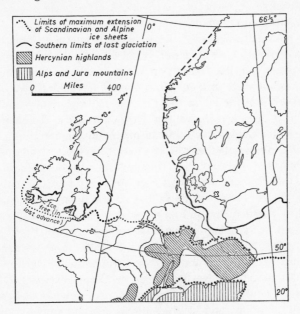

Fig. 2. Limits of maximum and of last glaciations.
After Charlesworth and Woldstedt.

(b) Glacial topography

The northern half of Western Europe, and also the regions of the Alps and the Pyrenees were time and again during the Ice Age covered with ice-sheets radiating from thick ice-masses accumulated on the highlands. The southern limit of the maximum northern or Scandinavian glaciation was a line from the Bristol Channel across southern England and the Netherlands into Germany along the northern flanks of the Hercynian uplands (Fig. 2). Between this line and the independent Alpine glaciation, a broad wedge open to the Atlantic and blunted towards Bohemia remained free from ice except on isolated highlands. The Ice Age is estimated to have lasted over half a million years, and to have come gradually to an end 15,000 to 7,000 years ago, the existing Scandinavian ice-fields having formed since the disappearance of the ice-sheet. At least four main advances of the northern ice-sheets have been recognised, separated by inter-glacial periods long enough for normal erosion to reduce or remove much of the morainic deposits of the earlier advances. Thus it is the last glaciation which, though not the most extensive, has left the most clearly visible evidence of its effects in carving the highlands and strewing the plains with debris.

The mountain regions of Scandinavia, northern Britain, the Alps and the Pyrenees have been deeply chiselled by the powerful incisive action of moving ice, thickest in the pre-existing river valleys; the concentration of ice in them set in operation a cumulative process of vertical erosion, the ice in them increasing in thickness and erosive power as it deepened the valleys. Now clear of ice, these flat-floored channels excavated far back into the mountains facilitate human movement and invite settlement. Roads have been built without excessive gradients, and railways also (though often through long summit tunnels) over or under the cols between valley heads on either side. The flat floors of many of the valleys are warm and fertile enough for agricultural settlement; and now that the waterpower available from the ice-fed rivers and streams can be utilised as hydro-electric power, factories have been added to farms on the valley floors, as in Switzerland, the French Alps and Norway. In western Norway, where numerous glacial valleys have been so deeply excavated as to be submerged now as fiords, their calm waters provide sheltered harbours for shipping, and facilities for fishing and communication by sea between otherwise isolated coastal settlements.

The surface features and soils of the lowlands invaded by ice-sheets have been modified by the extensive deposition of rock waste. In some parts, as in East Anglia and the German Baltic coastlands, considerable tracts of nearly level or gently undulating fertile ground moraine, mostly boulder clay, have been laid down with settling of solid fragments from slowly melting sheet ice. In other parts, especially in northern Germany and Poland and in the Salpausselkä of Finland, massive hummocky terminal moraines, marking the outer edge of successive advances of the Scandinavian ice-sheets, stretch in concentric pattern for hundreds of miles. On the inner northern side of these terminal moraines, a belt strewn with drumlins and eskers commonly occurs; on the outer side another belt of outwash sands and gravels. Similar features appear in reverse order (from south to north) in places on the northern side of the Alps, though there the active rivers and streams have dissected the glacial debris, and re-deposited the transported material further north, notably in upper Bavaria.

On the southern margins of the former Scandinavian glaciation, beyond the limits of the moraines and outwash drift, lies a discontinuous belt of loess. This has been of special significance in the prehistoric settlement of Europe (p. 44), and owing to its natural fertility is intensively cultivated in the present age. The loess belt extends from northern France through Belgium and Germany into Eastern Europe, where it joins with the extensive Czernozem or Black Earth region. It hugs the northern edges of the Hercynian highlands, sometimes covering their lower slopes. It is interrupted here and there by northward projections of those highlands such as the Ardennes and the middle Weser uplands, but extends well into the intervening embayments in the Rhineland, Saxony and Silesia. Similar deposits occur also in Hungary, in Bavaria south of the Danube, and on the upper terraces of the Rhine Rift Valley. As the northern ice-sheets melted back, the dry anticyclonic winds, outblowing from the high pressure air mass over the retreating ice, caught up large quantities of fine particles from the drift-covered zone; these they deposited farther south on reaching the humid region penetrated by Atlantic air currents, where moisture was sufficient for grass and other vegetation to fix the fine-grained material as loess.

(c) Coastal features and harbours

North-West and Central Europe has an exceptional length of coastline in proportion to land area, no point within it being situated more than 300 miles from the sea, and also a great variety of coastal features in consequence of its complex geological structure. It has, in fact, a double coastline, an outer from western Ireland to northern Norway, and an inner, bordering the English Channel and the North and Baltic Seas. Moreover, the eustatic rise of general sea-level following upon the recession of the great ice-sheets has caused the sea to invade the land in numberless indentations; and the considerable tidal range on all coasts open to the Atlantic converts a number of river estuaries in effect into arms of the sea reaching far inland, e.g. the Firth of Forth, the Elbe Estuary and the Gironde.

In addition to tidal rivers other forms of inlets on the West European coasts that provide suitable harbours are the fiords of Norway, the rias of southern Ireland and some rock basin openings.

The latter, found on discordant coasts of submergence, often form excellent harbours, protected as they are in some instances by outlying islands. Good examples are seen in the harbours of Toulon in France and Helsinki in Finland. Worthy of mention is the lagoon type of harbours on low concordant coasts, such as those of Dunkirk, Sète and Esbjerg, though these have generally needed extensive dredging and constructional work to make them serviceable.

Attention has been drawn (p. 6) to the maritime outlook and activities of West European peoples. The development of these characteristics of their ways of life has been fostered by the abundance of useful natural harbours of various types. This endowment has been enriched by the construction of artificial harbours, and the improvement of indifferent natural harbours such as shallow tidal estuaries, in all of which West Europeans have displayed special aptitudes in keeping with their mechanical genius and their seafaring interests and traditions.

(d) Mineral resources in relation to physical structure

Of outstanding importance in the human geography of North-Western and Central Europe are the resources in coals, iron ores and salts, the foundations of its primacy (till recently) in industrial development. The distribution of each of these basic groups of minerals is closely related to some of the geological features among those described above. In particular, the highly important part played by the Armorican-Hercynian physical element will be apparent from the following account.

Coals comprise ordinary hard coals of Carboniferous age, and soft coals or lignite, most abundant in Germany where they are known as brown coals. The extensive late Carboniferous Armorican-Hercynian upheavals and flexures are mainly responsible for the preservation of the numerous West and Central European deposits of hard coals. The main axes of folding lay along the southern margins of the swamps previously covered by the Carboniferous forests, the remains of which were buried in the associated synclines. In addition, however, to the main E.–W. uplifts, subsidiary Armorican anticlines running N.–S. (such as the Pennines), and also E.–W., developed in places in the synclines, with the result that the existing coalfields occur in separate basins as well as in elongated forms. Examples of the former are seen in the Pennine and Midland coalfields, of the latter in South Wales, Belgium and the Ruhr. In accordance with this sequence of events, almost all the chief coalfields of both forms are situated in basins on the borders of the Armorican-Hercynian highlands, in a belt which on the Continent follows the northern margins of those highlands (Fig. 3).

The important continental lignite fields, those of the Rhineland, the middle Elbe basin and Nieder-Lausitz in Germany and the Ohře valley in Bohemia, are also associated with the Hercynian highland

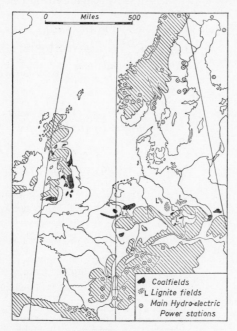

Fig. 3. Coal and Lignite fields and main hydro-electric power stations. It will be observed that the main coal and lignite fields lie in a diagonal belt between the two highland areas that are great sources of hydro-electric power.

system; but being of much later date than the hard coals, they differ much in form. Plant remains accumulated in the Tertiary period in slowly subsiding swampy basins between or on the margins of the Hercynian blocks, and were later covered with sufficient overburden to preserve them from decay. Being thus near the surface, these immature coals are worked by open-cast methods.

Richly endowed with solid fuels, this section of Europe produces little mineral oil. Only a few scattered deposits have so far been dis-covered, the most productive of which are situated in the northern plain on both sides of the Netherlands-German border. Hydro-electric power is relatively abundant, though scattered. Being dependent on large 'heads' of water, it is associated mainly, though not entirely, with high mountain areas, especially those which have been heavily glaciated. The three main areas of development are the Scandinavian highlands, the northern fronts of the Alps and the Pyrenees and the upper parts of the French Central Plateau.

FUEL AND POWER RESOURCES. PRODUCTION, AVERAGE 1958-9

	Hard Coal mill. tons	Lignite mill. tons	Hydro-electric Power 1000 mill. kWh.	Petroleum mill. tons
Austria	0·14	6·4	11·3	2·65
Belgium	24·9		0·15	
Czechoslovakia	26·15	55·3	2·35	
Denmark		2·4		
Finland			6·15	
France	57·7	2·25	32·4	1·5
{West Germany	130·1	93·7	12·1	4·8
{Saar	16·3			
East Germany	2·9	214·9	0·59	
Irish Republic	0·24		0·76	
Netherlands	11·9	0·23		1·7
{Norway			28·3	
{Spitzbergen	0·28			
Poland	97·0	8·4	0·66	
Sweden	0·32		28·85	
Switzerland			17·4	
United Kingdom	210·9		2·7	0·15
Totals	578·83	383·6	143·7	10·8

Assuming a thermal ratio of 4 tons of lignite to 1 ton of hard coal, the total equivalent coal production of the above countries was about 675 mill. tons p.a. as compared with about 400 mill. tons coal + lignite average in the same years in North America, and 75 mill. tons in the three southern continents.

Most of the European deposits of iron ore, like those of the coal-fuels, fall into one of two main classes according to origin, age and composition; these are the ancient, metamorphic, high-grade and the younger, sedimentary, phosphoric low-grade. The former, generally containing nearly 60 per cent of iron, are found in the Pre-Cambrian rocks of Scandinavia, especially of northern Sweden, where they form solid mountain masses resistant enough to have withstood prolonged erosion. The latter, averaging about half of the metal content of the metamorphic class, form extensive beds in the lower Jurassic rocks that outcrop in escarpments both in England and in Lorraine-Luxembourg (pp. 73, 199). They have been exploited on a large scale, usually by open-cast working, since the introduction of the Thomas-Gilchrist process whereby the phosphorus is eliminated. Besides these three main sources of iron ore, other smaller bodies that contribute appreciable supplies are those in Normandy (south of Caen), the Harz foreland (Salzgitter) and Siegerland in West Germany, and Styria in Austria.

Beds of common salt and of potash compounds occur in the rocks of the Permo-Triassic period, during which inland seas and waters dried up, owing to general climatic changes associated with the interception of moisture-bearing winds from the Atlantic by extensive Armorican uplifts to westward. Large deposits of common salt are worked in Cheshire and northern England, eastern France (Lorraine) and central Germany, where Triassic rocks appear at or near the surface. The more valuable potash salts are restricted to central Germany (see Fig. 69), and to a small area in upper Alsace in France.

BASIC MINERALS AND STEEL. PRODUCTION, AVERAGE 1958–9
(million metric tons)

	Iron Ore Metal content	Crude Steel	Salt NaCl content	Potash K₂O content
	Iron Ore *Metal content*	*Crude Steel*	*Salt* NaCl *content*	*Potash* K$_2$O *content*
Austria	1·07	2·5	0·32	
Belgium	0·05	6·2		
Czechoslovakia	0·87	5·8	0·16	
France	18·6	14·9	3·53	1·66
Finland	0·14	0·21		
{West Germany	4·2	24·3	3·6	2·08
{Saar		3·54		
East Germany	0·41	3·15	1·8	1·65
Luxembourg	1·72	3·52		
Netherlands		1·56	0·89	
Norway	1·0	0·39		
Poland	0·58	5·9	1·7	
Sweden	11·2	2·6		
Switzerland	0·03	0·25	0·13	
United Kingdom	4·1	20·2	5·3	
Totals	43·97	95·02	17·43	5·39

From the data in this and the preceding Table, several significant facts can be gathered. First, though the countries listed produce particularly large quantities of solid fuels, and relatively large amounts of hydro-electric power, their output of petroleum is small. Second, the production of crude steel is more than twice that of the metal equivalent of the iron ore, so that even though much scrap metal is used, large quantities of ore need to be imported from Africa and

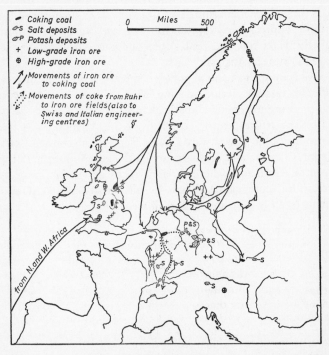

Fig. 4. Iron ore, coking coal and salt deposits; major movements of iron ores and of coke. (For details of localities see larger-scale maps in regional accounts). The map illustrates the special importance of Swedish Lapland ores and of Ruhr coal for the iron and steel manufactures of Western and Central Europe.

other distant sources; the only substantial surplus iron ore countries (in relation to steel production) in the above list are Sweden and France. Third, the three largest producers of coal are, as might be expected, the largest producers of steel. Fourth, over 70 per cent of the total hydro-electric power is generated in four countries, France, Norway, Sweden and Switzerland. Fifth, the total production of common salt is very great, apart from several million tons of potash salts mined in Germany and France, but here again most of the output is concentrated mainly in four countries, which therefore also hold leading places in the chemical group of manufactures.

(e) Highland regions and water-power resources

In the cool temperate climate of Western and Central Europe, highland areas are, in general, negative regions for human settlement. Except in some ice-deepened and trough-faulted valleys, they offer scanty opportunities for cultivation, and their mineral deposits are few. Their main resources have lain in the forests on the lower slopes and the rough grazings and summer pastures at moderate elevations.

However, with the progress in the present age in the use of electricity as energy converter the more elevated highlands, especially those of the Alpine system and of Scandinavia, have assumed increasing value as sources of power. The features that have rendered them useless for other purposes have been turned to account; their steepness, excessively low temperatures and heavy precipitation mainly as snow combine to make them eminently suitable for the generation of hydro-electricity. The snow and ice-fields serve as natural storage reservoirs contributing to a steady flow of melt-water, which can be supplemented by the construction of dams in the deeply-cut rocky valleys. These facilities are not confined to the mountains themselves; for the larger snow-fed rivers e.g. the Rhine, the Rhône, the Garonne and some of the Scandinavian rivers, which owe their volume and constancy to their mountain origins, plunge through rapids in their middle courses. Thus the concentration of output of hydro-electric current as shown by countries in the Table on p. 26 is largely coincident with the territorial distribution of the major highlands and their associated rivers.

Chapter 3

CLIMATE

EUROPE is situated in middle latitudes where the planetary winds in the upper air are westerly and fairly constant. These cause a general easterly movement in the sequence of weather conditions at the earth's surface in the temperate regions. Open to the Atlantic Ocean on the west and backed by the Eurasian continent to the east, Western Europe is subject to air-streams resulting from the interplay of air-masses centred north-west, south-west and east, namely the predominant low pressure over the North Atlantic near Iceland, the Azores High and the seasonal alternation of high and low pressure over Eurasia in winter and in summer respectively.[1] These air-streams are

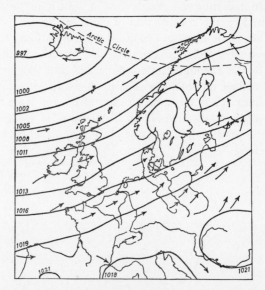

Fig. 5. The distribution of air pressure (isobars in millibars) and prevailing winds in January.

[1] Summer low and winter high over the continental interior are to be understood only as generalised expressions of prevailing pressure conditions. Depressions with

often separated by more or less sharp discontinuities, causing turbulence and stormy or unsettled weather. In the Atlantic borderlands
particularly a complex weather pattern results, and in them the climate
is a rather indefinable average of changing weather conditions.

In the North Atlantic mild, relatively moist tropical air comes into
contact with cold outward-spreading Arctic air in a zone known as the
Polar Front, which in winter extends in general from near Florida to

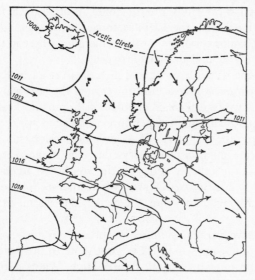

Fig. 6. The distribution of air pressure (isobars in millibars) and prevailing
winds in July.

south of Iceland. It is in this zone of convergence that many depressions or cyclonic storms are born, which owing to the upward movement of relatively light air in them give rise to the commonly prevailing low pressure of the so-called Icelandic Low south of Iceland.
These depressions tend to follow easterly or north-easterly courses,
and, fed over the ocean by warm moist air from the south, and by cold
polar air from the Arctic, they may gather intensity as they move
eastwards; they are responsible for much of the precipitation and for

their associated troughs sometimes follow easterly tracks over Central Europe into
Russia in winter, and extensive anticyclones may persist for days in summer over
Eastern Europe. Though the winter and the summer air pressure and weather
conditions there are subject to some variability, they are constant enough as a rule in
each season to act as general controlling agents.

the commonly changeable weather of the Atlantic borderlands of Europe.

The Azores High, though it contributes to the activity of depressions, itself extends far enough north to affect Western Europe only in summer, when it normally spreads into the Mediterranean and forms a wedge-shaped extension over Central Europe. In the Mediterranean area it gives rise to calms with dry sunny weather in the north-western sector, from which north-east winds blow into the Saharan Low in the west, and north-west winds into the South Asiatic Low in the east; in Central Europe it feeds the warm sectors of depressions which penetrate into the continent on its northern margins, where in the zone of instability convectional rain is liable to occur.

The Eurasian winter mass of cold high pressure air tends to spread outwards when most intense after the turn of the year when it sometimes extends westwards to affect much of Britain and France. Apart from the abnormally low temperatures associated with it, its chief effect is to split the main track of Atlantic depressions into two branches, one following a north-easterly course on its northern flank off Norway, and the other passing to the south-east across southern France into the Mediterranean area, where another front often forms between continental air from the north and warm air from the south.

The extensive Eurasian summer low pressure systems, on the other hand, cause inflowing winds. They contribute to the easterly movement of outflowing air from the Azores High. Winds normally blow from the Azores High towards the Icelandic area in winter; but in summer, more towards the continent when pressure there approximates to that of the Icelandic area. The continental and the North Atlantic low pressure areas then tend to link up over North Central Europe, and depressions from the Atlantic often follow tracks on the northern margin of the extended Azores High and may well reach into Russia, where the mean annual (summer maximum) precipitation exceeds 20 inches west of the line Leningrad-Kiev.

AIR-STREAMS AFFECTING WESTERN EUROPE

With changes in the positions and the relative pressures of these air-masses and their consequent variable interplay, air-streams from widely separated sources invade Western Europe in turn, particularly with the passage of depressions. Two of them are from the ocean, the Tropical and the Polar Maritime (including the Arctic and the Polar

Maritime Returning), and two from land areas, the Polar and the
Tropical Continental (Fig. 7).

Tropical Maritime air-streams originating in the sub-tropical zone
of the Atlantic reach Western Europe as warm, usually moist winds;
and the Polar Maritime from Greenland and the Arctic seas as relatively cold dry winds, having gained some heat but not much moisture
during their ocean passage; though if they are drawn round on a
longer passage as returning streams, they gain more of both. Polar

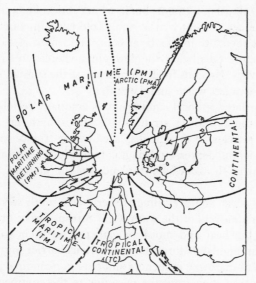

Fig. 7. Air streams affecting Western and Central Europe. Adapted after
A. A. Miller and C. E. P. Brooks.

Continental air-streams outflowing from Scandinavian anticyclones
or the continental high pressure area, are commonest in late winter
when continental influences gain the mastery at times in Western
Europe. Tropical Continental air-streams affect North-Western
Europe but rarely, and only in summer. Originating in North Africa
or the Sahara, they are liable to be hot and dusty in their passage over
the Mediterranean lands where they sometimes have a withering
effect upon vegetation; north of the Alpine chains they are still warm
and fairly dry, having gained some heat by compression. At Kew,
a typical West European station, these various air-streams in all are
active on the average some 57 per cent of yearly time (according to

12-year observations), out of which the Polar Maritime minus the Arctic occupies about 35 per cent and the Tropical Maritime 9·5 per cent. This overwhelming predominance of winds from the open Atlantic over those from other (mainly continental) sources is embodied in the term Prevailing Westerlies.

At intervals, however, especially round midsummer and midwinter, these wind systems are interrupted by more or less stationary masses of descending air known as anticyclones, which generally persist for several days. In them the air is warmed by compression in its slow downward movement; but in winter anticyclones the upper air is arrested in its descent by the stable cold layer in contact with the ground, the moisture in this layer being condensed as fog whenever the temperature falls below the dewpoint; whereas in summer anticyclones dry air descends freely from above to the surface, and spreading out there causes warm sunny weather.

Sooner or later, as local equilibrium is gradually restored between the upper and the lower strata of the atmosphere, an anticyclone declines or retreats. It may be displaced by the tropical maritime air of an approaching depression bringing rain, which at its onset is often convectional in the zone of turbulence on the margins of summer anticyclones.

Over the ocean the prevailing westerly and south-westerly winds are the prime movers of the warm Gulf Stream Drift; over the land they carry the heat and moisture gathered on their passage. The Scandinavian highlands form the only serious barrier to the eastward penetration of maritime influences and only in Scandinavia is there a fairly sharp transition from the maritime to the continental type of climate. The north-east Atlantic is in fact, a great reservoir of transferred heat of equatorial or tropical origin.[1] Over a large area between 55° and 70° N. January temperatures are 30° to 40° above the normal for latitude. This winter 'Gulf of Warmth', partly caused and mainly made effective in Western Europe by the prevailing westerly winds, has the effect of raising the average temperatures of that area above the normal for latitude, and of making it possible for permanent settlement there to advance beyond the Arctic Circle.

---

[1] The South Equatorial Current is divided against the projecting angle of South America, and the northern branch reinforces the North Equatorial Current. The combined currents make their way into the Gulf of Mexico, where their waters are canalised through Florida Strait as the Gulf Stream at a temperature of 75° F., which, continued as the North Atlantic Drift, contributes most to raising the temperature of the North Atlantic surface waters.

The moderating effects of air-streams from the Atlantic are naturally greatest on the western coastlands and most of all in the winter
season when the sun is weak. The isotherms of mean January temperatures trend N.–S. across the parallels of latitude in maritime
North-West Europe. The average January temperature at Tromsø
nearly 70° N. in Norway is very little lower than that at Hamburg; on
the other hand, London, Berlin, and Warsaw, all nearly the same

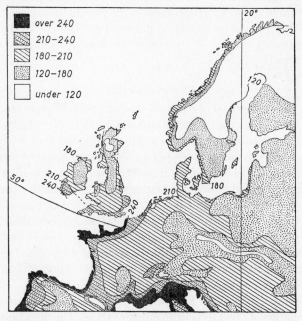

Fig. 8. Average numbers yearly of frost-free days. Source: the Agricultural
Geography of Europe and the Near East. U.S. Department of Agriculture.
Miscellaneous Publications. Publication No. 665, 1948.

latitude and differing little in average July temperatures, have mean
January temperatures of 39°, 31·5° and 25·9° F. respectively. In
summer, however, the sun asserts its role as the main determinant of
temperature. Then latitude and insolation are of greatest significance;
the July isotherms are more or less aligned with the parallels of latitude, but have a northward trend inland as cloudiness diminishes and
the land surface accumulates heat.

In North-Western and Central Europe, considerable parts of
which lie north of 50° N., temperature conditions have much influence

upon the range of crops and forms of agricultural production, and also upon the habitability of northern marginal areas. Of particular significance in this connection are the average lengths of the frost-free period (Fig. 8) and of the growing season as indicated by temperatures over 50° F. There is some difference in areal distribution between the former and the latter which is an expression of the contrast between the winter and summer temperature distributions noted above; maritime influences play an important part in lengthening the frost-free period in areas exposed to them in the west, whereas insolation as indicated in general by latitude is the main determinant of the length of the growing season, as shown by the northern limits of various staple crops (Fig. 11).

PRECIPITATION

Over the greater part of North-West and Central Europe, including nearly all the lowlands, the mean annual rainfall is moderate in amount, between 20 and 40 inches. This, combined with the likewise moderate amount of loss by evaporation averaging about 15 inches per annum, and the slow run-off from the lower ground, is generally sufficient for varied agriculture, especially as the rainfall is normally well distributed throughout the year. Excessive precipitation falls on the north-western highlands of the British Isles and Scandinavia, and on parts of the Alps and the Pyrenees, but these areas are in any case unproductive. Similarly, the only considerable area of marginal low precipitation, namely the northern part of the Baltic Shield, is too cold and barren for agricultural settlement.

The rainfall in Western Europe may be cyclonic or convectional, or a combination of orographic with either of these. The first, brought by depressions, accounts for the greater part of it, at all events on the western lowlands. The track followed by these disturbances — north-east off Scotland and Norway, east over Britain and the Central European Plain, and south-east over France — ensures a general wide distribution. The considerable additional orographic or relief rainfall on the north-western highlands and other mountainous regions accounts for their excessive precipitation, more than twice the average of the lowlands. Convectional rainfall, commonly associated with summer thunderstorms, occurs widely on the continent away from the coasts, and also in eastern England.

Though nearly all parts of the whole area have some precipitation in most months, the seasonal distribution varies from one part to another according to changes in the general air circulation. In western France and in most of the British Isles and Norway, the autumn and early winter months are commonly the wettest and the spring months the driest. As autumn advances cyclonic activity increases, but it diminishes in spring with the decline in the pressure gradient between the Azores and the Icelandic systems over the ocean, and with the levelling up of temperatures over land and sea. In the course of the spring season a general reversal of the air-streams over Central Europe takes place, with pressure falling over Eurasia; by early summer the easterly winds of winter are replaced by prevailing westerly air-streams carrying moisture which contributes to summer maxima of rainfall throughout Europe north of the Mediterranean, except in the western maritime parts mentioned above.

Climatic Regions

North-Western and Central Europe extends upwards 30° in both latitude and longitude; and though climatic differences are small compared with those in other areas of similar extent in the temperate zone, five or six regional types may be distinguished according to rainfall and temperature régimes and the average temperature of the coldest month (Fig. 9). (1) The maritime or oceanic of the British

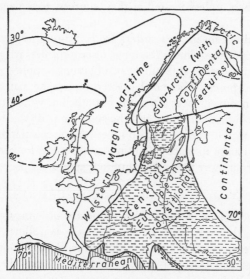

Fig. 9. The major climatic regions of Western and Central Europe. January and July isotherms in degrees F.

Isles and a coastal belt from northern Norway to the Bay of Biscay, generally equable but changeable in weather conditions, humid with autumn maximum rainfall in most parts; (2) the transitional becoming increasingly continental in the east, where the range of temperature is about twice that of London (40° at Warsaw) and the rainfall shows a distinct summer maximum; (3) the sub-arctic or boreal, marked by a short summer growing season (100–120 days above 50° F.), by temperatures below freezing for 6 months or more, and by light precipitation mainly in the summer months; (4) the arctic of the northern coastlands; (5) the Mediterranean of south-east France showing the usual Mediterranean characteristics of temperature and rainfall régimes. In addition there is the mountain type of the Scandinavian axis and of the higher Alps and Pyrenees, these highlands (but not the Hercynian except at isolated points) rising well above the tree line.

The transitional type covers the larger part of the whole area, for beyond a couple of hundred miles inland (considerably less in western Scandinavia) the continental influence begins to be felt with greater range of temperature and summer maximum rainfall. This summer rainfall is beneficial for agriculture and for navigation on inland waterways; it compensates for the loss of moisture by evaporation and by the active transpiration of growing crops, and it maintains the flow of rivers when, unless ice-fed at their sources, they would shrink in volume.

The Mediterranean area suffers from its summer drought which parches the pastures, limits the range of crops unless irrigation can be provided, and entails difficulties in obtaining supplies of water for common purposes. The north-western maritime parts of Europe escape the inconveniences attending both the low winter temperatures of interior continental areas, and the summer aridity of the Mediterranean region; but their climate on the Atlantic coastlands is apt to be cloudy and damp, in places too humid and sunless for healthy human existence or for more than a very limited range of crops.

THE CYCLE OF SEASONAL CHANGES

From the above account the sequence of climatic conditions throughout the year may be summarised as follows. In winter, vigorous depressions generated along the Polar Front commonly travel on north-easterly or easterly courses towards the Norwegian Sea or the British Isles, less often across southern France. These bring stormy weather, with strong but relatively warm south-westerly winds veering to north-west, and heavy precipitation on the Atlantic coastlands. At the same time the Eurasian high pressure system, often well established over Eastern Europe, extends as a wedge over Central Europe towards the Alps, dividing the tracks of depressions, and bringing very cold dry weather often as far west as the Elbe, sometimes even to eastern Britain.

Hence the winter weather of the Atlantic borderlands and of Mediterranean France is changeable, with rainfall at intervals, and is also comparatively mild in both areas, though with occasional cold spells in the former; that of the interior lands tends to be continuously cold with light precipitation mainly as snow caused by occasional depressions. The line of demarcation between these contrasted types follows the highland axis in Scandinavia, but south of that shifts across a belt between the longitudes of Berlin and London, not only during a particular winter, but also between one winter and another.

As spring advances, depressions from the Atlantic become less vigorous, and with the gradual weakening of the continental high pressure system, they tend to move eastwards more frequently over Central Europe. As the air over the land becomes at the same time less cold relatively to that over the sea, and therefore less effective as a condensing agent, spring is in general the season of lowest rainfall over North-West Europe.

Summer brings further developments in the distribution of air-pressure. The generally prevalent low pressure system, by then established over the heated land surface, reinforces Atlantic air-currents over Central Europe from the Azores High, shifted north; these air-streams and weak depressions penetrating eastwards, supply moisture which contributes to the partly convectional summer rainfall on the interior mainland. If, as sometimes happens however, the Azores High holds back in summer, and the low pressure area near Iceland retains its identity, moderately intense depressions may travel eastwards over Western Europe, afflicting it with unseasonably cool wet summer weather, as in 1956 and 1960. If, on the other hand, the Azores High spreads exceptionally far north, dry sunny weather is experienced well beyond the Mediterranean.

During the autumn months the land loses heat relatively to the sea, and the pressure gradient between the Azores High and the Icelandic area is gradually restored. Depressions moving east from the Atlantic become more vigorous and the moisture carried by the warm south-westerly winds is more readily condensed on the land, then colder than the sea. Autumn is accordingly a season of heavy rainfall on the maritime parts of Western Europe, where nearly all stations record an October–November maximum. These conditions persist into winter, when anticyclones occasionally develop, giving rise to cold spells and fogs.

The march of the seasons brings changes in the prevailing types of weather experienced in North-Western Europe: what sort of weather throughout depends partly upon the alternate high and low continental systems, largely upon the results of the play of forces out in the North Atlantic.

Chapter 4

NATURAL VEGETATION;[1]
HUMAN SETTLEMENT;
THE CULTURAL LANDSCAPE

FOLLOWING the final retreat of the ice-sheets of the Quaternary Age, a plant cover consisting largely of deciduous trees and bushes, but with coniferous trees and humbler plants on the higher ground and sandy soils, crept northwards and westwards over Central and Northern Europe. On reaching the loess belts the forests became less continuous, broken here and there by stretches of steppe vegetation (mainly grasses) on the less compact porous soils. Between the loess belt and the North Sea–Baltic coasts, in the zone of glacial moraines and outwash sands, and also in the unglaciated lands bordering the English Channel, a mixed vegetation gradually appeared. This eventually consisted of deciduous and coniferous forest, together with stretches of marsh and heath plant-associations; all corresponding to the endless variety of soil texture and drainage in the glaciated country, and to the varied relief, geological formation and soil composition in southern Britain and northern France.

On the northern side of the Baltic Sea, beyond about 60° N. in Scandinavia and Finland, the slow clearance of the ice-cover delayed the establishment of plant life in that area, much of which may have been colonised from Russia. There the short growing season and the commonly moist, acid soils have always been unfavourable to trees other than some species of conifers and the hardiest deciduous trees and shrubs such as birch, willow and alder. Coniferous trees, mostly spruce, Scots pine, and Siberian larch and fir, physiologically adapted for quick growth within the restricted open season, have been able, in the absence of serious rivals, to form extensive forests continuous with, and containing some species found in those to the east in Russia.

---

[1] 'Natural' Vegetation here and elsewhere in this book is used in the sense of the plant forms that have existed according to the climatic conditions prevailing in the past, or that would now exist if undisturbed by man.

The present forms of natural vegetation in North-Western Europe, or those that would be established if human intervention ceased, fall broadly into five regional groups: mountain flora on the upper parts of the Scandinavian highlands and Alpine ranges above the tree limits, merging upwards into tundra, bare rock and ice-covered wastes; coniferous forest as described above in most of Scandinavia and Finland and also predominant on the Hercynian plateaux; moorland and bog plant-associations on the highlands of the British Isles and Brittany, as well as on the sterile, sandy glacial deposits (Geest) in the Netherlands and North Germany; grasses with scattered belts of trees on the stretches of loess; and finally, a broken pattern of deciduous trees and bushes covering the rest of the lowlands and uplands.

The greater proportion of the whole area is the domain of the deciduous type, in the sense that, given free competition among plants, deciduous trees and bushes would in general prevail, though their continuity would be broken by other forms, especially coniferous, better suited to special soil conditions; hence the use of the generic term deciduous or mixed to designate the characteristic vegetation of the West and Central European lowlands. Likewise also, even in the northern coniferous belt where pure stands of trees are the rule, certain hardy deciduous genera such as the birch and alder occur in patches, and actually extend beyond the northern limits of the coniferous trees on to the margins of the tundra.

Of the actually existing vegetation, much is the result of modification by human activity. The mountain and moorland and bog floras, however, are mostly or entirely indigenous, having persisted in their unfavoured habitats undisturbed by man or by competing forms of vegetation. The northern coniferous forests are also indigenous in a sense, being composed mainly of native species self-seeded or re-planted as cutting has proceeded, though in Scandinavia some exotic species and hybrid varieties have been widely planted. In the highly variegated pattern of the present plant cover on the broad medial mainly lowland area, cultivated crops and man-made pastures predominate; though some of the grasses, especially those of hill pastures, are indigenous. The woods and forests, still moderately extensive on the mountain slopes, the Hercynian highlands and other less fertile parts, are commonly more what forestry than nature has made them.

The post-glacial establishment of forests as the prevailing vegetation of North-Western Europe became climatically possible when the shrinkage of the ice-sheets and their associated anticyclonic air-masses left the way open for depressions and moist Atlantic winds to penetrate into Central Europe. While North-West Europe was covered by ice, the major track of depressions lay well to the south across the Mediterranean and North Africa. Thus regions of North Africa and South-West Asia, now desert, were then covered with a rich forest or steppe vegetation. The inland regions in Anatolia and the Aral–Caspian basin and the Near East also became progressively arid in the period 12,000 to 6,000 B.C., providing less and less sustenance for the primitive hunting and herding populations that occupied them. Driven by hunger, they pushed out by whatever land and sea routes they could make their ways — into Western Europe, the Mediterranean peninsulas and Northern India. The basic racial stocks in all these lands, especially in North-Western Europe, are the issue of migrations following upon the northward shifting of climatic and vegetation zones towards the close of the Ice Age.

The constitution of the original deciduous forest varied considerably, as do its surviving modified remnants, according to local soil and other physical conditions, the commonest being the oak-elm-hornbeam association with considerable undergrowth. Such forest impedes human movement, provides little in the way of food, and was generally avoided by primitive man. On the other hand, the beech forests growing on calcareous soils overlying chalk or limestone, being free of undergrowth and comparatively open, did not present such serious barriers to early migration and settlement as the more widespread 'closed' forests.

These closed forests were naturally avoided by early man who lived mainly by hunting. Likewise the Neolithic groups migrating westward later from the Danubian lands, who practised agriculture, though largely of the shifting kind, and who were able to clear small tree growth by burning and felling, sought the relatively open loess country, more wooded probably then than now.[1] Hence early human migrations across Central Europe were directly influenced by the contemporary pattern of natural vegetation, being canalised along the two discontinuous loess belts of steppe and woodland on either side of the forested Hercynian highlands. The northern less broken belt bounded northwards by forests and marshes led from the Russian steppes and Danubia across Germany to the chalk uplands of northern France and southern Britain. The southern belt provided a way, also

---

[1] See *Geographical Journal* CVI (3, 4), 'The Loess Regions of Central Europe in prehistoric times', by A. Garnett.

from the Russian steppes via the Danube Valley and the Belfort gap to
the limestone uplands of eastern France. The latter route, though
constricted at the Iron Gate and at the Austrian Gate, widens out in
Hungary and Bavaria into open country with tracts of loess. These
doubtless provided halting places for consolidation of the successive
waves of migrations on their westward movements (Fig. 10).

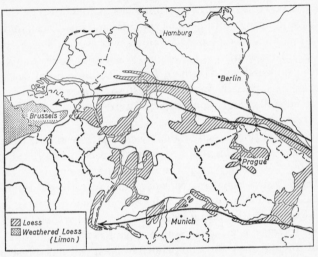

Fig. 10. Early migrations via loess belts. Loess and limon deposits
generalised after Charlesworth and Woldstedt (following earlier investigators).

In the West European lowlands, after centuries of occupation by
peoples equipped with means for destroying trees, little of the original
deciduous forests remains. These grew best on the agriculturally
productive brown forest soils, since taken into cultivation. The
scattered existing deciduous and mixed woodlands have generally
been selectively developed with commercially desirable species cut
out on reaching maturity. This holds still more of the large stretches
of coniferous forests planted on the Landes in France, on the sandy
soils of the North German Plain, on moorland areas in Great Britain
among others. In some regions, however, in particular the dry limestone country of south-east France and the Scottish moorlands, a
secondary degenerate form of natural vegetation has been established,
after destruction by man of the original forests. In south-east France
erosion of the soil previously held by the forest cover has contributed

to the present scattered bushy flora of brooms, dwarf oaks etc, sometimes in thickets (maquis), sometimes in open formation (garigue);
on the Scottish Highlands removal of the trees has facilitated the
spread of heathers and bogland plants, which, by forming a spongy
surface layer, aggravate the tendency to waterlogging of the soil in a
distinctly humid climate.

DISTRIBUTION OF FORESTS AND WOODS

The proportions of forested land to total area differ greatly among
the various countries. In general, forests occupy lands intermediate in
quality between those suitable for arable or pastoral farming on the
one hand, and barren wastes on the other, whether mountain heights
or sterile moorlands or bogs and marshes. Naturally the proportions
of such intermediate quality land vary from one country to another.
In the fully settled countries of Western and Central Europe human
agencies have also played a significant part (by deforestation and
afforestation) in combination with the purely physical. More attention
has been given to forestry in some countries, notably in Sweden and
Germany, than in others, by corporate organisations in the forms of
State-sponsored forestry departments and land reclamation authorities, as well as by private initiative.

LAND UNDER FORESTS AND WOODS, PER CENT OF TOTAL AREA

Sweden	51·1	Switzerland	24·5	Denmark	8·1
Finland	64·3 (51·3)[1]	Austria	36·1	Netherlands	7·0
Norway	23·2 (15·3)[1]	Bohemia and		United Kingdom	6·3
Germany	28·1	Moravia	30·0	Irish Republic	1·8
France	20·5	Belgium	18·7		

These countries contain in all some 320,000 sq. miles of forests and
woods = 33 per cent of total area.

Any human agencies that have contributed to bringing about these
differences have been guided by the basic physical conditions and
competing forms of land use. The high proportions of forest lands in
Finland and Sweden correspond to the large areas of land which are
not suitable for farming, nor yet too cold and barren for trees to grow
to maturity. The much lower proportion in Norway (well below the
average) is the result of adverse physical conditions, chiefly the large

---

[1] The bracketed percentages are of productive forests. Finland and Norway both
extend into the Arctic regions of scattered stunted deciduous tree vegetation.

areas of barren mountains; while in the lowland countries, Denmark and the Netherlands, the very low percentages arise from the commonly sharp transitions from fertile farmlands to the sterile geest of the glacial outwash, leaving little room for woodlands or forests, except by reclamation of the latter.

Most of the other continental countries listed in the Table contain highland or mountain regions, either Hercynian or Alpine, on which forests are a characteristic landscape feature, as indicated by the names Black Forest, Thüringer Wald, the Forest Cantons. Thus over 20 per cent of the area of each of those partly mountainous countries is under forest. At the lower end of the scale are the countries round the North Sea — Great Britain, the Netherlands and Denmark — in all of which the proportions of farm land (including rough pastures in Great Britain) are unusually large. In the Irish Republic, however, it is not so much the extent of land utilised for farming, as the numerous bogs and the exposure to Atlantic gales in most western parts that have hitherto restricted the proportion of land under woods and forests — the lowest among cool temperate countries.

Apart from the 'native' forests of Scandinavia, Finland and some mountainous regions, most of the existing woods and forests in Western and Central Europe are an integral element in the cultural, as distinct from the natural, landscape. Some woods have been planted and some forests preserved mainly for game shooting, or to add variety and beauty to the landscape. In general, however, forestry in its various forms has a commercial basis. The timber cut is in the nature of a crop, involving an inevitable long-term lock-up of capital wherever afforestation is carried out, or cut-over forest is replanted. It is for this reason that the larger afforestation projects are usually undertaken by organs of the governments. As there is a strong demand for softwoods of coniferous trees from both constructional and the paper-manufacturing industries, and as, moreover, coniferous trees make timber much faster than the deciduous hardwoods, the former are favoured in practical forestry at the expense of the latter. Man's interference with the natural vegetation of Western Europe, guided by economic motives, has resulted both in the wholesale disappearance of the original forests, and in the displacement of deciduous by coniferous trees on afforested land, previously occupied by the former.

A broad survey of the human occupation of North-Western Europe, from prehistoric to modern times, in relation to the natural vegetation, especially the forests, reveals the revolutionary technical progress made by European man. In the palaeolithic age the forests were fixed negative features in man's environment, forcing him to turn aside elsewhere; they were for him master elements in the landscape. In modern times the tables have been completely turned. The forests have been removed, remoulded and replanted at man's will to suit his near or distant ends; they have become plastic features of the environment.

The Cultural Landscape

The above brief survey of the transformation by active human intervention of much of the original forest vegetation of Western Europe is a conspicuous example of the process by which the existing rural landscape has come into being. Except on uninhabitable high mountains and sterile moorlands, this is the product of an intimate association of human activity with the natural conditions and of action and reaction between them. Few of the long-settled inhabited parts of North-Western Europe are as nature alone would have made them; and yet nearly all its man-made features, including cities, towns and villages, are expressions of a continuous quest for adjustment to natural conditions — a law of life for human beings, as it is for the plant world.

Whether land is left waste or afforested or farmed, and likewise what are the forms of farming, if any, are profoundly influenced by relief, soils and climate. It is true that here and there land has been 'made', e.g., the Dutch polders reclaimed from the sea, or has been redeemed for farming by the addition of chemical fertilisers, as in parts of the Netherlands-German Geest, or has been converted by drainage works from unwholesome swamps into fertile farm land; but all that man has done is to modify the landscape in co-operation with Nature, which is ready to resume control if he relaxes care and attention.

As natural conditions are the designers of the agricultural landscape scenes, so also do they shape the lay-out and modes of the whole range of constructional engineering works — the draining of marshes, the building of railways, the cutting of canals, the excavation of dock basins on tidal estuaries, the construction of hydro-electric power plants. The concentration of manufacturing industries on coalfields, formerly the rule, is yet another example of the shaping force of nature's physical pattern; geological structure determines the location of coal-mines, and also of petroleum wells and all other forms of mining activity. Man's conquest of nature is in reality a loose expression; whatever seemingly wonderful mutations he performs, or forces he releases in the physical realm, arise from his increasing knowledge of its properties and of the laws that govern it.[1]

In Western and West Central Europe the mature cultural landscape is seen in its most attractive forms in many fully-settled unspoilt rural regions, where it is the result of long human experience, guided by intelligent understanding of natural conditions. Its aesthetic quality arises from the harmony between the human element and the physical setting. Its pervading character is the skilful adaptation and modification of the natural elements of the environment to meet human needs and desires. It reveals the process of man working hand in hand with natural conditions and forces as they operate in time.

The numerous cities, towns and villages of the densely populated lowland regions of Western and Central Europe, together with the interconnecting means of transport, constitute an essential part of the cultural landscape. All the larger centres are closely related in their lay-out to the concrete expression of natural lines of least resistance i.e. the means of transport, the towns often developing tentacles along the main arteries of movement. This feature is an expression of their dependence, especially if they are manufacturing centres, upon the inward and outward movement of goods and persons. While it is true that many inland towns have arisen at convenient river crossings and at points of convergence of lines of least resistance of movement, some of the radiating strands in the present-day webs of communications are subsequent to and consequent upon the growth of the towns themselves. Here cause and effect are often intertwined. In the development of large cities such as London, Paris or Cologne, every addition of strands to the webs of surface or air transport, which their expans on induces, leads to further expansion of the city with further additions to the system of transport.

Though the modern facilities for transmission of power by electric current from hydro-electric or thermal stations favour the dispersal of industry, other factors such as transport costs, supplies of workpeople and access to markets enter into the choices of location of factories. Some electrically-powered industries, especially those of the lighter forms or those using large amounts of current, are be-

---

[1] 'Naturae enim non imperatur nisi parendo' — Francis Bacon. For we cannot command nature except by obeying her.

coming more dispersed, but the majority of new factories tend to concentrate in or around already existing industrial towns or great cities, the populations of which are in general growing faster by this and the above-mentioned developments than the country-wide totals.

Chapter 5

THE PATTERN OF FARMING;
CULTIVATED CROPS AND LIVE-STOCK

A TRAVELLER on a journey through any of the populated rural areas of North-Western and Central Europe will observe that farmland is the prevailing element of the landscape. If his journey takes him any considerable distance, he will notice that the types of farming vary according to changes in the physical conditions of relief, soil and climate. As noted above, Western Europe viewed as a whole is marked by physical diversity, and the closely adjusted pattern of land use for farming or horticulture is correspondingly complex. Its complexity is all the greater by reason of the widespread practice of rotation farm-

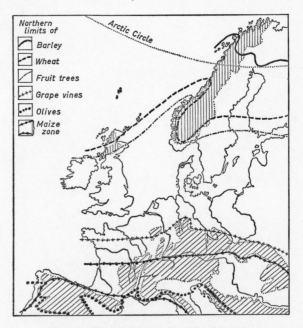

Fig. 11. The northern limits of leading crops.

ing, and the interlocking of animal husbandry with arable farming, by way of fodder crops, in the rotations. Nevertheless some broad distributional features of crops, pastures and live-stock in relation to geographical factors and farming practice can be recognised, which contribute to the understanding of the diverse cultural landscapes and of the economic geography of the various countries.

The relatively high latitude of this section of the continent makes it a marginal area for the leading temperature crops and fruits, in the sense that the northern limits of their successful cultivation are reached within it (Fig. 11). Of the cereals the most important as bread grains are wheat and rye, neither of which can be grown much beyond 60° N., except in parts of Sweden and Finland where the continentality of the summer climate is a favourable factor. Barley, however, which has the greatest climatic range of all cereals, will ripen inside the Arctic Circle in Scandinavia and Finland, and, if need be, takes the place, as bread grain, of wheat and rye beyond their northern limit. In common with all other cereals, tropical or temperate, the three so far considered require moderately dry, sunny weather in their ripening period to produce good yields of grain suitable for milling, or for malting in the case of barley.[1] In the humid climate of the Atlantic margin — in the western parts of Brittany, Ireland, Scotland and Scandinavia — oats, which ripen satisfactorily even in wet weather and are fairly tolerant of the commonly acid soils of these maritime lands, are the leading cereal crop. More oats than barley are, in fact, grown in most Western and Central European countries, though mainly for animal fodder.

The only other grain cultivated on any appreciable scale in Western Europe north of the Mediterranean is maize, which, owing to its climatic requirements of at least five months frost-free period and hot summers with considerable rainfall, is restricted to the Aquitaine Basin and lowlands and valleys east of it in the same latitude. It does not succeed without irrigation where the summer drought is marked, as in parts of the Mediterranean lands, so that in general it has a southern as well as a northern limit. Maize is also grown as a green cattle fodder crop north of its limit as a cereal, and can be, though rarely is, ripened in exceptionally warm summers as far north as the Netherlands.

---

[1] In North-West Europe these cereals vary in yield of grain suitable for milling or malting in direct proportion to the amount of sunshine, and in inverse proportion to the amount of rainfall.

AREAS UNDER SELECTED CROPS, AVERAGE 1955–8 (1000 hectares)

	Wheat	Rye	Barley	Oats	Maize	Sugar Beet	Pota-toes	Grape-Vines
Austria	261	208	173	181	49	47	179	37
Belgium	220	68	90	145	1	64	82	
Czechoslovakia	740	509	670	522	175	230	618	22
Denmark	71	120	706	220		89	86	
Finland	120	81	222	428		13	91	
France	4642	356	1713	1548	567	327	982	1435
East Germany	430	1096	324	441	3	221	790	
West Germany	1262	1479	875	916	5	270	1090	74
Ireland	166	1	125	186		32	107	
Luxembourg	22	4	6	17			7	1
Netherlands	105	151	77	148	2	73	132	
Norway	11	1	140	59			54	
Poland	1458	5140	720	1724	14	348	2761	
Sweden	306	104	278	524		53	117	
Switzerland	110	12	25	19	1	6	54	13
United Kingdom	875	10	1083	948		175	330	

Among the points that may be inferred from this general reference Table are: (*a*) a marked concentration of crop production in a central zone which comprises the United Kingdom, France, the Low Countries, Denmark and Germany together with Poland and Czecho-slovakia; (*b*) a close association of sugar beet (in rotations) with grain

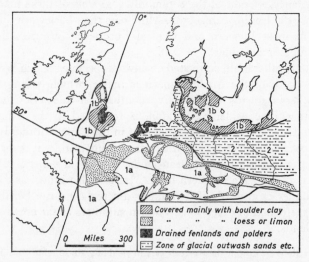

Fig. 12. Cereal zones in relation to drift deposits. 1a. Main wheat and barley belt. 1b. Northern wheat and barley areas. 2. Rye-potato belt.

crops; (c) the larger areas given to rye than to wheat in five countries, Denmark, the Netherlands, West and East Germany and Poland, across which lies a broad belt of glacial outwash (Fig. 12); (d) the definite climatic limits of cultivation of both grape-vines and maize.

The genera wheat, barley and oats each comprise various species. The urge to extend the climatic ranges and the yields of these cereals has led to the breeding of special varieties suited to particular conditions of climate and demand. Thus the oats grown in Scotland differ from those native to, and cultivated in, North Africa, though the former may include the latter among their parent stocks; the hard macaroni wheats of the species *Triticum durum* grown in Italy do not succeed in the moist British climate, where soft varieties have been developed from the species *Triticum vulgare*. Whereas formerly slow progress was made by individuals following haphazard trial and error methods, in recent times the tempo of specialised improvement has been greatly accelerated by scientific breeding at research stations to increase the yields and/or to improve the qualities of cereals, as well as of many other cultivated plants. West Europeans both in Europe and North America have been foremost in this branch of technical progress, which from them, often under guidance of their experts, has spread to other, even tropical lands.

Fruit-bearing trees and plants cultivated in North-Western Europe, though of diverse kinds, may be considered as a group. The northern limit of the hardier temperate deciduous fruits e.g. apples, plums, lies a little south of that of wheat cultivation, as these require well over 100 days frost-free period to complete their foliage and fruiting cycle. Grape-vines grown for wine require dry sunny weather with temperatures of 70° F. and over during at least three months. Being deep-rooted plants, they can tolerate the summer droughts of the Mediterranean region where they flourish. Their northern limit in Western Europe is accordingly the line beyond which a cool and humid oceanic climate prevails. As great importance is attached to the flavour qualities of wines, and as these depend upon special conditions of soil and climate as well as upon the traditional skill of the growers, the production of branded wines is highly specialised by districts, e.g. Burgundy, Champagne. Moselle; though ordinary wines have a much wider range of production i.e. in France south of the Loire, and in favoured districts in Switzerland, the Rhine Rift Valley and Austria. Olives demand much more accentuated Mediterranean climatic conditions than vines, and are thus confined in the above-listed countries to a small triangular region round the Rhône delta in southern France.

Various members of the fleshy and tuberous root families of plants have found congenial conditions in North-Western and Central Europe, where they are extensively cultivated — two of them, namely sugar beet and potatoes, primarily for human food, others such as turnips, swede turnips and mangolds mainly for animal fodder. All five hold important places as rotation crops in mixed farming.

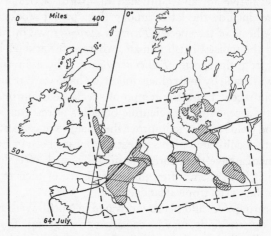

Fig. 13. The sugar beet rectangle. The areas of cultivation shaded produce 80 per cent of 8 to 8½ million tons p.a. of beet sugar produced in Western and Central Europe.

Sugar beet are grown as a dual purpose crop. In addition to the sugar extracted from them, they provide 'soft' fodders in both the green tops and the pulp residue, especially valuable to balance the 'hard' rations of hay etc. in the winter stall-feeding of cattle. Like other root crops they fit well into rotations in which wheat and barley are the cardinal crops, though they require much labour for weeding and singling. In order to succeed well, sugar beet require a fairly rich loam type of soil, temperatures over 60° F. with abundant sunshine for the three summer months, a moderate, well-distributed rainfall in the growing period, and fairly dry autumn weather with cool nights to promote the storage of sugar. These conditions are best satisfied in a group of scattered areas within a rectangle intersected lengthwise by the north-eastward trending July isotherm of 64° F. (Fig. 13).

Potatoes are much more widely cultivated than sugar beet. They are grown in quantity in every country of Western and Central Europe, especially on the belt of glacial sands in Germany and Poland (Fig. 12), where they occupy 20 to 25 per cent of the land sown to the leading crops. Though sensitive to frost, most varieties of potatoes mature within four months of planting, and can therefore be grown in high latitudes, as in Finland, and at comparatively high altitudes (being native of the high Andes), provided the frost-free period exceeds 120 days. They are, however, susceptible to disease in wet summers, when the crops may fail, though this misfortune is rarer now that field spraying is generally practised. Though potatoes are grown mainly for human consumption, the surplus crops and rejects are utilised, notably in Germany and the Netherlands, for pig fodder and the distillation of alcohol.

Soils as well as climatic conditions are a significant factor influencing the distribution of a number of the above crops. Reference has been made to the special soil requirements of sugar beet. Wheat also and barley for malting require good medium loam or heavy loam soils, naturally well suited to the root crops grown in rotation with those cereals. Whereas wheat, brewer's barley and sugar beet, being exacting in their requirements, are in general restricted to the more fertile soils, rye and potatoes succeed on the less fertile sandy soils if these are treated with the appropriate artificial fertilisers. On such lands oats also, more tolerant than wheat of soils as well as of climatic conditions, are an important crop. Broadly classified, the chief crops cultivated in Western and Central Europe fall into three groups: the rather exacting wheat, malting barley and sugar beet; the relatively tolerant rye, oats and potatoes; and roots, temporary grass and other fodder plants grown in rotation with crops of the preceding groups.

THE STRUCTURE OF MIXED FARMING

We now pass on to a survey of mixed farming as commonly practised in this section of Western Europe, with which fodder crops for live-stock may be conveniently considered. As a general rule, animal husbandry for the production of meats, dairy products, eggs etc. goes hand in hand with the cultivation of cereals and other food crops, and is in many areas and in some whole countries, e.g. Denmark and the Irish Republic, the predominant element in the farming industry. Permanent pastures are insufficient in all the countries to carry the stocks of cattle and sheep through the winter season, so in general considerable quantities of fodders in addition to hay have to be provided for them. These are largely grown on farms, but they have to be supplemented by imported concentrated fodders such as maize and by various by-products, e.g., milling offals, molasses, brewers' grains and oil-cakes derived partly at least from imported materials.

The crop rotations commonly followed vary from four to seven years in different parts. In almost all the rotations, cereal crops, (wheat, barley, oats, rye, according to climate and soils) are grown in at least two years; and potatoes, root crops or sugar beet, green fodders and/or temporary grass in the remaining years. Temporary pastures down for about three years are a characteristic feature of the more humid regions where cattle and dairy-farming are more important than the cultivation of cereals except of oats, used chiefly as live-stock fodder. In the long as well as the short rotations, root crops (turnips etc.) or green fodder crops, e.g. clover, kale, rape, occupy the land for one or two years. Hence mixed farming of one kind or another, in which dairying or the carrying of beef cattle or sheep is the leading feature, prevails throughout the maritime parts of Western Europe, as the most advantageous way of utilising resources in keeping with the demand for farm products in terms of relative prices.

	Numbers of live-stock 1957–8 (millions)			*Permanent grass mainly rough grazings (mill. hectares 1958)*
	Cattle	Sheep	Pigs	
Austria	2·3	0·20	2·9	2·317
Belgium	2·6	0·17	1·42	0·725
Czechoslovakia	4·09	0·89	5·4	1·94
Denmark	3·27	0·035	5·35	0·37
Finland	1·9	0·40	0·5	0·28
France	17·9	8·6	8·13	12·29
East Germany	3·7	2·0	8·25	1·3
West Germany	12·0	1·13	15·5	5·66
Irish Republic	4·47	4·17	0·90	3·36
Luxembourg	0·14		0·11	0·06
Netherlands	3·2	0·5	2·47	1·27
Norway	1·12	1·8	0·42	0·19
Poland	8·2	3·88	11·96	4·18
Sweden	2·54	0·14	2·03	0·68
Switzerland	1·66	0·2	1·19	1·73
United Kingdom	10·96	26·2	6·48	12·285
Totals	80·05	50·315	73·01	48·637

It will be noted that some 35 million sheep, nearly two-thirds of all those in the European countries listed, are in the United Kingdom and France, which between them contain half the total of rough hill and mountain pastures. Sheep can survive where cattle would starve.

Throughout the lowlands of Western and Central Europe, in fact, cattle hold a much more important place in farming than sheep. It will be seen from the Table above that their total number exceeds that of sheep by nearly 60 per cent, and that they are more numerous in every country except the United Kingdom and Norway, in the former of which, as in France, the large areas of hill and mountain grazings account for the unusual number of sheep. Moreover, as in fodder requirements and in salable products, one head of cattle is held equivalent to from five to seven sheep, the numbers of cattle should accordingly be multiplied by six in order to arrive at a true comparison, which gives an effective overall ratio of cattle to sheep in the above countries of Europe of nearly 10 to 1. In point of fact, sheep are steadily losing ground to cattle in this part of the world, where they are now not much more numerous than in New Zealand; if present trends continue, that small country, less than one-ninth of North-West and Central Europe in area, will soon have a greater number of sheep.

Pigs are also more numerous than sheep in this section of Europe, and as they provide a much more rapid 'turnover', are immensely more important as sources of meat supplies. They are commonly closely linked with the dairy industry wherever the by-products skim-milk, buttermilk and whey are available as valuable adjuncts to their rations. Their solid feed consists of the surpluses and residues of farm crops — inferior corn and potatoes, roots such as swedes, and milling offals — supplemented by imported fattening fodders such as maize. For the production of high quality bacon, the ideal basic rations are skim-milk and barley meal, and in Denmark where the emphasis is on quality, large quantities of barley are grown expressly for pig-feeding.

In contrast with the large-scale, extensive type of cultivation in the so-called new countries, or even in Eastern Europe, farming in North-West and Central Europe is characterised by an intensive, many-sided and complex utilisation of the land resources. With the exception of the wine-producing districts of France and elsewhere, monoculture is extremely rare. Yet even in those districts as in the regions of general mixed farming, the guiding principle in practice is to adjust the forms of production to a pattern set by the great variety of combinations of climate and soils, but all subject to modification by the conditions of demand for the products as expressed by market prices, modified in their turn in various countries by protective tariffs and subsidies in favour of the farming industries. These human factors are subject to changes according to variations in economic conditions and in government policies; the role of nature, expressed as a combination of the fixed elements terrain and climate, remains the basic factor contributing to the varied forms of agricultural production.

Chapter 6

THE BRITISH ISLES. GENERAL SURVEY

THE British Isles are the unsubmerged portions of the European continental shelf which extends outwards to the 100 fathom line 50 to 100 miles west of Ireland and the outer Hebrides. During the Pleistocene Glacial period, when large quantities of sea-water were impounded in the ice-sheets and the level of the oceans was lower than it is now, much of this shelf must have been dry land. Britain then formed a western extension of the continental area, being united with it across the Straits of Dover and the Narrow Seas, as it had been intermittently in previous geological times. The severance was apparently a gradual process consequent upon the release of water from the melting ice-sheets, accompanied by a slow subsidence of the North Sea and Channel regions. The lowering of the land surface relatively to sea level, still apparently in progress in south-east England, has enabled the sea to creep up the lower valleys of many rivers in both Great Britain and Ireland, so forming tidal estuaries and rias.

However, a land bridge at the present Dover Straits persisted long enough, until about 5,000 B.C. as estimated, for the flora and fauna to be replenished after the Ice Age by immigrant continental species, and for the early Neolithic peoples to make use of a land crossing. The final break may have been induced by the overflow from the North Sea basin into the English Channel of the glacial melt-water plus the river-water of the Rhine-Meuse-Thames system. At a later stage when, with the general rise of the sea-level caused by further melting of ice-sheets, Atlantic tidal waters broke through from the Channel, the separation of Britain was complete. At the same time the climate became warmer with the establishment of sea-water round, and of maritime conditions over, the British Isles. The Goodwin Sands, exposed at lowest tides, are in part a remnant of the former land connection, pointing to the comparatively recent encroachment by the Narrow Seas.

The westward extension of continental structural elements into the British Isles bears witness to former continuity of the land surfaces

(Fig. 1). These formations in order of age are, as noted in Chapter 2, the Caledonides in the north-west and fringing the Irish Sea; the Armorican, most conspicuous in the south-west peninsulas of both islands and also in the Pennines; and the outer waves of the Alpine upheavals in the scarplands of eastern and south-eastern England.

The first of these groups comprise not only the Scottish Highlands and the broken remains of their continuation into north-west Ireland, but also the Southern Uplands in Scotland, the cores of the Cumbrian highlands and of the Isle of Man, the Cambrian Mountains of north and central Wales, and the Mourne and Wicklow Mountains facing their British counterparts across the Irish Sea. Since their original folding, these ancient highlands have more than once been reduced to peneplanes by prolonged erosion, and subsequently re-elevated with much faulting and extensive granitic intrusions now forming some of the highest parts; while their sedimentary rocks have been crumpled and become generally metamorphic. The highland areas, composed mainly of resistant crystalline rocks from which moving ice in the past and subsequent erosion have removed much of the weathered material, are commonly bare or have a thin covering of soil. Yet the British Isles owe their continued existence as land areas in no small measure to these Caledonian highlands, both because of their considerable extent, and because they are so disposed as to form protective buttresses against the vigorous aerial and marine erosion from the North Atlantic.

The Armorican group comprises as its more characteristic elements the denuded anticlinal ridges in Devon and Cornwall, in South Wales, and in Kerry and Cork in south-west Ireland, together with the Mendip Hills and a buried anticline under the London Basin, all with a general east-west trend. In addition, the Malvern and Shropshire Hills and the Pennines in England, and various outliers rising from the Central Irish Plain, were re-elevated as horsts, or originated in the extensive Armorican upheavals. In England a fan-like arrangement of the axes of uplift can be observed; they turn from E.–W. in the south, to N.–S. (as in the Pennines) against the resistant Cambrian and Cumbrian massifs. In Ireland the axes curve S.–E. against the Wicklow massif in the direction of those of South Wales and Exmoor. The Armorican folding at the close of the Carboniferous period has been largely responsible for the preservation of coal-measures in synclinal basins in Britain as also in continental countries (see pp. 24–5). In Britain these basins occur in the Central Lowlands of Scotland, on the flanks of the Pennines, between the anticlinal 'ribs' of the Midlands, and on the southern margin of the Brecon Beacons ridge in south Wales.

The Alpine waves of folding reached as far as the Exe-Tees line in England, throwing the accumulated thick beds of soft Mesozoic rocks into a series of anticlinal and synclinal flexures in the South-East. Their axes, like those of the Armorican anticlinal structures to the west of them, are arranged in fan-like pattern, the 'ribs' of which, hinged on east Devon, turn from an easterly direction in the Weald to a northerly one in Lincolnshire and Yorkshire. Rapid erosion of the unresistant Jurassic and Cretaceous limestones, sandstones and clays has deformed the anticlines into a succession of escarpments. On the whole, Britain was not greatly affected by the Alpine orogenesis. Apart from the moderate folding of strata in south-east England, tectonic disturbances occurred in the Caledonian highland zone in association with the foundering of Atlantis. These highlands were fractured and re-elevated in parts, and extensive outpourings of basalt lava occurred in western Scotland and northern Ireland, together with intrusions of numerous dykes extending into northern England.

The prolonged glaciation of the Ice Age has left its marks upon the surface features of the British Isles as on those of the northern mainland. Ice-sheets advancing across the floor of the North Sea from Scandinavia were joined by others from the ice-caps on the northern British mountain masses, reaching a maximum extension along a line approximately the northern boundary of the Thames Basin (Fig. 2). The ancient north-western and western highlands have naturally been most affected by ice-erosion. Their summits have in general been planed off into rounded forms, though in some parts, for example the Cairngorm Mountains in Scotland, the Snowdon Range and the Carantuohill district in Kerry, cirques (corries) and arêtes have been carved out of the mountains. In the Scottish Highlands and in Cumbria deep flat-floored valleys also have been excavated, often containing ribbon lakes characteristic of glaciated highlands, or forming fiords where deepened below sea-level on the west Scottish coast.

On the lowlands and the scarplands the effects of glaciation, though much less striking than on the mountainous areas, have a highly important bearing upon agriculture. Masses of rock waste removed from the highlands by ice have been transported southwards over distances up to several hundreds of miles and deposited as a mantle of glacial drift. This consists, notably in East Anglia, of gently undulating stretches of fertile boulder clay, though in some parts, especially on the Central Irish Plain, there are numerous morainic ridges, eskers and drumlins, composed of sand and gravel mingled with clay. Disturbances of the pre-existing drainage pattern are not uncommon. Some rivers such as the Yorkshire Derwent and the Cheshire Dee have been diverted either by lobes of the ice-sheets or by moraines athwart their old courses; and on the Irish Plain the numerous eskers have impeded the flow of naturally sluggish rivers, thus aggravating the tendency to the formation of bogs.

UTILISATION OF HIGHLANDS AND UPLANDS

The older Caledonian and Armorican highlands differ from the younger Jurassic (Oolitic) and Cretaceous (Chalk) scarplands not only in height and structure, but also in the extent and the forms of their utilisation under human occupation. Considerable parts of all the former lie between 1,000 and 3,000 feet in elevation, and being exposed to the full force of the Atlantic storms, are windswept and excessively wet. Their leached and generally acid soils carry a mixed moorland, bog and coarse grass vegetation, interspersed with patches of pasture grasses in less unfavourable situations. Though these mountain uplands are quite unsuitable for ordinary mixed farming, they are widely utilised for hill sheep-farming. Large numbers of sheep all told are pastured on them, part of the year at least, being brought down to lowland farms in very severe weather, and also for fattening. The intermediate slopes, between 1,000 and 500 feet, of many of these ancient highlands are more productive; live-stock (chiefly cattle) farming with some cultivation of fodder crops is practised wherever climate and soils permit. Below 500 feet mixed farming is common, for the lowland types of farming can generally be pushed up to that elevation, and well above it in southern England and Ireland.

The Oolitic and Chalk scarplands seldom rise above a height of 1,000 feet. Because they are situated in the drier and sunnier parts of the country, and their soils tend to be lime-rich and acid-free (except on the Greensand ridges), mixed farming with cereal and other field crops often extends towards their summit levels. Where thin soils overlie the chalk, however, and short grass is the natural cover, sheep-pasturing is common. An interesting development of post-war years has been the extension of arable farming on these scarplands, with sugar beet and cattle-fodder crops in the rotations at the expense of turnips formerly fed to sheep. The course of this development is reflected in changes in the total number of sheep in the United Kingdom, which fell from 27 millions in the 1930's to under 23 millions in 1954, but rose again to over 27 millions in 1959 with a decline in the wheat acreage (p. 68).

Except for the long worked tin, copper and lead ores of Cornwall and of the hematite iron ores of south Cumbria, no substantial deposits of metallic ores have been found in the older highlands of the British Isles. Nor are these highlands capable of providing more than limited supplies of hydro-electricity. Though precipitation on them is abundant, their moderate elevation restricts the utilisable 'heads' of water to the heavily glaciated regions of the Scottish Highlands and North Wales. In the former, numerous projects, some large, and some involving considerable diversion works, have been completed or are planned. The power stations already in operation are situated in or near Glenmore, such as those at Foyers, Kinlochleven and Fort William, or in the upper Tay area, e.g. Loch Rannoch, Loch Tummel and Pitlochry. In North Wales power has been developed from falls on streams descending into the Ffestiniog and Conway valleys. The heavy precipitation on the north-western British highlands, together with a terrain that lends itself to the construction of reservoirs, has been utilised for water supplies by towns far and near; Manchester for example obtains its water from the Lake District, Liverpool–Birkenhead from North Wales, Birmingham from central Wales, and Sheffield, Derby and Leicester from the Pennines.

The coal-measures associated with the Pennines belong strictly speaking to the adjacent industrial regions of the outer slopes and plains, with which they are described in the next chapter. On the other hand, extensive deposits of low-grade iron ores occur interbedded in the strata of the Jurassic escarpment, notably in Lincolnshire and Northamptonshire; these contribute a substantial share of the ore supplies for the British iron and steel industry. Rock materials also, such as limestone, slate and granite, have been quarried at various places in the older highlands, and chalk in the chalk escarpments. Of these, far the most important nowadays is limestone (including chalk), widely used for the manufacture of cement and for liming agricultural land. The use of limestone, sandstone, slates and granite as building materials has declined with the introduction of alternative fabricated products, costing less in terms of human labour.

CLIMATIC CONDITIONS IN RELATION TO AGRICULTURE

The general references to the British climate in Chapter 3 leave some points of detail to be noted. From Figs. 14 and 15 it will be observed that (a) in both Great Britain and Ireland the mean annual rainfall exceeds 40 inches in most western parts, and exceeds 60 inches on sections of the highlands, (b) whereas the proportion of total area

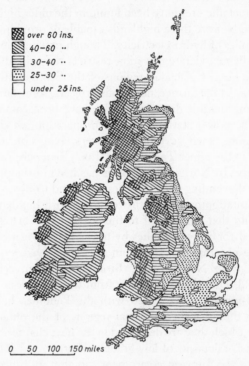

over 60 ins.
40–60 ··
30–40 ··
25–30 ··
under 25 ins.

0   50   100   150 miles

Fig. 14. The mean annual rainfall of the British Isles. Based on the *Climatological Atlas of the British Isles*. H.M. Stationery Office 1952: mean annual rainfall 1901–30.

that receives less than 40 inches is over three-quarters of England and Wales, it is under one-half of both Scotland and Ireland, and still greater differences appear in the proportions receiving less than 30 inches, which in Scotland and Ireland are very small, (c) winter temperatures are some 4° F. higher in the west where Atlantic influences predominate, than in the east where these are modified by continental influences; (*d*) summer temperatures are some 6° F. higher in southern than in northern Britain, owing to the combined effects of latitude and distance from the continent, then warmer than the seas, (*e*) the tempering influence of the Irish Sea is shown by the wedge of warmth over it in winter (over 42° F.), replaced by a bridge of relatively cool air in summer (under 60° F.).

Most significant on these maps are the isohyet of 40 inches mean

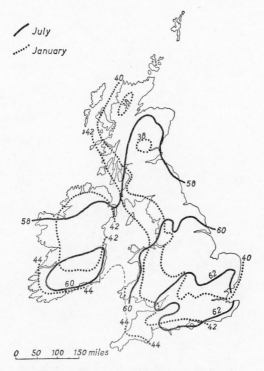

Fig. 15. Selected isotherms of January and July mean temperatures in the British Isles. Source as for Figure 14.

annual rainfall and the July isotherm of 58° F., in that they indicate limits beyond which the range of farming is restricted. Thus north-west Scotland, which is cool in summer and wet throughout the year, is well-nigh useless for farming except of the poor crofter kind. Though the rest of Britain and the whole of Ireland below about 600 feet are warm enough in summer for the cultivation of a variety of crops besides the crofter's mainstays, oats, turnips and potatoes, considerable areas in both islands, especially in Ireland, which receive more than 40 inches of rainfall per annum, are too wet for reliable returns from the more desirable temperate crops such as wheat, barley and sugar beet. In effect, full-scale farming is restricted to eastern Ireland excluding the Wicklow Mountains, eastern Scotland as far north as Inverness, and much of lowland England and the Welsh borderland (Figs. 16, 17, 41).

The complex pattern of mixed farming in Western Europe with

Fig. 16. The distribution of grain crop cultivation in Great Britain. Based on Ministry of Agriculture Returns of Acreage, June 1959.

(1) 80 per cent of total wheat and 82 per cent of total barley acreage.
(2) 18 per cent of total wheat and 12 per cent of total barley acreage.
(3) Little grain cultivation except of some oats and mixed (fodder) corn in valleys.
(4) Scattered cultivation of oats outside main cereal areas (1) and (2).

Notes. I. The proportions of total *production* of wheat and barley in areas 1 and 2 are greater even than the acreage percentages owing to higher yields there.
II. While the cultivation of barley declines westward sooner than that of wheat, oats (grown also extensively in areas 1 and 2) have in effect no western limit in Great Britain, as they have in Ireland (Fig. 41).

variations of emphasis on this or that product or group of products, according to the climate, the soils and market conditions described in the previous chapter, are well illustrated in the British Isles, where special types of live-stock and arable farming are associated with particular regions.

Of the three chief kinds of live-stock, cattle are kept mainly on the lowlands where their relatively large requirements of provender such as meadow grass, hay and fodder crops can be grown on the farms, supplemented by readily accessible supplies of oil-cakes and milling offals made largely from imported materials. In England both beef and dairy cattle are more numerous in the western than in the eastern counties, in keeping with the higher proportions of pasture lands to cornfields in the former, though dairy cattle have been increasing in the latter mainly for the production of liquid milk for town supplies. In Scotland the eastern coastal belt is noted for beef cattle, while the south-western region, being adjacent to the Clyde industrial belt, leans rather more to dairy than to beef cattle. In Ireland, where beef cattle are more numerous than dairy cattle, the areas of greatest concentration are the counties Meath and Kildare behind Dublin and the south-western counties Limerick and Cork, in the latter pair of which dairy cattle also are numerous (Fig. 40).

Pigs are reared chiefly in the lowland areas of general mixed farming, especially in eastern England, where farm-grown fodders together with imported concentrated feeding stuffs are available; they are also numerous in the West Country belt from Cheshire to Cornwall, and in County Cork in Ireland, where they are associated with specialisation in dairy-farming.

Contrary to the common impression, the majority of the sheep in both Great Britain and Ireland are raised on the western highland areas where the rainfall is 40 to 60 inches. Being in the nature of residual claimants upon farm land in these islands (see p. 57), sheep tend to be relegated to the rough hill and mountain pastures, in particular those of Wales, Cumbria, the Southern Uplands and the western Scottish Highlands, which cannot be usefully farmed in any other way; and the breeds favoured are such as can withstand the harsh climate of these rain-drenched highlands. In Ireland a similar concentration of sheep in wet inhospitable country is to be observed; the area of greatest density is actually County Galway in the far west in which the seaward parts are covered with rugged highlands, lakes and bogs, and the overall average rainfall is some 50 inches.

CEREALS AND SUGAR BEET

As shown on the map, Fig. 16, a striking feature of the distribution of cereal cultivation, especially in England and Wales, is the general transition from east to west in order of the series barley,[1] wheat, oats. First barley, then wheat dwindles, until finally oats grown mainly for fodder are the only significant cereal crop. The major area for barley is the easternmost belt of England comprising East Anglia and a narrowing extension northwards beyond the Humber, where the fertile glacial soils, the low rainfall of 24 to 30 inches and the warm summers are favourable conditions. For wheat, which requires much the same conditions, the major area of cultivation covers that of barley, reaching somewhat farther inland in areas of under 25 inches rainfall. The cultivation of both barley and wheat extends on a reduced scale across the Midlands and thence south to the Channel Coast; but west of a line Liverpool-Exeter, little of either is grown apart from some fodder barley. The area sown to wheat in 1954 in Great Britain and Northern Ireland was 20 per cent greater than the average of the years 1935–9, and that under other grains combined was over 60 per cent greater. This expansion was achieved by extending cereal cultivation on to marginal lands where costs are relatively high. It was made possible by Government subsidies, paid as a kind of national insurance premium to reduce dependence upon imported grains.[2]

In Scotland wheat is grown on a limited scale in the east round the Firths of Forth and Tay, and some barley also in the same area and in others here and there on the eastern lowlands from Berwick-on-Tweed to Inverness, where climatic conditions are similar to those in Eastern England, though with lower summer temperatures. In Ireland barley has been long a relatively important crop in an area south and west of the Wicklow Highlands. In recent years, however, wheat has become a leading crop in the Republic, occupying upwards of 50 per cent greater area than barley. Under Government encouragement its cultivation has expanded in the eastern lowlands wherever it is likely to succeed.

---

[1] That is, barley suitable for malting. Only good quality grain is accepted by the brewing trade; inferior qualities commonly grown on farms outside the eastern cereal belt are used for feeding pigs and other live-stock. Barley is less tolerant of excessive moisture even than wheat.

[2] By 1959 the wheat acreage had declined by 10 per cent from that of 1955–6, which, however, was offset by an increase in the area under barley and oats, indicating some change-over to live-stock at the expense of bread grain.

Oats are cultivated more widely than either of the above cereals throughout the British Isles. They are, in fact, grown on a majority of the farms in England and Wales, chiefly for animal fodder, both in the regions that specialise in wheat and barley, and beyond them to the west and north where the climate is too wet and sunless and the soils generally too acid for those grains; but in much greater proportion of the total arable in the latter than in the former. The extension of oats

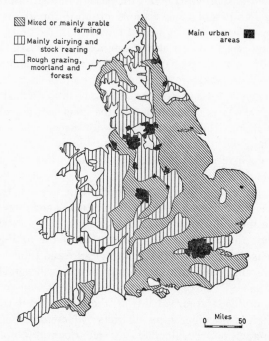

Fig. 17. The major types of farming in England and Wales.
Adapted after W. B. Mercer and others. *British Farming.* H.M.S.O. 1951.

to the climatic margins of cereal cultivation appears in both Ireland and Scotland. In Ireland even this crop dwindles away westward as the rainfall increases above 40 inches (Fig. 41). Likewise in Scotland, where rain-tolerant oats occupy more than half the total tillage, the 40 inch isohyet marks the general westward limit of their cultivation except for parts of the western Central Lowlands and scattered patches in the western Highlands.

Sugar beet is grown extensively in the eastern cereal belt from central Essex to the Vale of York, where soils, climatic conditions and the structure of mixed rotation farming (see p. 54) are suited to their cultivation. The moderate rainfall and relatively high proportion of sunshine in that area are favourable to the formation of sugar in the roots, now averaging 20 per cent of their weight; the great majority of the extraction factories in Great Britain, 15 out of 18 in all, are situated within this belt. As sugar beet is a bulky crop, production has to be concentrated on farms as near as possible to the factories in order to minimise transport costs. Thus the pattern of distribution is in the form of a number of constellations grouped round the scattered factories, each located in an area of intensive mixed arable and livestock farming. Sugar beet is also grown in a narrow coastal belt round the Firth of Forth in Scotland (one factory) and in another belt in Shropshire-Worcestershire (two factories), both favourable by reason of their relatively dry sunny climate. In the Irish Republic the cultivation of sugar beet is concentrated in the chief cereal-growing area, that of the Barrow valley and the south-east corner. There and also in Great Britain the industry has been established and its expansion fostered by Government assistance, without which its chances of success would have been small.

Commercial production of both orchard and small fruit in the British Isles is concentrated largely in three major and three secondary areas. The more important are north Kent with an extension into south Essex, the Spalding-Wisbech district of the middle Fenland with the neighbouring parts of Cambridgeshire and Lincolnshire, and the West Country region of the lower Severn valley including the highly specialised Vale of Evesham. The less important are the Carse of Gowrie in Scotland for small fruit, the Hampshire basin, also for small fruit, and the cider apple districts of Hereford, Somerset and Devon. In addition, considerable aggregate quantities, not definitely known, are produced in private orchards and gardens, chiefly in eastern, central and southern England.

Very little fruit is produced commercially in Ireland, and the Carse of Gowrie is the only district of much importance in Scotland, the chief limiting factor in both countries being lack of sunshine. Of the six areas mentioned above, the five that specialise in dessert fruit[1] are situated in the drier parts of Great Britain, where the relatively warm and sunny summers are favourable to proper ripening; three of them are in the eastern coastlands, while the Hampshire and the lower

---

[1] Much of the dessert fruit grown in the Fenland, the Vale of Evesham and the Carse of Gowrie is canned or made into preserves.

Severn areas are on the lee sides of the chalk uplands and the Welsh Highlands respectively. In the West Country belt from Hereford and Gloucester to south Devon, cider apples are grown in quantity both commercially and privately on farms for the production of a traditional West Country drink.

FUEL AND POWER RESOURCES

The Table, p. 26, of outputs of fuel and water-power in North-Western and Central Europe shows that Great Britain produced about 37 per cent of all the hard coal and almost one-third of the total thermal equivalent of coal and lignite combined, but only about 2 per cent of the hydro-electric power. It is evident that Britain's place as an industrial country rests upon coal, her most conspicuous endowment of natural resources and the mainspring of her industrial functioning. The tendency still apparent, in spite of decentralisation with the increase of thermally generated electric power, for industry in general, and heavy industry in particular, to be concentrated near pithead supplies of coal, gives the distribution of coal output by districts special significance; it is, in fact, a key to the localisation of large sectors of industrial activity.

	Average 1931–2	*Average 1958–9* (*including open-cast*)
Scottish	28·8	19·9
Northumberland & Durham	41·9	39·44
Cumberland	1·3	1·02
Yorks, Notts-Derby	65·6	85·07
S. Derby & Leicester	3·3	7·3
N. Staffs.	5·5	6·03
Lancashire & Cheshire & N. Wales	16·7	15·98
West Midlands	11·5	11·05
South Wales	36·0	22·4
Western (Forest of Dean & Bristol-Somerset)	2·0	1·12
Kent	1·7	1·62
Totals	214·3	210·93

Output of coal in Great Britain (millions of tons).

In the interval of 27 years covered by the above Table, the production of the Scottish and the South Wales coalfields declined appreciably, owing in the former to the partial exhaustion of the Lanarkshire field, now producing little over half the tonnage of 1931–2; and in the latter to a similar working out of seams in the northern 'outcrop' section of the Glamorganshire field. These are instances of the onset of conditions common to old coalfields. Even in the newer productive sections, as the more accessible or richer seams are worked over and old pits are closed, new shafts have to be sunk farther out from the outcrops and to greater depths to reach the generally downward-dipping seams — a feature illustrated by the graphs in Fig. 29 showing the locations and the average depths of the active pits in the south-east Pennine coalfield. Though the British coal reserves, estimated at over 40,000 million tons, are still large, considerable capital expenditure is required to keep down working costs.

From 1950 to 1959 the total output of coal was maintained round about 210 million tons per annum in three ways: by stabilisation of production from a number of the smaller high-cost pits, by open-cast workings and by considerable expansion in the largest and richest group, that of the south-east Pennines. The first of these was possible as long as overall demand for coal showed an upward trend, but the increasing internal substitution of oil fuel for coal in industry, by the railways and by domestic consumers, and the shrinkage of exports, have necessitated the closing of high-cost pits. In view of this still growing competition and of that of hydro-electricity in continental countries formerly customers for British coal, coal-mining in Britain will have to be concentrated, it seems, in the more productive areas, with a lower total output than in the past. Coal is likely to lose further ground as the main source of British supplies of fuel and power.

The following Table shows how consumption was distributed in 1958-9 compared with 1946.

	1946	Average 1958-9
Electricity Works	26·2	46·15
Coke Ovens	20·1	26·75
Gas Works	22·7	23·65
Railways	15·1	10·8
Industrial Consumers	37·8	32·55
Collieries	10·6	6·15
Domestic Consumers (Merchants' disposals and Miners' coal)	36·1	35·3
Miscellaneous	17·6	15·35
Totals	186·2	196·7

Inland consumption of Coal, Great Britain and Northern Ireland (million tons).

The largest increases recorded in this Table were in Electricity Works and Coke Ovens, for both of which expansion of industrial activity was largely responsible. Factories have been using electricity for power in place of raw coal, and the output of coke ovens is taken chiefly by blast furnaces and smelting works. Exports and ships' bunkers accounted for an average of 6·5 million tons in 1958–9. The partial eclipse of the British coal industry is illustrated by comparison of present-day overall production and exports with those for 1913, which were 287·4 million tons and 94·4 million tons respectively.

IRON ORES: THE IRON AND STEEL INDUSTRY

In the two years 1957–8 production of iron ore in Great Britain averaged 15·7 million tons, the metal content of which, however, was only about 4·2 million tons. Except for less than half a million tons of hematite ores produced in Cumberland and South Wales, the rest consisted of 'lean' ores averaging only 27 per cent of iron, quarried at various places in the Jurassic escarpment; about half of them in the Lias beds from north Lincolnshire to Oxfordshire, and the balance in the Inferior Oolite from south Lincolnshire to Rutland (Fig. 23). The distribution of output (million tons) in 1957–8 was as follows: Yorkshire (Cleveland) 0·56, Lincolnshire 6·4, Leicester and Rutland 2·04, Northants 4·86, Oxfordshire 1·4. Both N. Lancashire and the Scottish Lowlands, formerly sources of hematite and blackband ores respectively, have ceased production.

These domestic supplies furnish less than a quarter of the metal equivalent raw material requirements of the British iron and steel industries, whose output of steels rose from 10·4 million tons in 1938 to an average of over 20 million tons in 1957–9, and to 24 million tons in 1960. Almost half the balance was covered by scrap, and the rest by imports of the required alloys and some 12 million tons of high-grade ores, mainly from Sweden, Canada, North Africa, Venezuela and Sierra Leone. The supplies from Spain, formerly an important source, have declined to less than 5 per cent of the total imported.

The bulky raw materials and finished products of integrated iron and steel works enforce their location in sites where combined transfer costs (for fuel, ores and finished products) are minimised — generally in proximity to coking coal; though where low-grade domestic ores are used, the works may be located on the ore-fields rather than on or near coalfields, such as at Scunthorpe (Lincolnshire) and Corby (Northamptonshire). As imported ores form the larger half of total effective supplies, several large and expanding works are situated in or near ports on the margins of coalfields, as in South Wales and on the North-East Coast. In 1958 the regional distribution of the total 19·566 million tons of steel of all qualities produced was as follows: S. Wales 4·48, N.E. Coast 3·87, Sheffield 2·5, Lincolnshire 2·25, Scotland 2·116, Lancashire–Cheshire–N. Wales–S. Yorkshire 2·11, W. Midlands 0·97, E. Midlands & Essex 0·94, N.W. Coast 0·33.

FISHERIES[1]

The weight of fish of British taking landed at ports in Great Britain averaged upwards of a million tons in the years 1954–8, most of which was absorbed by the home market. Though part of the landings was exported, mainly as cured fish, this was offset in a large measure by imports of wet and canned fish. Large as the British catches are, they are exceeded by those of five other countries, notably of Japan and the United States; among European countries the U.S.S.R. and Norway are easily in the lead with landings two and a half times and twice the British total respectively. Even so, the supplies of fish available in Great Britain, at the rate of 40–50 lbs. per head of the population per annum, form a highly important element in the nation's diet. Fish, like meat, contain protein; and inasmuch as the great bulk of fish consumed in Britain is landed by British fishing vessels, there is a saving in expenditure on imported protein foods of animal origin.

Great Britain owes the development of its fishing industry to the valuable fishing grounds of the Continental Shelf round its shores, especially those of the North Sea, yielding both surface-swimming fish and bottom-feeding kinds such as haddock. As these waters are actively fished by other West European nations, joined recently by the Russians, competition for catches is apt to result in shortage of supplies, if not in some depletion of the stocks of young fish. Partly for this reason, and also because cod and plaice (constituting nearly half the British catches) are most abundant in the cold northern waters, British fishing fleets operate especially round Iceland and the Faeroes and in the Barents Sea (north of Russia) as well as in the near waters of the Continental Shelf. Nearly half the total landings of British catches is classed as from distant waters.

There may well be some contraction in these catches following upon Great Britain's withdrawal in 1961 (to become fully effective in 1964) to the Icelandic extension of the fishing limit for foreign trawlers from

[1] See also Chapter 24, pp. 351 and 352-4.

3 to 12 miles. Now (1963) the Faeroese authorities are making a similar claim, the implementation of which, even in a modified form, would clearly make it still more difficult for the British fleets to maintain their catches of cod.

A feature of the industry in recent years has been a decline in the landings of herrings to less than half those of pre-war times owing to smaller shoals moving south to their spawning grounds in the North Sea; apart from the probable over-fishing mentioned above and the taking of an undue proportion of immature fish, a decline in the shoals may arise from a low survival rate of young herrings on the spawning grounds some years earlier. However, the decline in the landings of herrings has been partly offset by larger catches of haddock. Another feature of a different order has been the introduction of factory ships operating with the fleets in distant waters, on which larger fish such as cod are prepared for immediate freezing and for direct distribution on landing as frozen fish or fillets.

Fishing has been carried on from over 40 ports in Great Britain and its adjacent islands, but many of the smaller ones, working mainly inshore fisheries, have lost trade to the larger centres which have better handling equipment, transport facilities and marketing organisation. Of the latter Hull and Grimsby lead in volume of landings, followed by Aberdeen and Fleetwood. Yarmouth and Lowestoft, formerly in the front rank of British fishing ports when herrings were plentiful in the North Sea, have lost some of their specialised trade with the decline in the catches.

Chapter 7

SOUTHERN ENGLAND AND WALES

SOUTHERN England and Wales may be divided into the six regions shown in Fig. 18, each of which is defined by some distinguishing features of location, of physiography and human geography. Their boundaries correspond in the main with those of physical and structural elements, except that the East Anglian boulder clay extends southwards into the London Basin, and the Jurassic Escarpments of central England continue as a narrow belt through south-west England to the Channel Coast.

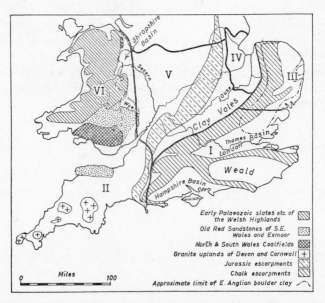

Fig. 18. The geographical regions of Southern England and Wales. I. South-eastern scarplands and basins. II. South-West England. III. East Anglia. IV. Fenland. V. Central England. VI. Wales and the Welsh borderlands.

I. The South-Eastern Scarplands and Basins

This complex region comprises the chalk escarpments and plateaux east of the Salisbury Plain inclusive, enfolding the London and the Hampshire Basins and the denuded anticline of the Weald. These various anticlinal and synclinal components are all physically related as products of the Alpine earth movements, and the dominating influence of London pervading throughout gives the area as a whole a large measure of functional unity also.

In early Tertiary times most of this area was covered by the sea, in which continental and marine sands and clays were deposited. With the elevation of a pronounced anticline in the Weald, continued westward into Wiltshire as a broad monoclinal fold, and of a narrow parallel anticline across the Isle of Wight into south Dorset, synclinal troughs developed on either side of the former with central axes from Reading to the Thames Estuary and from Dorchester to Chichester.

Subsequent erosion has removed the soft Tertiary deposits from the anticlinal ridges, thus exposing the lower Cretaceous sands, clays and sandstones in the Weald, and the upper Cretaceous chalk strata in scarp formation on its margins; west of the Weald these chalk beds appear as partially dissected plateaux on the northern sides of the Hampshire Basin, and as a narrow ridge across the Isle of Wight and South Dorset. In the London and Hampshire-Dorset synclines, on the other hand, the Tertiary sediments have been preserved, covered in places with later deposits, glacial and alluvial in parts of the London Basin, and downwash in the Hampshire Basin. The London Basin is bounded on its north-western side by the Chiltern chalk escarpment which rises gently from the Basin to its crests overlooking the Clay Vales.

The various stages in the evolution of south-east England have given rise to a great variety of soils. The South Downs and the western chalk plateaux have generally a thin covering of soil held by short, springy turf; while the dip slopes of the North Downs and the Chilterns have a moderately thick cover of clay-with-flints. In the Weald, clays and sandstones alternate in parallel longitudinal bands according to the outcrops of Cretaceous strata composing the original fold, now exposed by erosion as shown in cross-section (Fig. 19).

Similarly in the London Basin various Tertiary deposits, mostly clays, sands and gravels, have been exposed by differential erosion; though these are masked by patches of boulder clay towards the northern margin, and in the lower valley belt by clays, gravels and river alluvium deposited by a once more powerful Thames swollen by melt-water from the retreating ice-sheets. The surface soils of the Hampshire Basin are mostly the residual materials from the rapid erosion of the northern chalk uplands. These materials, re-sorted by the rivers, have been deposited in diverse forms — as fertile alluvium along old and existing river valleys, as medium to poor sandy loams elsewhere, merging into stretches of heathland sands and gravels.

The forms of land use in farming, horticulture and market gardening correspond in large measure to the motley soil pattern, though relative accessibility to markets for the disposal of products is also a factor. There can be little regional uniformity in areas where different types of soil appear on neighbouring farms or even on one and the same farm. Nevertheless, some general and some particular features of regional specialisation can be distinguished. Sheep-farming persists, in spite of the extension of cultivation, on the South Downs and on the Hampshire and Dorset Downs, where well-known breeds have been evolved. On the North Downs and the Chiltern Hills, however, where the soil cover is deeper than on the uplands just mentioned, corn crops and cattle including dairy cattle occupy most of the farm land.

Mixed farming in which dairy cattle are a leading feature is general on the clay belts of the Weald, in contrast to the intervening generally infertile belts of the Greensand and of the central ridges, where heaths, commons and woods occupy much of the land. Though the Weald as a whole is far from being a productive agricultural region, good loam soils occur in the lower Medway Valley and on the adjoining north-facing slopes of the North Downs. There, as in some fertile parts of the Hampshire Basin, fruit-growing and market-gardening are highly developed, with the addition of hop cultivation in the Medway district. In the remaining productive parts of the London and Hampshire Basins, mixed farming is general, with emphasis upon this or that product according to soil and location. Wheat and other cereals are grown in the Hampshire Basin and east Kent; sheep are kept in large numbers on Romney Marsh; and market gardening is a specialised industry on the fertile alluvial and brick-earth[1] tracts of the Thames Valley above London.

The development of the drainage system is of special physio-

---

[1] So named because formerly used for making bricks. It is thought to have been formed from a kind of loess of glacial origin, deposited in still water where it settled as a sediment.

graphical interest, and its results have a conspicuous bearing upon the present-day human geography. The Thames, flowing east into and along the London syncline, has cut a gap above Reading, where it is joined by the Kennet. Thus graded routes lead from the London Basin to the West Midlands and the West Country; while the formation of a tidal estuary by partial submergence of the lower reaches of the river has contributed much to the growth of London as a leading world port. Gaps have also been cut in the chalk plateau of the Chil-

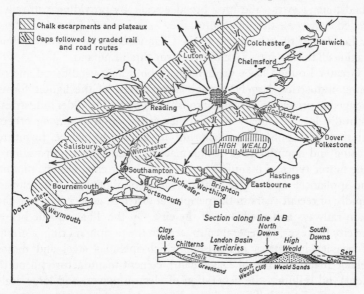

Fig. 19. The London and Hampshire Basins. Inset section through the London Basin and the Weald. The map shows the dominating situation of London in this area.

tern arc, probably by swollen glacial ancestors of the present shrunken streams, providing expedient routes for roads and railways from London to the Midlands and the North.

In the Hampshire Basin the existing short rivers are fragments of the earlier system, the main axial stream of which followed an easterly course marked by the Dorset River Frome-Solent-Spithead. The dismantling of parts of the coast by erosion and submergence has produced the two-way sea approaches to the Southampton Water Estuary, and this together with the double tides has provided the physical setting for the rise of Southampton as a major port.

The drainage system of the Weald and its existing configuration as well, is the result of the marked development of subsequent streams along the weaker outcrops, as tributaries to the master consequent rivers. The reduction of the whole inner zone thus effected has enabled the rivers to cut numerous gaps in the outer edges of the chalk strata, now surviving as inward-facing escarpments. Two special developments have followed in the human occupation of the area: these gaps, serving as exit funnels for convergent lines of movement from the Weald, have given rise to towns on their inner sides, e.g. Guildford, Maidstone, Lewes; and on a broader scale, by providing naturally-graded transverse through routes, they have facilitated the absorption by London of the whole area to the Channel coast into its orbit, thus making all that an integral part of metropolitan England.

Greater London has a great range of both long-established and of newer industries, largely, though not entirely, of the lighter forms engaged in preparing or making consumer goods. The older industries, naturally located chiefly in the inner area, comprise among others printing and publishing, tailoring in all its branches, furniture making and manufactures of pharmaceutical and toilet preparations. The newer types of manufactures, e.g. of motor cars, electric motors and appliances, and of electrical and radio equipment, have developed rapidly in recent years in the peripheral districts, especially along the main railways and roads out of the city. On the Thames-side below the city however, in general contrast with the peripheral ring, a group of heavier industries has arisen, which includes steel and motor vehicle manufactures (at Dagenham), cement manufacture (in north Kent), oil refining, the generation of electric power, and large-scale sugar-refining and flour-milling. Engaged in almost every type of manufacturing and processing industry, London employs a greater number of industrial workers than any other urban centre in the world. It is also the chief seaport and commercial centre of the British Isles, conducting a large trans-shipment trade with both British and neighbouring continental ports.

Metropolitan south-east England has by now become the greatest industrial region of Britain. Yet it has no internal sources of fuel and power apart from less than 2 million tons of coal per annum from the Kent coalfield. It depends almost entirely upon coal transported from the Midlands and the North by rail or by sea, and also increasingly upon imported oil fuels. Much of the coal and of the fuel-oil is used to produce electricity at large generating stations from which current is readily distributed to many places. It is the flexibility of electric transmission together with the transportability of fuel oil, that has enabled manufactures, especially of the newer kinds, to be established over a wide radius both within the London area and outside it.

Greater London, having a population of over 8 millions out of 40 odd millions in England and Wales, is naturally the hub of the inland transport system not only of the South-East, but also of Great Britain as far as Glasgow and Edinburgh. In metropolitan England, within a radius of 75 to 100 miles from London, no major independent town has arisen except perhaps Southampton which, however, is in no small measure an outport for London. The seaside towns from Southend to Bournemouth obviously serve as resorts for the metropolitan area, and Portsmouth and Chatham are primarily naval bases for its defence. The larger inland towns such as Reading in the Goring gap, Luton in a Chiltern gap, and Winchester and Salisbury in the Hampshire Basin, have arisen mainly as local transport, administrative and market centres; and though some have expanded with the establishment of special manufactures, as of motor cars and engineering products at Luton and of food products and farmers' requirements at Reading, none has as yet grown to more than a medium-sized town.

II. South-West England

West of a line Gloucester-Trowbridge-Weymouth, the Cretaceous chalk and sandstones that form the framework of south-east England give place to older rocks, except for outliers of the Cretaceous in west Dorset and east Devon. The change in structure is accompanied by a change in the scenery and the atmospheric conditions. The landscapes are more varied, more romantic in their forms; and the general mildness and freshness of the air, together with the open windswept skies, betoken the predominant Atlantic influence.

This western area is built up of two main structural elements, Armorican in Somerset, Devon and Cornwall, and Jurassic Escarpment in a N.-S. belt east of Bristol. The former comprises two main E.-W. axes of uplift, one represented by Exmoor and the Quantocks bordering the Bristol Channel, and the other by the granite bosses of Dartmoor and Bodmin Moor, with a synclinal depression between Dartmoor and Exmoor. A third shorter axis runs through south Cornwall, terminating in the granite plateau of the Land's End Peninsula. Yet another Armorican axis of uplift runs through the Mendips, probably continuing into South Wales, separated in its turn from the Quantock-Exmoor uplift by the broad depression of the

Somerset Plain. The Jurassic Escarpment, pushed up from the south-east in the Alpine 'storm' against the old resistant blocks in Wales and Devon, is a dissected plateau of broken uplands in South Dorset which terminate in the so-called Isle of Portland, but rises north of Bristol in a continuous belt towards the Cotswolds (Fig. 20).

South of the Dartmoor-Bodmin Moor axis, sandstones and other rocks of Devonian age, the uppermost of which have weathered into fairly fertile soils, occupy a belt across Devon into Cornwall, inter-

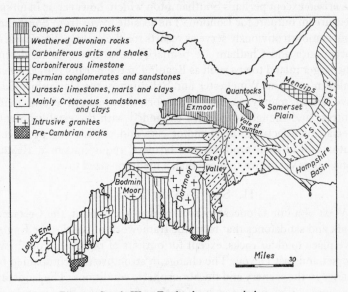

Fig. 20. South-West England: structural elements.

sected by deep and picturesque valleys. The broad depression between Dartmoor and Exmoor, on the other hand, has been filled with carboniferous grits and shales, producing indifferent soils on the whole. East and north-east of Exmoor, newer rocks, Triassic and Recent, form the floors of the Severn and Somerset Plains, lying on either side of the Carboniferous limestone ridge of the Mendips; and Permian sandstones and conglomerates, producing the red soils characteristic of the farmlands of east Devon, occupy the Exe Valley Basin and the coastal strip southwards to Torbay.

Elevated at the close of the Carboniferous period, the once massive Armorican chains were reduced by prolonged erosion, and now only stumps for the most part remain. In geologically recent times, however, the Devon-Cornwall Peninsula was elevated several hundred feet, so that platforms of marine denudation at about 400 feet above sea-level are of common occurrence; in these the rivers, notably the Dart, rejuvenated by the general elevation, have cut gorge-like valleys. The later post-glacial rise in the general sea-level (p. 59) has caused the lowermost courses of many of the rivers to become tidal, and in some of them branching ria-type inlets have been formed, as at the mouths of the Tamar and the Fal. These tidal-river inlets and various sheltered bays provide good natural harbours which have furthered the age-long sea-faring activities of the inhabitants of this Atlantic peninsula, not greatly endowed with land resources, and removed from the main centres of population. In the Somerset-Bristol area also, where swampy plain and undulating lowlands are backed and in a measure walled off by limestone escarpments, oversea trade centred on Bristol has been, and still is, an important source of income for the people.

Apart from the recent marked industrial developments in the Bristol area, and smaller-scale manufactures in Yeovil, Exeter and Taunton, farming dominates the inland scene. The mild Atlantic climate with relatively high proportion of sunshine is favourable to the growth of pasture grasses, root crops, potatoes, and fodder cereals such as oats and mixed corn. Thus dairy cattle and pigs are numerous, though some sheep are pastured on the moorland margins of the residual highlands in Devon and East Cornwall.

Market gardening is widespread, more especially in the Penzance district and the Fal valley in south Cornwall, the lower Tamar valley in Devon and the Scilly Isles, where early vegetables, small fruits and spring flowers are intensively cultivated. In general, the proportion of land classed as arable is high, though much of it is worked on long rotations in which temporary pastures and fodder crops for cattle (and sheep also) are the basic features.

With some notable exceptions such as the Triassic Vale of Taunton, the soils are but moderately fertile. The heavy rainfall averaging 40 inches or more upon the generally dissected and sharply undulating lowlands of Devon and Cornwall tends to cause leaching of the soluble constituents; and the Somerset Plain is apt to be waterlogged in the stretches between the 'islands' of older rocks such as Glastonbury. Continuous cultivation of crops as in East Anglia would promote soil wash, hence the practice of incorporating several years of temporary grass in the rotations, and of keeping the steeper slopes under permanent pastures.

Fishing has been a substantial industry at various small ports, of which the chief surviving centres are Newlyn and St Ives in Cornwall and Brixham in south Devon. Far more widespread and important as a source of income than fishing nowadays is the 'tourist' industry, i.e. catering for holiday visitors, attracted to these parts by the mild climate and the distinctive coasts, with their succession of bays, coves and rocky headlands in the peninsula, and by the fine stretches of sandy beaches along the Severn Estuary. Among the many resorts some are outstanding and have grown into fair-sized towns: Penzance,

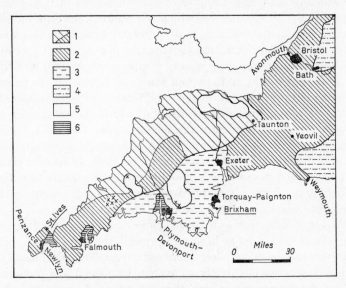

Fig. 21. South-West England: local forms of land use.

1. Stock-rearing with dairying, especially in west-central Devon and south-west Cornwall. 2. Predominantly dairying. 3. Mixed farming with considerable arable. 4. Mixed farming with grain crops. 5. Mainly sheep farming on moorlands. 6. Chief horticultural districts.

Note. Even in this limited area, there is a general transition eastwards from mainly pastoral to more intensive forms of farming with larger proportions of arable and cash crops.

The crosses indicate china clay quarries and the names of the chief fishing ports are underlined.

Falmouth and Newquay in west Cornwall; Torquay-Paignton in south Devon; Weston-super-Mare in Somerset.

The mining of tin and copper ores has now almost ceased; but china clay is worked on a considerable scale in the altered granites of Bodmin Moor and south-west Dartmoor. The inland towns are for the most part local agricultural market centres, and as such, few except Taunton and Yeovil have developed regional importance at all comparable with that of each of the three main centres — Bristol, Exeter and Plymouth. Bristol (with Avonmouth) and Plymouth-Devonport are national ports, the former for the south-west Midlands and the West Country, the latter for the naval dockyard and some transatlantic traffic. Exeter, situated in the main gateway into Devon and Cornwall, at which rail and road routes from London and the Midlands converge and then fan out westward north and south of Dartmoor, is the cultural capital of the South-West Peninsula; and Bristol, formerly a leading port for West Indian trade, has developed, as a heritage of that, large tobacco and chocolate manufactures, to which large-scale construction of aircraft and general engineering have more recently been added. Falmouth, formerly important as a last and first port of call for sailing ships and later for steam ships (to get orders) before the introduction of wireless communication, has declined as a port, but has found some compensation in the expanding tourist traffic.

Weymouth, like Plymouth-Devonport, is a Channel naval base, and is besides the port for shipping connection with the Channel Islands. These islands, of which Jersey and Guernsey are the largest, belong structurally to Normandy, but are tied up economically (as well as politically) with Great Britain. They specialise in the production for the English market of early potatoes and tomatoes, for which the mild climate and the long open season give them distinct advantages over their mainland competitors. Like Cornwall, but more on the highly organised Swiss model, they have developed a large tourist business, this invisible item of exports, like the visible, being ordered to meet demand from England.

III. East Anglia

This area, characterised physically by its moderate to low elevation and the gently undulating surface of its widespread mantle of glacial drift, covers most of the County of Norfolk, all of Suffolk and a small northern part of Essex, where it merges into the London Basin (Figs. 18, 22). It is traversed lengthwise towards its western border by a section of the chalk escarpments of low elevation averaging some 300 feet, which runs in a shallow curve from the northern end of the Chiltern Hills to the eastern side of the Wash. On the west of this escarpment the land falls in steps (in which the underlying Greensand is exposed in places) down to the Fens and the lowlands east of Cambridge; on the eastern dip slope the Cretaceous rocks sink under Tertiary beds and the overlying mantle of glacial deposits.

The escarpment watershed separates the East Anglian drainage system from that of the Great Ouse basin. From it the Bure-Wensum-Waveney system and other short rivers flow east, the mouths of those three rivers and that of the Alde in Suffolk being diverted by sand-bars, while south of the Alde the rivers terminate in large tidal estuaries. The shallow enlargements of the tripartite Norfolk system, known as the Broads, occupy hollows in what was once a shallow bay, which were formed in part at least by the removal by earlier inhabitants of some of the peat accumulated in hollows during the intermittent silting up of the bay. From the western side of the chalk ridge shorter rivers flow to join the Great Ouse, some of which, particularly the Little Ouse, have cut far back into the chalk escarpment by head-

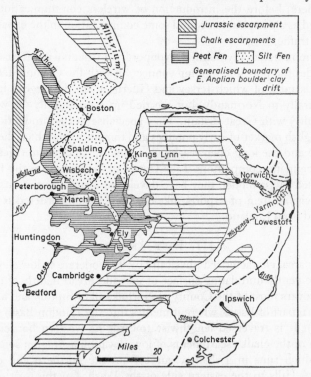

Fig. 22. East Anglia and Fenland. Based on O.S. 'Ten-mile' Drift edition
geological series England and Wales, sheets 12 and 16.

ward erosion, thus furnishing graded transverse routes followed by railways and roads.

Diversity in the composition of the surface deposits has resulted in a variety of regional soil types in East Anglia. Though boulder clay and glacial loams predominate, sandy gravels occur in the Cromer morainic ridge, mainly sandy deposits in the Sandlings belt of east Suffolk, and moderately fertile sandy glacial soils in north-west Norfolk. On the west central side of the chalk upland, a relatively small area known as Breckland is covered with blown sand, and is consequently more or less sterile heathland. In some of the higher western parts, however, the chalk is exposed free of drift, giving rise to typical downland topography and landscape.

The climate of East Anglia is more continental in character than elsewhere in the British Isles except in the Fenland. The mean annual rainfall is less than 25 inches over a large part of the area, and little more on the escarpment belt and in central Norfolk. The summers are relatively warm and sunny, the average July temperatures being about 62° F., and the winters rather cold with mean January temperatures about 38° F. The considerable range of temperature, 24° F. compared with 17° F. in Cornwall, is more favourable to arable than to pastoral farming, to cereals than to meadow grasses.

East Anglia is the leading agricultural region of the British Isles. It shares with the Fenland the greater part of the chief cereal belt (Fig. 16) which produces large proportions of the wheat and barley and also of the sugar beet grown in the British Isles, in addition to which East Anglia raises pigs and fattens beef cattle, both in large numbers. The region is noted for its intensive farming worked on special crop rotations, e.g. the famous Norfolk four course (wheat, turnips, barley, clover or beans) modified according to changing conditions of demand for the various products. In particular, sugar beet is now widely grown instead of turnips, with a consequent decline in the number of sheep, offset by an increase in that of dairy cattle which consume the by-products of the sugar beet. In all the rotations, fodder crops, especially roots and clover, hold important places, and these together with the residues of the corn and sugar beet crops, enable East Anglia to supply also a variety of animal products — milk, poultry and eggs, besides fat pigs and cattle.

Industrial development has been restricted by distance from sources of coal and iron. The earlier Norfolk woollen textile industry has died out, and present-day manufactures are related directly or indirectly to the prime agricultural industry, e.g. of shoes, flour and starch at Norwich, and of agricultural machinery and fertilisers at Ipswich. The old-established milling and malting industries are naturally widespread, though they too tend to become concentrated in the two leading centres, Norwich and Ipswich. These two semi-industrialised towns are the largest, both numbering over 100,000 inhabitants. Other towns with special functions that have enabled them to grow beyond the modest proportions of agricultural market centres are Colchester on the Colne, Harwich as a port for shipping to and from Denmark and the Netherlands, and Yarmouth and Lowestoft as North Sea fishing ports.

Though there is some coastal trade between the ports and the Thames region, the farm produce of the whole area is moved by land to London and other large centres of population; but in order to save needless transport, and to utilise on the farms the valuable by-products, such as sugar beet pulp and milling and malting residues, preliminary, if not final processing is commonly carried out within the area; and industries of this kind are, in fact, an integral feature of the functions of the smaller as well as the larger local market towns.

IV. The Fenlands

This area, formerly marshland, but now completely drained, extends inland from the Wash to about the 50-foot contour along an irregular line which encircles an area of over 1,000 sq. miles in south Lincolnshire, the Isle of Ely (Cambridgeshire) and the western fringe of Norfolk. Previous to the Ice Age the Fenland basin was submerged in a bay now reduced to the Wash; but during that period drift materials were deposited in it, the higher mounds of which have formed 'islands' of boulder clay in the marsh. Since then the area has been built up round these 'islands' with marine clays and sands, with silts deposited by the four sluggish rivers Ouse, Nen, Welland and Witham, and by the growth of swamp vegetation. The Fens now comprise two main zones: an arc of silts some 20 miles in width round the Wash, and an inner zone of peat fen, narrow in the north, but widening out to upwards of 25 miles in the southern lobe round Ely.

The drained Fens are extraordinarily fertile and are intensively cultivated under cash crops which occupy fully three-quarters of the total area. Few cattle are kept because larger returns can be obtained from field crops, and because animal manure is not essential to maintain the fertility, at all events of the peat fen. Corresponding to the difference in soil texture and composition between the Fenland zones, there is a contrast in land use. On the peat fen potatoes, sugar beet and wheat, grown in rotation, occupy most of the land, and some sheep are kept, fed on the sugar beet residues. On the silt fen a much greater variety of crops is cultivated, especially of the market garden and horticultural types, such as peas, carrots and other vegetables, flower bulbs and small fruit, all on a large scale, as well as potatoes and sugar beet. The Fenland as a whole, with its rich, fine-grained soils, is the leading area in the British Isles for the cultivation of potatoes and of 'greedy' plants such as celery and bulbs; and with East Anglia it supplies upwards of two-thirds of the beet sugar produced in Great Britain. It is, however, less important than East Anglia for wheat, which requires fairly stiff clay soils.

Within the exclusively agricultural area of the Fenland proper, the towns, none of them large, are primarily collecting and marketing centres. Such are Spalding, Wisbech, March and Ely situated on 'islands' of boulder clay. Of these Spalding, Wisbech and Ely have also processing industries — sugar beet factories at Spalding and Ely, and large works for canning fruit and vegetables at Wisbech. King's Lynn and Boston, accessible by small vessels from the Wash, are minor ports. Two other towns, Peterborough and Cambridge, situated on the inland margins of the Fenland, have economic ties with it. Both have other special functions that have enabled them to grow beyond the modest proportions of local agricultural market towns. Peterborough is an old cathedral city, on the outskirts of which large brick-works and some engineering establishments have arisen in modern times, and Cambridge is the seat of a great University dating from the thirteenth century.

V. CENTRAL ENGLAND

This roughly rectangular area comprises the west and the north-east Midlands, the central sweep of the Jurassic Escarpments (including the Cotswolds, and the Northampton, Leicester and Lincoln Uplands), and the belt of Clay Vales extending south-west from Cambridge. Its borders are ill defined, except along the chalk scarp-faces in the south-east, and in parts on the west by ridges of old rocks: it merges on either side of the southern Pennines into the northern industrial regions, into the Welsh Borderlands along a line Chester-Shrewsbury-Hereford, and into the inner Fenland in the east. Though agriculture is well developed, the dominant feature of this physically composite area, common to its several parts, is the varied and highly developed manufacturing industry in over a score of towns from Stoke and Derby on the border of the Pennines to Bedford, Oxford and Swindon in the Clay Vales (Fig. 23).

The Jurassic Escarpments extend in a continuous arc from south Lincolnshire to Gloucestershire, their dip slope strata sinking beneath the Clay Vales, which narrow gradually from a width of over 30 miles towards the Fenland border to less than 10 miles beyond Swindon. In contrast with these two physically more or less homogeneous regions, the Midland Triangle lying south of the Pennines is structurally complex. In broad outlines, it is a Triassic plain, covered in parts with glacial drift, from the surface of which anticlinal ridges and masses of Carboniferous, pre-Carboniferous and even Archaean rocks

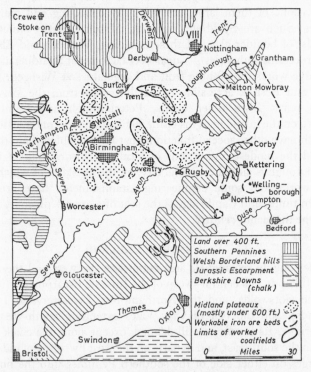

Fig. 23. Central England: physical features, and coal and iron ore fields.
Worked coalfields (numbered 1 to 7, and part of S.E. Pennine marked VIII) based on N.C.B. maps 1958. Workable iron ore deposits generalised from 1:625,000 maps of the National Planning Series.

project with a general N.–S. alignment. Some of these upland masses are broad enough to form plateaux, for example the Staffordshire-Warwickshire Plateau from Cannock Chase to the Clent and Lickey Hills, the east Warwickshire Plateau including the Nuneaton Ridge, and the Forest of Dean in the extreme south-west. On the Welsh borderland margin, narrow ridges rise from the elevated ground in Shropshire, e.g. the Wrekin, Wenlock Edge and the Clee Hills; and farther south another ridge of ancient rocks appears in the Malvern Hills on the Herefordshire border. Charnwood Forest in Leicestershire, on the other hand, is the denuded remnants of a dome composed of the ejecta of Pre-Cambrian volcanoes.

The Carboniferous rocks dipping southwards from the Pennines, and forming with their surviving coal-measures the sub-strata of parts of this Midland Triangle, have been the basis of its long-established industrial greatness. The coal-measures occur at workable depths on the flanks of the denuded anticlines mentioned above, and also in the intervening synclines, in various coalfields, the average production of which in the years 1957–8 in millions of tons was as follows:

South Derby and Leicester	7·29
North Staffs	6·03
Cannock Chase	4·28
South Staffs and Shropshire	1·49
Warwickshire	4·63
Total	23·72 + opencast 0·66 = 24·38

None of these coalfields is extensive; several of them, moreover, have been worked for upwards of two centuries, and their combined output including opencast is now less than 12 per cent of the British total. Yet upon this comparatively narrow base of fuel and power resources a great industrial structure has been erected, comprising a great variety of specialised manufactures. The only other significant industrial resources are the low-grade Jurassic iron ores in south Lincolnshire, Northants, Rutland and Oxfordshire (see p. 73 and Fig. 23), the fire-clays of the coal-measures, and the 'earthenware' clays of the Potteries district.[1]

Three river systems share the drainage of more than three-quarters

---

[1] Resources that contributed to early growth, however, were iron ore associated with the coal-measures in the Black Country, and local chinaware clay in the Potteries.

of the whole area: the Severn-Avon, the Trent, and the upper Thames; their basins cover all except the south-eastern section lying between the crests of the Jurassic and the Chalk Escarpments, which is drained to the Wash by the Welland, Nen and Great Ouse. Within the Midland industrial triangle, the Warwickshire Plateau is a centre of radial drainage from which tributary streams flow in different directions to join the Trent, the Severn and the Avon. This nodality in the drainage system gave the Birmingham district a key position in the days of canal transport, which was paralleled in the lay-out of the roads, and also of the railway net-work when it came into being. All this contributed to the specialisation in the manufacture of transport equipment that has long characterised this geographical centre of England and Wales.

Central England as defined above contains a considerable variety of generally fertile soils, with little really unproductive land. The weathered Triassic sandstones and marls and their overlying stretches of boulder clays form good arable land in general, while the Jurassic uplands and Clay Vales produce first-class pastures on the heavier soils, and are well adapted to mixed farming on the loams and lighter soils, especially those of the chalky glacial drift on the eastern Clay Vales. Though the proportion of farm land under permanent grass is comparatively high, oats, root crops, fodder crops (e.g. clover) and potatoes are widely cultivated, together with some wheat; large quantities of fruit are also grown, especially in the Avon valley; and market garden produce for the large industrial population, and also for London, e.g. from east Bedfordshire. Dairy cattle and pigs are numerous, and beef cattle even more so, fattened on the rich pastures supplemented by fodder crops. Except on the Jurassic scarplands, sheep are relatively scarce in this area where the pasturing of beef cattle and mixed farming with dairy cattle are the leading features of the agricultural industry.

Industrialisation has spread far and wide beyond the old traditional areas in central England. Almost every type of manufactures is represented, each on a considerable scale: steel manufacture and heavy engineering, non-ferrous metal industries, light engineering of every possible kind; textile and hosiery manufactures; the production of leather goods and of earthenware, pottery and chinaware; and the construction of heavy transport equipment and of motor vehicles, cycles and aero engines, for the last of which groups this is one of the most highly specialised regions in the world. It is impossible to give in

limited space inclusive details of the location of these and other industries, but some general features of their areal distribution by products can be recognised: i.e. iron, steel, steel alloy and non-ferrous
metal goods of every variety in Birmingham and the Black Country
towns such as Wolverhampton, Walsall and West Bromwich; rayon
filament at Wolverhampton and Coventry and at Spondon near
Derby; pig iron and steel at Corby, Wellingborough, Kettering and
Melton Mowbray on the Jurassic iron belt; hosiery and knitted wear
in the north-east Midlands, especially at Leicester and Nottingham;
boots, shoes and leather goods in the cattle country towns Northampton and Leicester; earthenware and pottery at Stoke-on-Trent, Derby
and Worcester; motor vehicles in the Birmingham, Coventry and
Oxford districts; railway rolling-stock at Derby, Crewe, Gloucester
and Swindon; electrical apparatus at Rugby; generalised and specialised engineering products in the Birmingham district and in the string
of Midland railway towns, Bedford, Wellingborough, Kettering,
Leicester, Loughborough and Derby. There is, it will be seen, considerable overlapping of the groups arising from the specialisation in
various directions of a number of the larger centres in this fully
developed area.

Transport by railways and road and on a smaller scale by inland
waterways is highly developed. Efficient means of transport are indeed
essential for this inland area, whose diverse activities necessitate the
inward movement of large quantities of raw materials, the outward
movement of a great array of finished products, and extensive internal
transfers of bulky minerals, semi-manufactures (e.g. components) and
of farm produce. Reference has been made above to the centrality of
Birmingham in the transport system. Among other towns that have
developed partly by reason of the convergence upon them of lines of
movement are Leicester in the Soar Valley between the coalfields to
the west, and the scarplands to the east with their rich pastures and
iron deposits; Rugby in an analogous situation 20 miles farther south;
Crewe in the Cheshire Gate leading to Lancashire and the north-
west; Nottingham on the Trent where routes from the Midlands
skirt the south-eastern corner of the Pennines; and Bedford and
Oxford, market centres for the lower and middle enlargements of the
Clay Vales respectively. For the very large external trade which the
area as a whole transacts, there is a choice of the four major ports
situated one near each of its four corners, namely London, Liverpool,
Hull and Bristol, of which the first two being terminals of shipping

services to many parts of the world have the largest shares of this Midland traffic.

VI. WALES AND THE WELSH BORDERLANDS

Structurally this area extends eastward to an outward curving line from the Dee Estuary through the Wrekin in Shropshire and the Malvern Hills to the Severn Estuary; it thus includes the North Wales coalfield, most of the Shropshire Basin and the whole of the Hereford Basin, enclosed between these outliers and the Massif itself to the west. Thus defined, the Welsh province consists of three major elements: the Massif proper occupying the northern, central and western parts to a diagonal line joining Radnor Forest and St. Brides Bay; the Armorican formations south of a line through the Brecon Beacons; and the Old Red Sandstone triangle between these two and a N.–S. line through the Malvern Hills. Two sub-regions, the North Wales coalfield and the western Shropshire Basin, fill out the north-east segment (Fig. 18).

The Massif is composed of ancient Palaeozoic rocks, first systematically studied there, as indicated by the terms Pre-Cambrian, Cambrian, Ordovician and Silurian of Welsh associations, now used by geologists the world over for rocks of corresponding ages. These Welsh Highlands retain conspicuous NE.–SW. trends in witness of their origin in the Caledonian orogenesis. Their long subsequent history has been marked by episodes common to old West European highlands — peneplanation, re-elevation, faulting and glaciation. They now form a dissected plateau, 1,500 to 2,000 feet in average height, intersected by deeply-cut valleys which divide it into several upstanding blocks. Some of the highest points in these, e.g. Snowdon, Berwyn and Cader Idris, are composed in parts of old volcanic rocks that have resisted erosion; the country rock consisting of compacted and crumpled early Palaeozoic grits and slates rises above 2,000 feet only in Plynlimmon.

The generally rugged relief of the Welsh Highlands, especially in the north, together with the heavy precipitation and exposure to strong winds, restricts settlements to the coastal margins, the valleys and the eastern uplands. Minerals of economic value are scanty, other than the slates quarried on a declining scale in the north,[1] and the coal

[1] Especially at Penrhyn and other places in Caernarvonshire, and at Festiniog in Merionethshire. The output is now only about 90,000 tons compared with upwards of 500,000 tons at the end of the nineteenth century.

worked in a Carboniferous annex to the Massif in Flint and Denbigh.
For the rest, the mountainous country with its harsh climate and indifferent pastures is suitable only for the support of hardy sheep,
mainly the Welsh mountain breed, which number $4\frac{1}{2}$ millions in the
counties within the border.

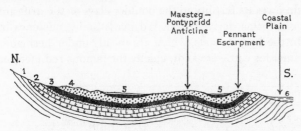

Fig. 24. N.–S. section through the South Wales coalfield.
1. Silurian and Devonian. 2. Carboniferous Limestone and Millstone Grit.
3. Lower coal-measures. 4. Pennant Grit. 5. Upper coal-measures and
surface deposits. 6. Mesozoic and later beds.

South Wales is the result of post-Carboniferous Armorican folding
with characteristic E.–W. trend. A northern anticlinal axis runs
through the Brecon Beacons and thence almost due west. This is
separated from a southern axis of uplift, bordering the Bristol Channel,
by a synclinal basin which is widest in the east and contracts westward, until in Pembrokeshire it is squeezed into narrow limits where
the rocks are huddled together and are so contorted and faulted that
coal-mining there has now ceased. A third axis of uplift, the Maesteg-
Pontypridd anticline, traverses the main basin lengthwise, bringing
the valuable lower coal-measures within reach of the surface (Fig. 24).
The Glamorgan-Monmouth field is noted for the high quality and the
variety of its coals. Anthracite containing 96 to 99 per cent carbon
occurs in a limited north-western zone, from which the seams grade
eastward in the Aberdare-Rhondda section into smokeless steam coals,
formerly in great demand for ships' bunkers. These pass southwards
and south-eastwards into ordinary bituminous and coking coals
containing less carbon and higher proportions of volatile constituents
(Fig. 25).

The relatively low elevation, the moderately fertile soils and the
mild Atlantic climate of the three southern peninsular extensions of
South Wales and of the Towy Valley inland, are favourable to mixed
farming pivoted on fodder crops for beef cattle, dairy cattle and pigs.
Large quantities of green vegetables are also grown, especially in the

Vale of Glamorgan, all farm products being readily absorbed by the mining and industrial populations of the area.

The Old Red Sandstone triangle comprises two major parts, the fertile middle Wye-Hereford Basin, and the inner wedge of bleak and barren highlands dividing the Caledonian massif from South Wales. The Basin owes its fertility to the boulder clays of the drift areas and to the light loams derived from red marls and sandstones in other parts. On the heavier soils, which are mostly under permanent pastures, numerous cattle are kept, chiefly the famous red Hereford beef

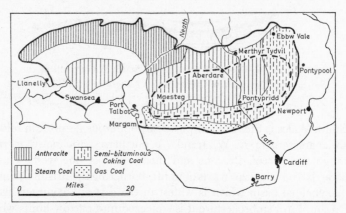

Fig. 25. The South Wales coalfield: types of coal. The shaded areas contain nearly all the active collieries, and the area enclosed by a broken line (associated with the Maestig–Pontypridd anticline) fully two-thirds.

breed; on the lighter soils a wide variety of crops is cultivated, including wheat, hops, orchard fruit, cattle fodders and some sugar beet; while on the surrounding hills and on the ridges within the basin, sheep-farming is practised. This basin situated in the lee of the Welsh Highlands has the climatic advantages for agriculture of relatively low rainfall (26·3 inches at Hereford) and a correspondingly high proportion of sunshine. The Hereford Basin merges northward into a region of detached highlands separated by open valleys, beyond which lies the Shropshire basin — an extension of the Triassic plain of the Midlands and Cheshire. In this basin, as on the adjoining Cheshire Plain, intensive mixed farming is general, with special emphasis upon beef and dairy cattle and the fodder crops required to support them.

The chief natural resources of Wales are the coal-measures in South Wales (Glamorgan) and in the north-east (Denbighshire) which produced in 1958–9 averages of about 24½ million tons and 2 million tons respectively. Upon the two coalfields and their peripheral zones nearly all the industrial activity and some two-thirds of the population are concentrated. The output of coal from both fields has declined (see pp. 71–2), and with that, the importance of coal-mining as an industry, and of coal exports from South Wales. Many of the mining villages strung out along the narrow valleys deeply cut in the Pennant Grit[1] in the northern part of the coalfield, have become derelict in consequence; and there is little hope of their survival with the general shift southward of the South Wales mining industry. Similar misfortune has overtaken the north-eastern coalfield, where a number of pits has been closed in Flintshire owing to exhaustion of seams and difficulties of mining in this faulted area; here also the industry is shifting southwards, into Denbighshire. The small Forest of Dean coalfield, producing less than half a million tons a year, may be included as an eastern outlier of the South Wales field. The coal-measures there have been preserved in a circular basin, and are worked chiefly in the neighbourhood of Cinderford, but workable seams are more or less exhausted.

Foremost among the coal-using industries in both South and north-east Wales are iron smelting and the manufacture of steel, much of which is rolled into sheets and other semi-finished or finished forms.[2] In South Wales the largest concentration of this group of industries is in the coastal belt from Llanelly across the neck of the Gower Peninsula to Swansea and thence east beyond Port Talbot to Margam; blast furnaces and steel works are also in operation near Cardiff and at Ebbw Vale (in the north-east corner of the coalfield), and there are rolling mills at Pontypool and other places on the eastern edge of the coalfield. In north-east Wales iron and steel works have been established at Mostyn and Hawarden Bridge on Deeside and near Wrexham in Denbighshire, although no iron ore is now produced in that part of the country. South Wales is almost equally dependent upon external sources of ores for its much larger iron and steel industries; apart from a little over 100,000 tons of hematite mined in south-east Glamorgan the balance of ores required, amounting to several million tons, has to be imported, chiefly from African sources. For this reason

[1] A hard sandstone not unlike the Millstone Grit of the Pennines, which composes thick beds, separating the upper from the lower coal-measures in South Wales.

[2] South Wales produces more steel than any other region in the British Isles. See outputs, p. 74.

nearly all the blast furnaces and the larger steel works are located on or near the coast, and, because fuel is also needed in large quantities, in that section of the coast adjacent to the active coalfield. For the same reasons the large copper and zinc refineries and aluminium works are in that part of the coastal belt, in particular round Swansea.

A million tons or more of the steel produced in South Wales are absorbed by the galvanising and tin-plate works. The galvanising works, situated mainly in the Swansea district, manufacture zinc-coated sheets of all kinds (for roofing and hollow-ware) as well as

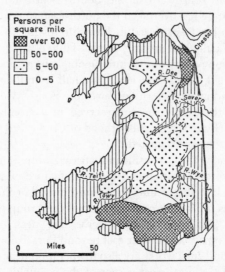

Fig. 26. The distribution of population in Wales and the Welsh border-lands (generalised).

fencing wires, both classes mainly for export; the tin-plate works, concentrated in the Llanelly-Swansea district and the valleys behind, also produce in large part for export. The marked dependence of both South and north-east Wales upon the coal trade and a narrow range of metallurgical industries has rendered them highly vulnerable to adverse external market conditions. In order to offset this liability and to remedy unemployment, various new industries, catering in large measure for the home market, have been established in both areas, for example manufactures of electrical equipment, motor cycles, clothing apparel and nylon in South Wales, and of rayon, aircraft and light engineering products in the North-East.

Reference has been made in passing to the importance of seaborne commerce in the economic structure of South Wales. In this connection it has the advantage of a string of ports along the Bristol Channel, chief among which are Cardiff, the commercial capital of the South and the administrative capital of Wales, Swansea, the centre of the metallurgical industries, and Newport on the River Usk. North Wales, on the other hand, having no comparable facilities for shipping (the Dee Estuary is silted up), depends mainly on rail transport. Both the northern and the southern regions are traversed each by a trunk railway which with branches links all the more important centres with one another and with the Midlands and London. The roads and railways across the Massif north of the Brecon Beacons, however, perforce follow valleys encompassed by steep mountain sides, and are thus in the nature of through-traffic routes. Here the intervening highland areas remain in comparative isolation, as through the ages, and their inhabitants tend to retain the physical characteristics and the speech of their distant ancestors — attributes that have been largely modified or lost by external contacts in the lowland parts. Owing to the relative unattractiveness of the highland core, it has been losing population to the periphery, and the proportion of those speaking Welsh in the total population has been declining.

The physical build of Wales and the concentration of industry on the two coalfields account in the main for the remarkably uneven overall distribution of the population (Fig. 26). The hill sheep-farming of the highland belt from the Snowdon Range in the north to the Brecon Beacons in the south requires many acres per sheep and more still per inhabitant; and were it not for the scattered valley settlements, its population would be still less. For the rest, away from the coalfields and some seaside resorts, the density of the population, mainly rural, varies considerably in keeping with the ridge and valley texture of the marginal lowlands, corresponding closely with the extent to which arable farming of one kind or another is possible.

Chapter 8

NORTHERN ENGLAND

NORTHERN England is largely, though not entirely, the product of the Pennine uplift in both its physical and its human geography. This upland zone, extending 150 miles throughout the length of the area from the Cheviot Hills to the great bend of the River Trent, is the master element in the structure, with which all others except the Cumbrian massif and the northern scarplands are closely associated. It forms the main watershed in which nearly all the larger rivers have their sources, and on its flanks are three major coalfields, the foundations of the great industrial developments in several parts of northern England.

The basic strata of the Pennines are massive Carboniferous limestones, exposed in places in the south and also notably in the Ingleborough district in west Yorkshire, but generally capped with millstone grit. The Pennine plateaux exceed 1,000 feet over large tracts, and rise to over 2,000 feet in north Yorkshire and farther north. The soils derived from the millstone grit sandstone are unproductive, incapable of supporting anything but moorland vegetation at higher elevations. Their poverty in plant food, owing to the small proportion of soluble matter in the parent rock, has one compensation in that abundant supplies of soft water (stored in great valley reservoirs) are available for the densely populated industrial districts of Lancashire and Yorkshire, and for use in the textile industries in which they specialise. Coal-measures that once apparently extended across the rising Pennines overlying the millstone grit, have been removed by erosion except in those places on the flanks where the Carboniferous strata dip under a protective cover of later rocks.

The Pennines are neither a continuous chain nor a simple dome-like anticline. They are broken into four block sections by the Tyne, the Stainmore and the Aire gaps (Fig. 27), which provide graded transverse routeways followed by roads and railways; and owing to great longitudinal faults in the west their cross-section profile is in general asymmetrical, resembling that of a monocline having a steep western face and a plateau-like upland surface gently sloping eastwards into the lowlands.

Thus in spite of the heavier rainfall on the western than on the eastern side of the Pennines, the principal rivers rise in the plateau crests well 'off centre' to the west, and have long upland courses before they emerge on the eastern plains. This feature in the drainage system has been followed in the main in setting the boundaries of the counties on either side, e.g., between Yorkshire and Lancashire and between Northumberland and Cumberland. Just as the Pennine uplands are mainly tributary to the eastern lowlands in the physical sense, so also are they linked with these both in their utilisation and their administration.

In view of the above, the line of the watershed crest of the Pennines forms the basis of a division of northern England into geographical regions, of which three lie to the east of it and two to the west. These are (1) the eastern Pennines in Yorkshire and counties to the south together with the adjacent Vales of York and Trent, (2) the Pennine and Cheviot uplands and the North-East Coast in Durham and

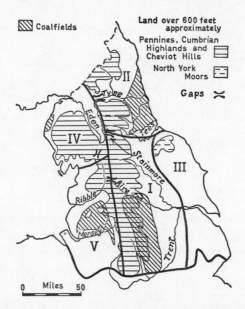

Fig. 27. The geographical regions of Northern England.
I. Eastern Pennines and York–Trent Vales. II. North Pennine–Cheviot uplands and N.E. Coast. III. Northern scarplands. IV. Cumbria. V. Lancashire–Cheshire lowlands and Western Pennines.

Northumberland, (3) the northern scarplands in Yorkshire and Lincolnshire, (4) Cumbria, (5) the Lancashire-Cheshire lowlands and
western Pennines (Fig. 27).

I. The Eastern Pennines and York-Trent Vales

This region corresponds closely with the Humber drainage basin.
The Pennine rivers in Yorkshire and southwards all belong to the
Ouse or the Trent systems, which collect the waters of the two Vales
also, to form the Humber waterway. In their long upper courses on
the dip slope of the Pennines the Yorkshire rivers occupy deep valleys
known as dales, e.g. Wharfedale and Airedale. These are generally
flat-floored and fairly open in their lower parts, and besides providing
useful routes for lines of communication, are fully utilised for mixed
farming. South of Sheffield most of the Pennine drainage is carried
southwards to the Trent by rivers, such as the Derwent, which likewise

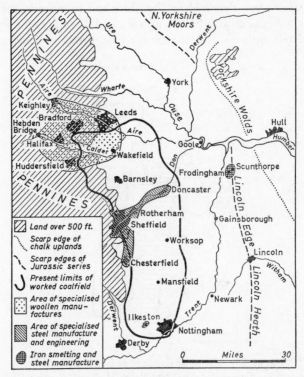

Fig. 28. The Yorks–Notts–Derby coalfield and surrounding parts:
specialised industrial areas.

occupy deep valleys followed by roads and railways. The undulating uplands between all these incised valleys contrast sharply with the valleys themselves. A few miles west of Sheffield in the Don valley, for example, the land rises to open unfrequented moorlands, of limited use even for hill sheep-farming.

The York-Trent Vales form a corridor of lowlands from 10 to 30 miles wide, which extends from the River Tees in the north to the neighbourhood of Nottingham. They are floored with Jurassic and Triassic beds covered for the most part with glacial drift or alluvium. The clay or loam soils are mainly fertile, but are apt to be rather damp,

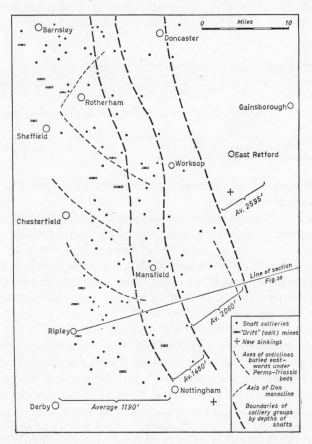

Fig. 29. Map to show increasing average depths eastwards of collieries in the E. Pennine coalfield south of Barnsley. Based on N.C.B. maps corrected to 1959 (depths of individual collieries taken as averages of landings).

so that permanent pastures with cattle-farming are widespread; though there is considerable arable land, especially in the Vale of York, producing cereals, sugar beet and fodder crops, for the cultivation of which the comparatively dry, sunny climate is favourable. Live-stock are, however, of first importance; large numbers of cattle, especially dairy herds, and of pigs are kept. This agricultural belt is complementary to that of the great industrial districts on the adjacent coalfield, supplying them with fresh produce, particularly milk and meat. The leading market towns are York and Northallerton in the Vale of York and Gainsborough in Lincolnshire; York is also a long-established ecclesiastical centre which in modern times has developed a number of food processing and manufacturing industries, and

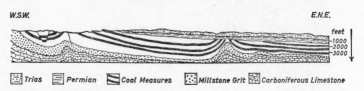

W.S.W.   E.N.E.

feet
-1000
-2000
-3000

▦ Trias   ▤ Permian   ◼ Coal Measures   ▦ Millstone Grit   ▧ Carboniferous Limestone

Fig. 30. Section E.N.E. from Ripley through E. Pennine coalfield showing anticlines and eastward dip. After Wilfred Edwards in Trueman's *The Coalfields of Great Britain* (simplified).

Gainsborough manufactures agricultural machinery and other engineering products.

The East Pennine coalfield, producing upwards of 90 million tons of coal per annum, is much the greatest of the British coalfields, and is second to the Ruhr in the whole of Europe. The seams dip gently eastward from the outcrop belt on the edge of the Pennines, and are worked without break in the distribution of the collieries over the 60 odd miles from Leeds to Nottingham and outwards beyond Doncaster (Figs. 29, 30). Upon this coalfield three major groups of industries have arisen: a northern one in the Aire and Calder valleys grouped round Leeds and Bradford which specialises in woollen manufactures of all kinds; a central one of steel and engineering works in the Don valley, dominated by Sheffield; and a southern one from Chesterfield to Nottingham[1] in which a great variety of manufactures,

[1] Nottingham has industrial affinities with both the Midlands and the East Pennine coalfield belt, on the southern margin of which it lies. Though the Notts-Derby section of the East Pennine coalfield is in the East Midland Division of the National Coal Board, and shares in some of the varied industries of the Midlands, e.g. knitwear textiles, it may perhaps, owing to the continuity of the great coalfield and of some of its associated industries, be properly included in the East Pennine region.

especially of the 'heavy' group, has developed, many of them on a large scale.

Woollen textile manufactures are of two main classes, of woollens and of worsteds. These two groups of industries in the West Riding are concentrated mainly in the Aire, the Calder, and their side valleys, in a rectangular area of which the corner points are Keighley and Leeds on the Aire, and Hebden Bridge and Wakefield on the Calder, with an extension southwards including Huddersfield (Fig. 28). Woollens are manufactured in both valleys, but more in that of the Calder; worsteds chiefly in the Aire valley, especially at Bradford, the metropolis for the production and marketing of this class of textiles. In addition, carpets are made at Halifax and Dewsbury, and shoddy (material made from discarded woollen rags) has been a speciality of the Batley, Dewsbury, Heckmondwicke group of towns. Some forty West Riding towns in all are engaged in one or more branches of the manufactures based on wool, with or without admixture of synthetic fibres; and as few of them confine themselves to one branch only, regional specialisation is not so apparent as in the Lancashire cotton industry (pp. 116–17). Halifax, Huddersfield and Bradford among others, for example, manufacture both woollens and worsteds.

The commercial capital and largest town of the whole constellation is Leeds which has developed a variety of industries, some of which are related to the predominant woollen group, chief among them being machine engineering, ready-made 'tailoring' and manufactures of leather goods. The Yorkshire woollen industries have owed their signal rise in but very small measure to supplies of raw wool from the adjacent Pennines, for these besides being poor in quality soon proved quite insufficient. The chief promoting factors have been water-power in the early days, from numerous Pennine streams, abundance both of soft water off the millstone grit and of cheap coal from the outcrop margin of the large coalfield, and facilities for obtaining imported wool (now accounting for 90 per cent of the supplies) via London or through the Humber ports direct or through Liverpool. Once the industry had established itself in competition with its forerunners in Norfolk and the West Country, the traditional skills developed by the alert Yorkshire people carried it forward, and have enabled it to retain its world leadership.

Another highly specialised area lies in the Don Valley between and including Sheffield and Rotherham, where the production of all kinds of steel and steel alloys, and of semi-manufactures, components, machines and tools made from these steels is supreme. For these secondary and finishing industries the area depends mainly upon supplies of pig iron and crude steel brought from elsewhere, e.g. from north Lincolnshire, to supplement those from the local smelting works. Though the millstone grit formerly used for making grindstones, and the water-power to turn them, may have directed the location of the above industries in the initial stages, the essential factors during the last hundred years have been, as they will remain, the Don waterway and the coalfield now worked along its course as far as Doncaster. The human factors in the forms of traditional skills and specialised technical experience have also played an important part in giving stability and momentum to this localised group of industries, as to the woollen group described above.

Iron-smelting and manufactures of a range of iron and steel products, together with coal-mining are the leading industries among others in a belt extending south from the Don Valley to Nottingham, in and around such towns as Chesterfield, Mansfield and Ilkeston. In Nottingham itself there is no 'heavy' industry; but large-scale manufactures of tobacco, drugs, bicycles and knitwear have been added to the long-established lace industry which has suffered a decline with change in fashion.

Railway transport is highly developed in this whole East Pennine industrial belt, linking it with the Humber ports Hull, Immingham and Goole for seaborne trade and with Hull and Grimsby for fish traffic; with the South Lancashire region via the Pennine tunnels, and with places far and near to the south and the north by the main lines from London to Scotland. The most direct of these is the main eastern line London to Edinburgh, which traverses the lowland belt of the York-Trent Vales, passing through Doncaster and York, the largest towns in the 150-mile stretch between Peterborough and Darlington. Both Doncaster and York are old towns built on the sites of Roman settlements, and both have become in this modern age important railway junctions on which lines converge from various parts of the whole East Pennine region to connect with the through main-line railway.

II. NORTH-EAST ENGLAND

This area extending from the River Tees to the Scottish Border, includes the whole of Durham and Northumberland and the Pennine fringes of Cumberland and Westmorland, as well as the Middles-

brough district south of the Tees estuary in Yorkshire. The Pennines
dominate the physical build of the area, occupying two-thirds of it.
They rise to between two and three thousand feet in their western
plateaux, beyond which they have been rent by a great fault with a
downthrow of 3,000 feet into the Eden Valley Trough. From this

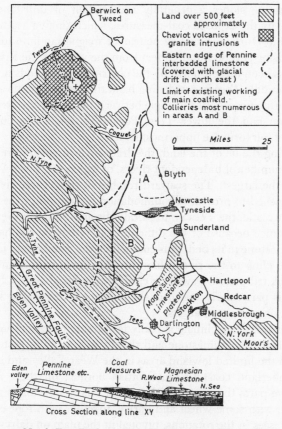

Fig. 31. North-East England: Physical features, coalfield and section.

summit belt the massive limestone strata incline eastwards at a low
angle forming extensive areas of moorland and rough grazings (Fig.
31). In the north the Pennine formations abut against the ancient
igneous rocks of the Cheviot Hills, and almost reach the North Sea
coast north of the River Coquet. Thence southwards they withdraw
from the coast, leaving a triangular area widening towards the Tyne

and again towards the Tees. They are broken in this northern section by the Tyne and the Stainmore gaps (Fig. 27), both of which, especially the former, provide serviceable E.–W. routes followed by railways.

The above-mentioned triangular area, of supreme importance in the human geography of the north-east, is not a level plain. On the lower Pennine slopes a generally narrow belt of millstone grit is succeeded by the exposed coal-measures, which sinking eastwards are concealed in Durham by a low plateau of magnesian limestone. This plateau, rising several hundred feet from the valley of the River Wear (which has been turned north by the obstruction), extends north-east from the middle Tees in a widening band till it ends in cliffs along the whole Durham coast. In the angle between the south-eastern edge of the plateau and the lower Tees, Permo-Triassic rocks containing deposits of salt form the uppermost strata.

Following the lie of the land, the drainage is almost entirely to the east by a number of independent rivers, of which the Tyne, Wear and Tees are the largest. The seaward reaches of these three rivers have been deepened to provide accommodation for shipping; the Tyne as far as Newcastle, the Tees up to Middlesbrough; but the Wear only a short distance because of the difficulties in removing the hard magnesian limestone in its bed, thus compelling the Sunderland industrial district to cling to the river's mouth. The Tyne, with its north and south bank tributaries traversing easily worked coal-seams, has been, and still is particularly useful in the movement of coal for shipment coastwise or to export markets.

Neither relief nor climate is really favourable to agriculture except on the Magnesian Limestone and the Triassic belts in eastern Durham, and the limited lowland areas in the Wear Valley and along the Northumberland coast to the Scottish border; on these relatively productive parts the East British type of mixed farming is generally practised, with some wheat and barley, together with root crops and fodder grasses in the rotations, pivoted in the main on dairy-farming. For in these districts the cattle are of prime importance, especially the dual purpose Durham or Shorthorn breed, which originated there and is now common in the herds in North America and the Southern Hemisphere. Inland on the slopes and in the valleys of the Pennines, the indifferent soils, where cultivated, are mainly under oats and other fodder crops for the winter feed of cattle and sheep. The large areas covered by the Pennine limestones and by the rugged Cheviot volcanics are of use only as grazing runs for hardy breeds of sheep, e.g. the Cheviots.

As the overall agricultural resources are distinctly limited, coal has become the life-blood of these north-eastern counties. Some 40 million tons of coal are raised per annum, much of it the excellent coking coal of Durham. Coal has long figured in the exports of the area, especially from Tyneside; and, though outward movements other than coastwise have declined, the whole group of coal-using iron, steel, heavy engineering and shipbuilding industries has expanded. In this connection it is proper to include the Middlesbrough iron-smelting and heavy engineering district, which, though south of the Tees in Yorkshire, depends on South Durham coal. The North-East Coast produces about 4 million tons of steel per annum (approximately one-fifth of the British total), using Scandinavian and other imported ores almost entirely, now that the Cleveland Hills deposits are be-coming exhausted. Most of this steel is produced round Middles-brough and eastward to Redcar, though blast furnaces and steel works are also in operation at Consett, not far from Newcastle, and at West Hartlepool.

Foremost among the industrial developments are shipbuilding, the fabrication of steel bridges (to be erected elsewhere) and the manu-facture of constructional steel and heavy railway requirements, in-cluding locomotives and rails. Shipbuilding is concentrated largely on Tyneside and at Sunderland, which together rival the Clyde as a leading world centre of this industry.[1] Some smaller ships have also been built on the Tees. Constructional steel products of all kinds are a speciality of the Tees-side mills, and locomotives and other forms of heavy railway equipment are built at Darlington on the east coast main line railway. In addition there is much general and electrical engineering as well as specialised engineering for the shipbuilding industry, the former in particular at Newcastle and Stockton, and the latter at various smaller towns adjacent to the Tyneside and Sunder-land yards. The salt deposits of south-east Durham are the basis of a wide range of chemical industries, including, as in South Lancashire, large-scale manufactures of soap products; the most striking develop-ment in recent times has been the establishment of large works by the Imperial Chemical Industries organisation at Billingham-on-Tees

[1] The Tyne–Wear–Tees yards have in recent years constructed over 40 per cent of the British total compared with about 33 per cent on Clydeside, but see p. 126.

and at Wilton across the river, for the manufacture of ordinary and recently evolved synthetic products.

In view of the concentration of industry at places on or near tide water and of population in the coastal belt, and in view also of the bulky imports of iron ores and pitprops and likewise bulky exports of coal and steel products, it follows that seaborne traffic fills a large place in the transport services. The major general-purpose port and regional capital of the whole area is Newcastle. Other ports such as Blyth, Sunderland, the two Hartlepools and Middlesbrough are limited in their functions to particular kinds of import and export trade. The main artery of internal transport is the trunk railway passing through Darlington, Durham and Newcastle and thence to Berwick-on-Tweed, connected with the west coast main line railway system via the Tyne and the Stainmore gaps. With one exception the towns mentioned above are mainly products of industrial development. The exception is Durham, situated on a limestone bluff formed by an elbow of the Wear; an historic town as its castle indicates, and the cultural capital of the north-east.

III. THE NORTHERN SCARPLANDS

The Northern Scarplands consist of (I) a belt of chalk uplands in the York and the Lincoln Wolds, on either side of the Humber Estuary, and (II) a mainly inland belt of Jurassic escarpments in the North Yorkshire Moors, separated by a wide gap in south Yorkshire from the Lincoln Edge and Lincoln Heath. Both the Chalk and the Jurassic uplifts have inward-facing scarps from which they dip eastwards. Towards the coast the chalk beds disappear beneath the glacial and marine clays of Holderness and the Lincoln Marsh; and an angular depression, the Lincoln Vale, lying between the Lincoln Edge and the Lincoln Wolds, is likewise filled with later deposits, mainly clays. This depression and also the Lincoln Marsh merge southwards into the Fenland.

Another depression, the Vale of Pickering between the North Yorkshire Moors and the Yorkshire Wolds, was at one time the valley of an eastward-flowing river, whose exit, however, became blocked by a moraine left by the Scandinavian ice-sheet. The drainage-water formed a lake which has been reduced gradually by downward cutting (at Kirkham Gorge) by a western overflow, which now forms the lower course of the present river, the Yorkshire Derwent, rising near the coast. Thus the drainage of the Vale has been reversed as the result of glaciation. Its nearly level floor, now completely drained, is covered with lacustrine silt of unusual fertility.

The North Yorkshire Moors are a plateau 600 to 1,000 feet in height, composed of sandstone and intersected by deep valleys. The siliceous upland soils are infertile, and little farming is possible except in the valleys. In the northern section including the Cleveland Hills large quantities of low-grade iron ore were formerly quarried for the Tees-side and coastal iron and steel works, but by 1959 supplies

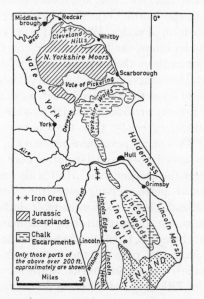

Fig. 32. The Scarplands north of the Wash.

from this source had fallen to little more than 3 per cent of the total output of England and Wales. The relatively small population of the Yorkshire Moors as a whole is concentrated in the valleys and along the coast from Whitby, a minor port, to Redcar where there is some 'heavy' industry.

The Lincoln Edge is a narrow belt of limestone rocks which rises steeply from the Trent Vale and falls away gradually on its dip slope into the Lincoln Vale. South of the Witham Gap, in which Lincoln is situated, the uplift is known as the Lincoln Heath. Of especial importance in these times are the thick deposits of rather lean iron ore in the Lower Lias beds in the northern section close to the Humber, where large iron and steel works are in operation around Scunthorpe (Fig. 28). Lincoln is an old town, the site of a Roman settlement (Lindum). It is a cathedral city and the natural market centre for the rich agricultural lands of the neighbouring vales and Lincoln Edge dip slope; it has developed manufactures of agricultural machinery as well as of diesel engines and excavating and pumping equipment.

The lower and intermediate slopes of the York and Lincoln Wolds are covered with fertile glacial drift, as are Holderness, the Lincoln Marsh and Lincoln Vale. All these, and indeed most of the Northern Scarplands except the North Yorkshire Moors, are good farm land with a high proportion of arable. Wheat and other cereals are grown together with fodder crops, the latter for sheep on the drier parts of the Wolds, and for cattle on the lowlands. Artificial drainage has been necessary in both Holderness and the Lincoln Marsh as well as in the Vale of Pickering to lower the excessively high water tables.

The Humber Estuary provides a through passage to the sea for the large external trade, especially with the Continent, of the inland industrial areas. Two major ports have arisen on it, Kingston-upon-Hull (commonly called Hull) and Grimsby. Both are great fishing ports situated near the Dogger Bank. Hull is also one of the leading British commercial ports, serving especially Yorkshire and the North-East Midlands, and has considerable industries based on imported products, e.g. oil-seed crushing and manufactures of oil-cakes, paints and chemicals. Goole, at the head of the estuary, has been created as an additional port for the industrially active Humber hinterland. Similarly the seaside towns, Scarborough at the eastern end of the Vale of Pickering and Skegness on the sandy Lincolnshire coast, owe their growth largely to the flow of visitors from the industrial areas of the East Pennine region and the North Midlands.

IV. CUMBRIA

This region is essentially that of the Cumbrian highland dome round the margins of which lie the Solway Plain with its extension along the Cumberland coast, the Eden Trough and the lowland at the head of Morecambe Bay. On the eastern border the Pennines rise steeply from the Eden Valley south of the Tyne gap along the line of the great fault. Here they average well over 2,000 feet, and reach nearly 3,000 feet in Crossfell. Small as the region is, it contains an unusual variety of structural elements and relief features.

The most interesting of these in both geological evolution and scenery is the Cumbrian massif. It originated in the Caledonian fold-ing, was subsequently peneplaned and probably submerged with the deposition of Mesozoic beds, and later re-elevated (during the Alpine disturbances) into a dome-like form, since when it has been subjected to vigorous erosion which culminated in sculpturing by glaciers in the Ice Age. The residual highlands, resembling the spokes of a wheel in pattern, average some 2,000 feet in height and attain their greatest

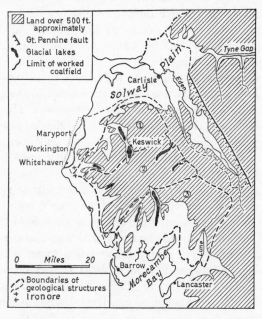

Fig. 33. Cumbria: structural features. (1) Palaeozoic slates, (2) old volcanics, (3) Silurian mudstones.

elevation in the 'hub' area where Scafell and Helvellyn both exceed 3,000 feet. Except on the outer margins, the massif is composed of Pre-Carboniferous rocks which are arranged in three diagonal bands — early Palaeozoic slates in the north, old volcanics in the centre, and compact Silurian mudstones in the south — all with a NE.–SW. Caledonian alignment (Fig. 33). These core structures are surrounded by broken rings of Carboniferous and Permo-Triassic rocks, the remnants of strata that probably covered the whole area prior to the final elevation.

In the peripheral areas where those strata have been preserved,

E   S.W.C.E.

Carboniferous limestones appear in a belt north of Morecambe Bay and also along the western margin of the Eden Trough, and coal-measures of Carboniferous age occur in the coastlands north of St. Bees Head, dipping westward with overlying beds under the Irish Sea. New Red (Triassic) Sandstones compose the floors of the Solway Plain and of the Eden Valley, and fringe the coast southwards from St. Bees Head inclusive. Finally, much of the surface of the marginal lowlands is covered with glacial drift, deposited by ice-flows from the Cumbrian and the Scottish ice-caps.

The Cumbrian massif shows a fine example of radial drainage which, it is thought, may have been guided by cracks formed when the area was uplifted as a dome. In the course of time such cover of Carboniferous limestones and Triassic sandstones as may have existed was stripped off, and the rivers, holding their initial courses, cut down into the ancient rocks regardless of their arrangement. The glaciers of the Ice Age followed these ready-made river valleys, chiselling their sloping sides into more or less vertical walls, and deepening their floors, in which they excavated hollows now occupied by ribbon-shaped lakes, some of them impounded by moraines. These flat-floored valleys penetrating far into the highland area contrast vividly with the rugged residual intervening limbs of the massif, both in physical form and in utilisation: lakes, green meadows, some fodder crops and cattle below; crags, moorland vegetation, mountain pastures and sheep on the Fells above.[1] The heavy precipitation (over 100 inches in exposed upland places) and frequent mists restrict farming to the pastoral forms. Otherwise the chief uses of the area are for recreational purposes and for water supplies, e.g. from Lake Thirlmere to the Manchester area.

The Solway and Eden Valley lowlands, their New Red Sandstone floors covered in part with Lias clays and glacial drift, are comparatively fertile; and as their rainfall is well under 40 inches (Carlisle 32 inches), mixed farming with varying proportions between arable and permanent pastures is the general rule. The chief rotation crops are oats, roots and sown grasses (for pastures and hay), all with a bias towards provision for dairy and beef cattle, together with potatoes grown mainly for human food.

Industrial development is concentrated mainly on the coastal coalfield between Maryport and Whitehaven, and in the Barrow

---

[1] A hardy type of sheep has been bred to thrive on the Fells, from which they are brought down only in very severe weather when they may be snowbound.

district in the south-west, in both of which iron-smelting and steel manufacture are the leading industry, with shipbuilding also at Barrow. Most of the iron ore supplies are now imported, local production being small and confined to the Egremont-Sellafield district behind Whitehaven.

Various miscellaneous industries including textiles have been established in the coalfield belt under the Special Areas Act; but the most recent and striking development is that of atomic plants in the Sellafield district e.g. at Calder Hall, now producing electricity fed into the national grid.

Carlisle, the natural focus of the lowlands of Cumbria, is an important transport and market centre, and the largest town in the whole region. Two main railway lines to Scotland, from London and the Midlands, reach Carlisle via the Eden and Lowther Valleys in the Eden Trough, and three main lines from Scotland and two others from Newcastle and the Cumbrian west coast also converge at Carlisle. Other towns beside the west coast mining and industrial group are small, depending mainly on tourist business, e.g. Windermere and Keswick.

V. The Lancashire-Cheshire Lowlands and Western Pennines

Between the Lune Valley in north Lancashire and the Midland or Cheshire Gate lies a plain broken on its seaward margin by the Ribble and Mersey estuaries, and eastwards by the Bowland and Rossendale spurs of the Pennines, which elsewhere rise steeply to their crests, thus giving the Lancashire rivers a high gradient in their upper courses. The plain is narrow in the north, but widens out south of the Bowland spur, and still more in the South Lancashire-Cheshire Basin, where it is some 40 miles in width.

This plain is generally fertile. Its floor, composed largely of New Red Sandstone, is covered with a mantle of glacial drift which yields soils that range from rich loams to heavy clays, with some patches of poor sands; towards the coast in south-west Lancashire there is a belt of blown sand and fertile peat soils. The grits and limestones of the Bowland and Rossendale uplands and of the steep western slopes of the Pennines produce generally thin and poor soils of little agricultural value.

Though the rainfall is heavy against the Pennines (50 inches above Manchester), it averages little more than 30 inches on the plain, and is only 24 inches in west Cheshire; and, while the atmosphere over the lowlands is more humid than to the east of the Pennines, sunshine is sufficient for the ripening of wheat. The more fertile lands, i.e. those in west Lancashire and north Cheshire, are intensively farmed with high proportions of field crops, among which oats, wheat, potatoes and temporary grasses lead in acreage; and market-gardening is very important on first-class land within reach of the urban centres. The Lancashire-Cheshire Plain specialises above all in live-stock, including dairy and beef cattle, pigs and poultry, with extraordinarily high densities of dairy cattle and pigs in Cheshire. Altogether the agricultural productivity of the region is great, though rather overshadowed by its industrial output.

The noted industrial activities of the area have been closely associated with the South Lancashire coalfield, and are located partly in the Ribble basin north of the Rossendale upland, mainly south of

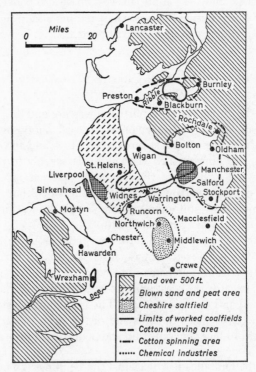

Fig. 34. The Lancashire–Cheshire Region: mineral deposits and manufactures.

it with extensions along Merseyside and into north Cheshire (Fig. 34). The 12 million tons of coal now raised, chiefly from the deeper seams towards the south, are insufficient however to meet all requirements, so that additional supplies have to be obtained from the East Pennine coalfield. On the other hand, the Cheshire salt-field, occupying a belt extending southwards from Northwich towards Crewe, produces more salt than is required by the Merseyside chemical and salt-using industries. Other bulky materials, such as iron ore for the steel and engineering industries, have to be imported.

South Lancashire has long specialised in cotton textiles; the initial advantages were supplies of soft water and water-power from the fast Pennine streams, the humid climate of the sub-Pennine valleys, and access to sources of raw cotton through the Mersey waterway and the port of Liverpool. The soft water from the millstone grit remains an asset, and likewise the inland waterway since enhanced by the construction of the Manchester Ship Canal; but water-power has long been superseded by steam-power generated from coal, and natural atmospheric humidity has lost its differential advantage with the introduction of artificial air-conditioning. The Lancashire cotton industry attained its zenith early in this century when exports reached their maximum. Two disrupting wars, the growth of cotton manufactures abroad in centres nearer to the sources of raw cotton and to markets for cotton goods, and the substitution of synthetic fibres such as rayon for cotton, have resulted in an absolute decline in output and a still greater shrinkage in exports both of yarns and of cloth.[1] A marked feature of the Lancashire cotton industry has been regional specialisation of processes: spinning in the towns round Manchester, such as Oldham, Bolton, Rochdale and Stockport among others; weaving in the Ribble valley in a group of towns, of which Preston, Blackburn and Burnley are the largest; and finishing in the intermediate district of the Irwell valley.

South Lancashire has found some compensation for the contraction of the cotton industry, by diversification — by expanding other industries and establishing new ones. Foremost among them is the engineering industry, which, beginning early with the manufacture of textile machinery and steam engines, has developed every branch, including that of steel-making, and some such as electrical engineering

---

[1] By 1960 production of cotton cloth had fallen to little more than a fifth of the earlier total, and for the first time for over a century the British exports of cotton cloth in 1958 were no larger than the imports.

at Manchester (Metropolitan Vickers) and machine-tool manufacture, on a very large scale. In recent years the production of
motor transport vehicles, e.g. at Leyland near Preston, has been a
significant addition. The chemical and soap-making industries of the
Merseyside towns, Widnes, Runcorn, Warrington and Port Sunlight,
using salt from Cheshire, have been long established; likewise glass-
making at St. Helens and shipbuilding at Birkenhead. On the other
hand, manufactures of artificial fibres and of rayon and mixed fibre
textiles, replacing to some extent those of cotton in the old cotton
towns round Manchester and in the Ribble valley, are comparatively
new developments. Macclesfield in east Cheshire and neighbouring
towns on the slopes of the Pennines where pure water is available,
have long been centres of the pure silk industry, but they too are now
using rayon as well.

The Cheshire salt-field (Fig. 34) has close economic ties with the
Merseyside and its chemical industries. The salt-beds, which lie at
depths of 200 to 400 feet, are worked by brine-pumping extraction in
a belt from Sandbach north-east of Crewe through Middlewich and
Winsford to Northwich. Some salt-refineries have survived, mainly
round Middlewich; most have been displaced by chemical works,
either on the salt-field or on Merseyside, e.g. at Weston Point, where
brine is delivered by pipe line.

Internal and external transport systems by land and sea and by
inland waterways are highly developed. The main west Pennine
railway London to Scotland gives direct connection from Crewe
through Warrington, Wigan (an important coal-mining centre),
Preston and Lancaster to Carlisle. Five main lines across the Pennines
(three with long tunnels) link Lancashire closely with the West
Riding; and a dense network in South Lancashire and Cheshire
converges on Liverpool, second among British ports, from which
shipping services are available to all parts of the world. The Manchester
Ship Canal opened in 1894 is the greatest man-made waterway in
Britain; it enables ocean-going vessels to reach the heart of the Lancashire textile and engineering region, making Manchester the rival of
Hull for third place among British ports by value of total trade. The
traffic it carries dwarfs that of the older barge canals, such as the
Liverpool and Leeds and the Mersey-Stoke canals, which have lost
relatively in importance as means of transport.

Chapter 9

SCOTLAND

Few countries in the world are composed of such clearly defined geographical regions as Scotland. The two great diagonal fault lines which mark off the Lowlands from the Highlands to the north, and from the Southern Uplands less distinctly in the south, divide Scotland into three regions, each contrasting with the others in geological structure and major relief forms, and correspondingly also in human

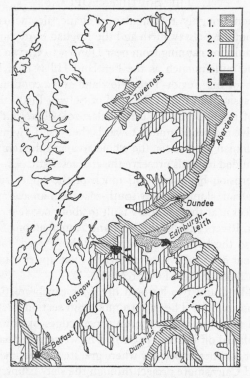

Fig. 35. Scotland: land use. 1. Cash crops and market gardening. 2. Mixed farming, partly or mainly arable. 3. Mainly dairying and stock-rearing. 4. Moorlands and rough grazings. 5. Main urban areas.

geography and density of population. Of these the mountainous Highlands with adjacent islands occupy more than half the area of the country, but hold only one-seventh of its inhabitants; while the Lowlands, less than a quarter of Scotland in area, contribute much of the agricultural and nearly all the industrial output, and contain little short of 80 per cent of the entire population. The Southern Uplands, less barren and mountainous than the Highlands, contain some moderately fertile valleys and coastal fringes but, apart from these, offer little to attract population. All three regions have retained distinctive marks of their genesis in the Caledonian revolution, which were first systematically studied in Scotland, hence the adoption by geologists of the term Caledonian applied to structures of similar origin all over the world.

I. THE SOUTHERN UPLANDS

This region, roughly rectangular in shape, lies across Southern Scotland from the Solway Firth and the English border in the southeast to the fault line running from near Dunbar to Girvan in Ayrshire, though some outliers such as the Pentland Hills stand beyond this line. Except for the Teviot-Tweed lowland and a continuation of the Carlisle Triassic plain round the head of Solway Firth, this region is composed of intensely folded early Palaeozoic slates and grits, with some intrusive masses of granite towards the west. Originally uplifted in the Caledonian orogenesis, the whole area and the remnants of the severely denuded uplands preserve the characteristic NE.–SW. trend. Prolonged erosion has planed off much of the upper surface to an irregular plateau, sloping gently south-east from an average height of over 1,500 feet near the boundary fault to about 600 feet on its southern margins. Rivers such as the Nith and Annan among others in the west and also the left-bank tributaries of the Tweed, following this slope, have cut deep valleys, gorge-like in their upper courses, widening out into 'dales' in their lower reaches.

Two highland and two lowland divisions can be distinguished in the region as a whole. The eastern mountain section is characterised by rounded forms in which the upturned edges of crumpled strata have been planed off in zebra pattern. The western highlands present more abrupt outlines, especially where granite masses such as those of Merrick and Cairnsmore project through the slaty country rocks, and where the rivers have sharply dissected the highlands. On the southern margin of this western upland lies a fringe of lowlands. These consist of an extension of the Solway Plain of Cumbria from the English border to near the River Nith, and west of that in the several peninsulas, of undulating, drift-covered country broken here and there by remnant ridges of former more extensive highlands. The fourth physical division, that of the Teviot-Tweed lowland, differs from the preceding in that it is carved out of Old Red Sandstone and Carboniferous rocks of later age than those elsewhere; in it a triangular area known as the Merse, its narrow apex reaching 30 to 40 miles inland, is covered abundantly with glacial drift, and is one of the most fertile and climatically favoured parts of Scotland.

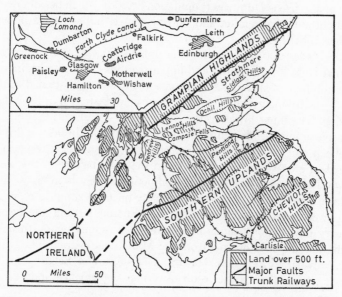

Fig. 36. Southern Scotland: relief features and trunk railways. Inset map of Forth–Clyde populous axial Lowland belt.

Climate as well as relief is a material factor in the distribution of farming activities in the Southern Uplands. The highlands above 500 feet in the west and 1,000 feet in the east are wet and misty, are mostly covered with moorland vegetation, and can be used only as rough grazings for the hardy black-faced breed of sheep. The dales, e.g. Nithsdale, Annandale, Eskdale, Lauderdale, are naturally drier, lying in the lee of highlands aligned across the direction of the prevailing south-westerly rain-bearing winds. In all of them some oats, turnips and fodder crops are grown for sheep and cattle, especially

E2

the former; and along them strings of settlements penetrate the more or less uninhabited uplands.

In contrast to the relatively dry and somewhat extreme climate of the lower Tweed Basin, that of the south-western lowlands is humid and mild. There much of the farmland is under permanent pastures; the chief crop is oats, grown for a couple of years in rotation with sown grasses down as pastures for seven years or more; and the whole agricultural economy is built up on cattle and sheep, especially dairy cattle. In this predominantly rural area population is distributed with the characteristic spread over the productive land. The only town of any size is Dumfries (population 87,000), which besides being an important local market and railway centre, has some textile and synthetic fibre factories.

The Tweed Basin, including the upland rim, is in some ways a singular area. Its wide outer and upper margins carry extraordinarily large numbers of sheep, pastured on the uplands and fattened in the dales — a striking example of an intimate combination of hill and dale farming. The inner lowland, the Merse, is in its turn an example of intensive arable farming in which oats, turnips and beans are grown for sheep and cattle; and also malting barley and wheat, especially towards the coast. In the upper basin the manufacture of the well-known Tweed cloth has survived competition from its much greater Yorkshire rival. Though based originally on local supplies of wool, and power as well as soft water from the numerous streams, the Tweed industry now imports much of its raw wool requirements (through Leith), and depends on coal from the Midlothian district. The siting of the towns, e.g. Peebles, Hawick, Galashiels and Selkirk, up the various river valleys is the result of former dependence upon direct water power.

In spite of the fact that the Southern Uplands extend across Scotland from the North Sea almost to the North Channel, they have not barred the ways and movement between England and Scotland, thanks mainly to the graded routes provided by the river valleys. The direct London-Edinburgh railway hugs the coast beyond Berwick-on-Tweed, but three other main lines, all from Carlisle, thread their ways through the highlands with but few troublesome gradients; one via the Liddel valley across the Tweed at Hawick and thence up Gala Water; another up Annandale and down Clydesdale, reaching both Glasgow and Edinburgh via Carstairs; and a third through Dumfries via Nithsdale into Ayrshire and thence to Glasgow. Roads by these and other routes have naturally been in existence from before the construction of railways. Partly because of these access routes, the Border country was for centuries the scene of strife, evidence of which remains in its ruined forts and castles. Its chequered history came to a close with the Union in 1707, since when the Southern Uplands region has become a transit zone between highly developed populous areas, but of secondary importance on its own account.

II. The Central Lowlands

Structurally a rift valley of Caledonian origin, modified by Armorican folding, the Central Lowlands are far from being an even-floored valley or lowland. The contrast between highland and lowland is most marked along the northern boundary fault from Stonehaven (near Aberdeen) to Helensburgh on the Firth of Clyde, especially to the north-east where the Grampian Highlands rise upwards of 3,000 feet from the Vale of Strathmore. Volcanic upthrusts and transverse anticlines, together with prongs and outliers of the Southern Uplands, have split up the region into a series of basins, floored in some parts with Old Red Sandstone, in other parts with coal-bearing Carboniferous strata. Most conspicuous among the volcanic uplands are those, dating partly from the Caledonian and partly from the Hercynian orogenesis, that form a belt parallel with the highland fault, namely the Renfrew Heights (south of the Clyde), the Campsie Fells and the Lennox Hills, the Ochil Hills and the Sidlaw Hills. On the southern margin anticlinal ridges, such as the Pentland Hills, have been thrust up, composed of ancient sedimentary rocks interbedded with volcanics. The volcanic hills rising to between 1,000 and 2,000 feet, (nearly 3,000 feet in the Ochils), are commonly steep-sided, as they tend to weather along the vertical joints in the lava rocks. Towards the southern boundary fault the so-called Lowlands rise steadily except in Ayrshire and in East Lothian, so that the distinction between them and the adjoining Southern Uplands tends to be effaced. Apart from Strathmore, the chief true lowland fragments are the Ayrshire Plain, Strathclyde, the middle Forth valley, most of the Fifeshire peninsula, the East Lothian coastland and the narrow belt between the Sidlaw Hills and the Firth of Tay (including the Carse of Gowrie).

The pronounced NW.–SE. courses of the rivers Tay and Forth and the almost parallel course of the Clyde, all three terminating in firths or estuarine inlets, are of special significance in the human geography of the region. The valleys provide useful transverse routes, with gaps through the volcanic belt at Perth, Stirling and Dumbarton, apparently cut by these rivers. The drowned lower valleys not only enable ships to proceed well inland, but also provide convenient sites for ports along their shores. Thus no part of the whole region is more than 25 miles from a seaport, and a very large proportion of the population is concentrated either in the numerous ports or within a

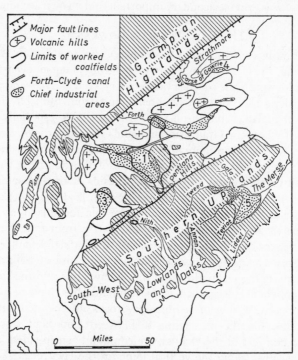

Fig. 37. Southern Scotland: general physical and industrial features. Industrial districts as numbered — (1) Clyde Valley and Clydeside. 2. S. Fifeshire and Stirling (3) Ayrshire (4) Dundee (5) Tweed valleys. Note. The Forth–Clyde Canal is now closed to shipping. Coalfields west to east — Ayrshire, Lanark–Clackmannan, Fife–Midlothian.

dozen miles of them. This access to tide waters, a singular feature in the conformation of the Central Lowlands, has contributed to, if not directed, its industrial development along lines that necessitate large imports and exports of bulky commodities.

The unusual variety of terrain in the relatively small area of the Central Lowlands has a direct influence upon the distribution of the various forms of agricultural utilisation; though this is influenced further by the broad difference in climate between humid west and comparatively dry east, and also by the varied composition of the glacial drift that covers much of the productive land. Within the limits set by natural conditions the Scottish Lowlands are one of the most intensively farmed regions in the world. This is true in particular of the eastern arable districts from Strathmore to the Lothians, where the rotation crops include wheat, barley, potatoes, sugar beet (in Fifeshire), and the usual root and fodder crops and sown grasses for sheep and cattle. On the other hand, the mild damp climate of the western and larger part, deficient in sunshine, discourages the cultivation of cereals except oats, and limits that of potatoes to certain special districts, but it is distinctly favourable to the growth of pastures whether permanent or sown. Thus beef and dairy cattle are kept in large numbers, as well as sheep brought down from the hills, i.e. the volcanic series and those adjoining the Southern Uplands, which cannot be used otherwise than as sheep runs. In addition to these general types of farming in the Central Lowlands, special forms of production have arisen in favourable localities, among them fruit cultivation in Clydesdale, Strathmore and the Carse of Gowrie, and large-scale production of seed potatoes in East Lothian.

Industrial activities are mainly responsible for the fact that the Central Lowlands, less than a quarter of the area of Scotland, contain over three-quarters of its population (4 millions out of 5·2 millions). These manufacturing industries have been built up on the supplies of fuel and power derived from coal. Blackband iron ore, which gave rise to the first iron foundries in Scotland, is no longer worked, and the oil shales mined in West Lothian yield only a small fraction of the industrial requirements of their products. Unfortunately also, the output of coal has been falling, the decline in that of the Lanarkshire field (still the largest producer) not being made good by increases in the outputs of the other fields.[1] Against this decrease in production, local consumption has been rising, so that little coal is now being exported abroad compared with the substantial amounts in pre-war times.

The iron and steel industries together with heavy and general engineering and shipbuilding are the chief consumers of coal, though part of the pig iron used in steel manufacture is obtained from other districts in Britain. The blast furnaces remaining in operation, and most of the steel works, are located either on the eastern outskirts of

---

[1] Output of deep-mined coal, average 1958–9: Lanarkshire 5·89, Fife 5·2, Ayr 4·42, Lothians 3·67 million tons. Total 19·18, compared with 28·8 tons in 1931–2.

Glasgow or above it in the Clyde Valley, i.e. on the western edge of the Lanarkshire coalfield, iron ore being imported mainly through the Firth of Forth. Here nearly all the Scottish production of steel, averaging $2\frac{1}{2}$ million tons in the years 1956–8, is concentrated.

Engineering industries are more widely distributed; general engineering in a number of the iron and steel centres such as Airdrie, Coatbridge, Motherwell and also at Kilmarnock; marine engineering, engaged in the construction of ships' engines and machinery, is naturally associated with the shipbuilding yards at Glasgow, Dumbarton, Port Glasgow and Greenock; and locomotive-building is important in the Glasgow-Kilmarnock district. Much of the steel and of the engineering products is incorporated in the finished ships delivered from the Clydeside yards, which launch about a third of the British tonnage, and which indeed for many years constituted the chief shipbuilding centre in the world. The relative importance of this area is all the greater, because a large proportion of the ships constructed there are of the liner class, more costly to build and more valuable by tonnage than the ordinary cargo ships or tankers. Some ships are also constructed at Leith, the port of Edinburgh, but the launchings there are insignificant compared with those of Clydeside.

The predominance in the Central Lowlands of shipbuilding together with the heavy industries that feed it with steel and machinery, is apt to overshadow other branches of industry there. Some of these are substantial. Foremost among them are the manufactures of ordinary structural steel and a variety of engineering and hardware products (similar to those associated with Birmingham) in the Clyde Valley towns. Linen and hempen goods are manufactured at Dundee and Dunfermline and other eastern towns, carpets at Glasgow and Kilmarnock, and knitwear at Kilmarnock and Ayr. Two specialised textile manufactures are distinctly localised, namely of sewing thread at Paisley, and of jute sacking and hessian at Dundee, the latter product being used as the base fabric of linoleum made in south Fifeshire, especially at Kirkcaldy. Of a different order are the paper-making and publishing trades of Edinburgh, in association with its role as the cultural as well as the political capital of Scotland; and different again is the manufacture of whisky (from imported grain) especially at Kilmarnock. Most of these manufactures are of long standing, but newer forms of industry have been introduced, partly to relieve the effects of depression in the inter-war period, among them the production of rayon in the Glasgow-Paisley area.

Unhappy experience has shown that the economy of the Central Lowlands is highly vulnerable to adverse trade conditions abroad. Its fortunes rise and fall with the world demand for its limited range of export products, mainly capital goods. More than most British industrial areas, it depends upon imported supplies of basic raw materials, iron ore, flax, jute and malting grain among others, as well as foodstuffs such as wheat. It thus derives its livelihood from the price difference between imported raw materials and the industrial products exported at a later stage, i.e. from the value of the labour and skill added in the interval. The terms of trade are of vital importance to it.

In response to the need for extensive movements of materials and products, internal transport is fully developed. A network of roads and railways covering the Lowland 'waist', links all important places in the populous belt served by the seaways that terminate in the fine natural waterways of the Firths of Clyde, Forth and Tay. The main foci of this system are Glasgow and Edinburgh-Leith. But owing to the disposition of the volcanic hills whereby routes converge on the Tay and Forth gaps, Perth in the former and Stirling in the latter are examples of historic as well as modern nodal towns, though their importance as route centres has declined in some measure since bridges were constructed over both the Firth of Tay and the Firth of Forth.

III. THE SCOTTISH HIGHLANDS

The Highland region comprises all the mainland and the islands that lie north-west of the great fault or series of faults from Stonehaven to the Firth of Clyde. Except for the Old Red Sandstone strip round Moray Firth and the basalt-covered parts of the Western Isles, it is composed mainly of masses of very ancient highly metamorphosed rocks, e.g. schists, slates and quartzites, with extensive intrusions of granite. Parts of it indeed, in the Outer Hebrides and the adjoining mainland, contain rocks (Lewisian Gneisses) which are among the oldest known to geologists. The Highlands themselves are divided by the Glenmore rift into the North-West Highlands and the Grampian Highlands which differ in several respects.

Folding in this area began apparently in Pre-Cambrian times, but the main folding took place in the Caledonian mid-Palaeozoic orogenesis with the characteristic NE.–SW. alignment that has persisted to the present day in the trend lines of the mountains, of the Glenmore rift and of the fault-guided river valleys, and also of many western coastal features. A remarkable development in the course of this Caledonian mountain-building was the thrusting from the south-east of great masses of Pre-Cambrian rocks over Cambrian in the North-West Highlands (the Moine thrust) in contrast with the over-thrust of Palaeozoic beds over Pre-Cambrian in reverse direction in Scandinavia (p. 303).

In the Devonian period subsequent to the elevation of the Caledo-nian mountain chains, Old Red Sandstone beds preserved in Glen-more and in the north-east coastlands were laid down in the basins between them. Prolonged erosion since then, together with extensive fracturing and re-elevation (the latter in progress now), has deformed the earlier mountain-system into the likeness of an elevated much-dissected peneplain, upwards of 3,000 feet in height, with a general gradual slope in both the north-western and the Grampian sections from north-west to south-east. The granite masses, intruded in the early phases of mountain-building, form the highest existing summits, i.e. Ben Nevis (near Fort William) and Ben Macdhui, and other peaks in the Cairngorms, all over 4,000 feet; while extremely resistant metamorphic rocks compose numerous other heights exceeding 3,000 feet. In addition to the NE.–SW. faults of Caledonian origin, many fractures trending more or less E.–W., developed in the western parts as a result of the Alpine earth storms, through some of which, especially in the inner Hebrides, basalt lava welled up to form exten-sive surface sheets.

Glaciation, the latest transforming episode in the long history of the Highlands, has left distinctive features in its train. The eastern parts of the Grampian Highlands have been rounded off in rather tame outlines between the ice-deepened valleys of the Spey, the Dee and other rivers; the western parts, being more rent by faults and fractures, have been carved into more rugged forms, and contain as the result of ice action numerous valley lochs (glacial lakes) and several striking sea lochs (fiords). The North-West Highlands are still wilder; they are dissected by numerous transverse valleys cut by rivers and ice in the shatter belts of the fractures, and their western coast is fretted by fiords. Thus glaciation has contributed to contrasts in physical forms, and consequently in human geography, between the western and the eastern highlands. The former have greater scenic attractions, abated however, by the excessively wet climate; the latter have rolling heather-clad uplands used as grouse-moors and rough grazings, and slower flowing rivers and streams sought by anglers.

The ice-sheets radiating from the mountains swept off the soil cover, depositing some of their load in the eastern valleys and lowlands, removing most of it away to the south or into the sea. The thin soils subsequently formed from the hard crystalline rocks may have carried a broken forest cover of Scots pine, mountain ash etc; but, since destruction of this cover by man, the leached, acid soils support little else but moorland, bog and coarse grass vegetation. In the humid mountainous wilderness of the western highlands, the scattered level patches in the valley bottoms and on the coastal terraces resemble oases, with their meadows and cultivated plots. The eastern highlands differ from the western not only in their lower rainfall (under 40 inches compared with 60 to 100 inches), but also in that the deeply penetrating valleys of rivers such as the Spey, the Don and the Dee form long ribbons of verdure intersecting the prevailing dun colour of the uplands and mountains. In these parts some hardy highland cattle and sheep are kept on the stretches of rough hillside grazings, and the general appearance of the landscape is kindlier than in the west.

The zig-zag belt of low and relatively low country from the Pentland Firth to Inverness, and thence round the coast to Aberdeen, is the most populous and productive part of the Highland region. The rainfall is quite moderate (27·6 inches at Inverness and 30·5 inches at Aberdeen). The Old Red Sandstone is a much more promising parent rock for soil production than the metamorphic rocks and granites of the mountains behind; and much of that formation as well as of the Aberdeenshire coastal platform is covered with more or less fertile glacial drift. These coastlands specialise in the production of beef cattle, especially of the Aberdeen-Angus breed, and have achieved a reputation as a source of Scotch beef. The mixed rotation farming, in which the common sequence is oats, turnips, oats and temporary grass, is adapted to the cool temperate climate and is designed mainly to provide fodder for beef cattle; some barley and food crops are also grown, in particular along the south coast of the Moray Firth.

In the mountain areas of the Highlands and on the western coastlands and islands, human settlement is restricted to the scattered and often isolated patches of productive soil. A somewhat primitive form of subsistence farming, supplemented where possible by fishing, is the mainstay of the small groups known as crofters. The range of crops is limited by the climate. On the family plots oats and potatoes are grown for food; and live-stock, chiefly sheep, pastured on the hillsides in summer, are sustained in winter with turnips and hay. As the crofters live mostly in isolated communities, they are necessarily self-contained, producing the bulk of their food and clothing requirements on the spot, and because, moreover, their natural increase tends to press on the generally scanty means of support, their standards of living are usually low, in spite of some emigration.

The development of hydro-electric power in the Highlands now in progress may help to relieve the hardships imposed by the limited agricultural resources. Though the heavy rainfall and moderately high relief in that region give rise to many fast-flowing streams, there are no really large heads of water, and power stations must accordingly be generally small and scattered. As conditions are thus unfavourable for the long-distance transmission of current in bulk from this remote area, miscellaneous manufactures in addition to the production of aluminium in the existing plants at the Glenmore stations (p. 63) may be established at various places following upon the further development of power resources in the Highlands.

In view of the small proportion of forests in Great Britain (see Table p. 45) and the large imports of timber and wood pulp needed to cover requirements, selected areas of little or no use for farming are being planted, mainly with the faster-maturing coniferous species. The most extensive areas have been found in the moorlands of the Scottish Highlands, hitherto used at best as rough grazings for sheep; and because the western highlands are in general excessively exposed and wet, the eastern slopes have been favoured, chiefly in the counties round the Moray Firth, though considerable areas of lower elevation are being planted in Argyllshire in the south-west. On the whole afforestation is not helpful towards re-settlement in the Highlands; its claims conflict in some measure with hill sheep-farming, and the trees must be given 12 to 20 years before the first thinnings can be taken.

Chapter 10

IRELAND

NOTE. The border between Northern Ireland and the Irish Republic has been fixed according to county boundaries, which correspond little with those of the natural regions. As some major structural elements accordingly lie partly in one of the political divisions and partly in the other, Ireland is treated as a whole in the survey of physical and general geography. But because Northern Ireland and the Irish Republic (Eire) are distinct political and economic entities, for which the relevant statistical data are published separately, they are reviewed in turn in respect of their economic geography.

PHYSICAL AND STRUCTURAL FEATURES

Like Scotland and Wales, Ireland is composed almost entirely of old rocks and structural elements. With the exception of the Antrim basalt lava sheet and trifling areas of chalk and of New Red Sandstone on the eastern and southern edges of the lava plateau, Ireland contains nothing later than Carboniferous rocks, and those mostly the lower and older massive limestones; though much of its surface is covered with Quaternary glacial drift which has greatly modified the details of relief and impeded the drainage, especially in the central lowland.

Structurally Ireland is a product of the Caledonian and the Armorican phases of mountain-building to which it owes the resistant protective wings of highlands round the central platform. In addition Armorican upthrusts have produced a dozen or more inliers, the highest being the Slieve Bloom and the Silvermine Mountains, that rise like islands from the floor of the central lowlands, but with a NE.–SW. trend in sympathy with the Caledonian system. Ireland is, in fact, an outpost of the Caledonian and Armorican structures of North-Western Europe. Their denuded remnants, broken into peninsulas converging on Galway Bay, reach in it their westernmost extension.

The Caledonian highlands follow three distinct axes, two in the north and the third in the south-east, namely the north-western in continuation of the Scottish Highlands, the Newry axis in continuation of the Southern Uplands of Scotland, and the Leinster axis of the Wicklow Mountains related to the Welsh Highlands. The north-western Caledonides occupy a broad belt from Loch Foyle to Galway Bay, broken by an encroachment of the Atlantic in the opening of

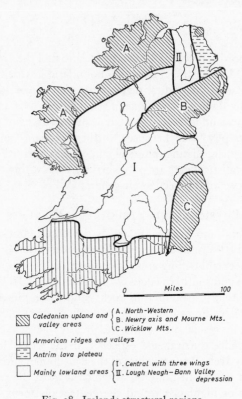

Fig. 38. Ireland: structural regions.

Note. The L. Neagh–Bann valley depression is actually a downwarped western extension of the Antrim lava plateau.

Donegal-Sligo Bay. They have been reduced to plateaux of moderately low elevation from which rise steep-sided ridges composed of highly resistant quartzites and granites, as in the Sperrin, Ox and Donegal Mountains. Separated from them by a continuation of the rift valley of the Scottish Lowlands lies the Newry uplift, which comprises the uplands south of Belfast and over the border into the Irish Republic. This group has been worn down to low hills except for a few residual heights, of which the Mourne Mountains, a granite boss rising to nearly 2,800 feet, is the highest. The Leinster chain, comprising the Wicklow Mountains and their continuation S.–SW. beyond Waterford, is an anticlinal arch with a twofold granite core bordered by old sedimentary rocks which sink into the Barrow Valley in the west and fringe the Irish Sea in the east.

The Armorican highlands in the south-west sector, south of a line through Tipperary, widen out from near Waterford into the whole Cork-Kerry peninsula, where Mt. Carrantuohill[1] exceeds 3,400 feet in height. They consist of a series of anticlinal ridges of compact Devonian sandstone with intervening synclines floored in the south with Carboniferous limestone which may have covered the whole area southwards from the interior plain, prior to the elevation of the anticlines. Sub-aerial and marine erosion of the less resistant limestone remaining in the synclines has contributed to the formation of the long rias between the Atlantic prolongations of the anticlines. The Armorican inliers mentioned above, that rise from the limestone of the plain, are composed of similar hard rocks, and like their counterparts in the south have generally rugged outlines.

The Antrim lava sheet, covering some 1,600 sq. miles in Northern Ireland, and exceeding 1,500 feet in its higher points, is a geologically late addition to the old structural elements of the rest of Ireland. Nevertheless, sufficient time has elapsed since the lava welled up through cracks and fissures formed in the disturbances of the Alpine orogenesis, for erosion to sculpture the surface of the plateau. A longitudinal valley has been excavated by the River Main flowing south to Lough Neagh; and deep, steep-walled, often gloomy glens have been cut by shorter streams flowing west or east, the erosive action of which has been facilitated by the characteristic vertical jointing of the basalt. In its high eastern part, the plateau is open moorland with some bogs, but westward it sinks into the drift-covered Bann valley and under Lough Neagh, beyond which it rises again and abuts against the ancient rocks of the Sperrin Mountains.

The old Caledonian highlands have been peneplaned, re-elevated and broken by fractures into blocks, which subsequent erosion has reduced to ridges of highly resistant rocks surrounded by lower hilly tracts; while continuous erosion has removed from the interior platform almost all the upper Carboniferous beds, including whatever substantial coal-measures they may have contained. The residual

[1] Also spelt Carrantuohil or Carrantual.

mountains and uplands, composed of siliceous rocks or granite, are commonly bare and barren, and the limestone platform where it is exposed in the west is likewise unattractive for farming. The best agricultural lands are in the eastern lowlands, though even there bogs are common in some of the river valleys, e.g. those of the Boyne and the Bann. The rise of the sea-level relative to the land (p. 59), combined possibly with some subsidence of the latter, has deprived Ireland of any extensive alluvial plains. It has been reduced to an exterior highland skeleton which, though broken here and there by gaps, more or less encloses an ill-drained lowland platform. On balance, natural forces have been unhelpful in shaping Ireland as a human habitat, and were it not for the mantle of glacial drift that covers much of its surface, it might well be less productive than it actually is.

GLACIATION AND DRAINAGE

The ice-sheets, which in their maximum, but not their latest advance southwards, covered the whole of Ireland, caused most of the lower ground to be thickly plastered with unassorted material dumped on their retreat. In particular, the central lowland has been covered with patches of boulder clay, most extensive in the east round Dublin, but much interspersed in the Shannon basin with swarms of eskers in the form of winding ridges of sand and gravel, and with drumlin mounds towards the north. The clay-floored hollows between and among these are often waterlogged and occupied by bogs, some of which, such as the Bog of Allen, cover many square miles (Fig. 39). Many of the deeper hollows contain seasonal or permanent shallow lakes fringed with reedy marshes. This interior basin of the plain suffers from a rare combination of conditions adverse to effective drainage: the low gradient of the Shannon (about 5 inches a mile) and of its tributaries, and the consequent slow run-off; a limestone base liable to be pitted with solution hollows; an irregular cover of glacial drift; and a persistently humid climate favourable to the spread of bog vegetation, especially of spongy mosses, which further impede the naturally poor drainage.

The numerous glacial ridges and mounds in the Shannon basin, being composed of better-drained soils, are generally covered with natural meadow grasses that make good cattle pastures; as also are the drift soils of the higher ground round the margins of the basin, especially in the northern and southern embayments. The valley lowlands in both Northern Ireland and the southern highland belt are likewise covered with glacial drift and later deposits which generally form fertile, though in places poorly drained, soils. Little of the central lowlands is, in fact, free of glacial or fluvial deposits except the westward extension of the Carboniferous limestone platform in County Clare, where the karst features of bare rock pitted with sink holes alternating with bogs give a hint of what the interior plain might have been without its cover of glacial drift.

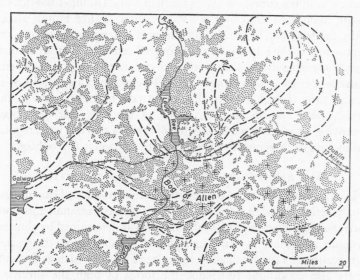

Fig. 39. Central Ireland: distribution of bogs. Source, *Geological Survey of Ireland*. The broken lines indicate eskers and recessional moraines (after Charlesworth). Note in this connection the alignment of the Dublin–Galway railway. The crosses indicate areas where bog peat is worked for the preparation of sod and milled peat used to generate electricity.

The low gradient of the Shannon river above Lough Derg is caused in part by the impounding of its waters by a ridge of hard old rocks below that lake, where a fall of over 100 feet is concentrated in the few miles of the Killalloe Gorge. This head of water has been harnessed for hydro-electric power, distributed to Dublin, Cork and many other places in Eire, thus compensating in some measure for the poverty of the country in coal.[1]

Other Irish rivers drain their basins better, not being impeded by

[1] Less than a quarter of a million tons of inferior coal are produced per annum, mainly in the Castlecomer district north of Kilkenny.

rocky ledges in their lower courses. The Blackwater, the Lee and the Bandon in the south-west, originally subsequent rivers, flow east along the graded synclinal valleys, and finally turn south along the courses of former consequents whose valleys are now largely submerged. The majority of the remaining longer rivers originate on the *inner* side of the highlands, and find their ways through or round them to the coast. Such are the Bann and the Foyle in Northern Ireland, and the Suir, Slaney and Liffey in Eire. Lakes (Loughs) are especially numerous in the courses of rivers north of a line Dublin-Limerick i.e. in the country covered by the last glaciation. Unlike typical glacial lakes, the Irish loughs are shallow sheets of water spread out over the depressions in the hummocky drift-covered country. They are accordingly most irregular in shape, studded with islands and fringed with marshes or bogs, as for example Lough Ree and the Upper and Lower Lough Erne. Lough Neagh, the largest lake in Ireland and in the British Isles, though shallow, is not of the type just described; occupying a basin formed by sagging of the lava sheet, it has a regular outline and its margins except on the south are largely free of bogs.

Natural Vegetation and Land Utilisation

In any country the forms of the natural vegetation and of land utilisation, whether actual or potential, are inter-related, inasmuch as both correspond to the variety of local conditions as determined by climate, structure and relief, and drainage. The relationship has all the greater significance in a predominantly agricultural country such as Ireland, where also conditions restricting the forms of both the surviving natural vegetation and land use are unusually pronounced. In this connection it is useful to note the broad regional distribution of various natural plant associations in Ireland, in conjunction with the corresponding forms of agricultural utilisation, where any is possible.

In climate there is the gradual transition from that of the relatively dry and sunny eastern lowlands where the rainfall is below or a little above 30 inches, to that of the humid western regions where the rainfall is nowhere less than 40 inches, and exceeds 60 and even 100 inches in exposed places, and where the rate of evaporation is exceptionally low in the generally more or less saturated atmosphere. In relief the relevant features are (*a*) the low gradient over a large central area, and consequent inactive drainage, (*b*) the highland tracts, which have a wet mountain clim   and are bare of soil in the steeper parts, and (*c*) the sheltered valleys, especially those in the lee of the southern highlands, warmed by compression of the air of the prevailing mild south-westerly air-streams.

In keeping with these conditions the land surface of Ireland may be divided into four regional classes, according to the predominant forms of vegetation and land use.

(1) The eastern lowlands and sheltered south-eastern mountain valleys, with which the open valleys of the southern rivers and of the two larger northern rivers may be included. In them the characteristic original vegetation was deciduous and mixed forest composed of European species; but most of this has been displaced by farm land, and meadow grasses are now the prevailing plant cover except where the land is under cultivation or is occupied by bogs. Outside these areas which now account for almost all the limited woodland in Ireland (less than two per cent of the total area), little deciduous forest has apparently ever existed in the island. The same relatively favoured eastern lowlands and river valleys account for nearly all the cash-crop arable farming in both Eire and Northern Ireland.

(2) The west central lowland, co-terminous in the main with the Shannon basin, the vegetation of which has been noticed above. The glacial ridges and other land clear of bogs carry more or less natural permanent pastures, interspersed with patches and stretches of cultivation (chiefly of potatoes and oats), especially on the better drained lands towards the south.

(3) The eastern highlands, covered with the typical British moorland vegetation above heights between 500 and 1,000 feet, varying with rock type, slope and situation; and the western highlands covered, where any vegetation exists, with blanket bog interspersed with moorland even on moderately steep slopes. Farming of any kind on these highlands is naturally very limited; though some small-framed sheep adapted to the unfavourable conditions are pastured on them.

(4) The lower ground with some sheltered valleys in the three western peninsulas, Donegal, Connacht (Mayo and western Galway) and Kerry-Cork, where patches of bog are again of common occurrence. In these windswept areas the natural vegetation is poor in West European species, especially of trees, but it comprises the Lusitanian group of special interest, now restricted to western Ireland and north-west Spain. In the south-western valleys and coastlands there are stretches of natural grasslands good for dairy cattle; but in Connacht and Donegal the lowlands, where not occupied by lakes and bogs, outcrops of bare rock and expanses of uninhabited moorland, are

little better than poor sheep-pasture lands, too damp for cultivation except on sheltered patches, where some potatoes and oats are grown. These two rain-drenched peninsular areas are characterised by low-level subsistence farming, supplemented by fishing on the coasts.

EXTERNAL RELATIONS IN HISTORICAL GEOGRAPHY

The situation of Ireland on the outermost fringe of Western Europe, combined with its comparative poverty in material resources, has in no small measure influenced the course of its human settlement, and the history and economic development of its people. Direct movements from the Mediterranean, by-passing Britain by way of northern Spain and Brittany, reached Ireland very early. By this route apparently Neolithic and Mediterranean peoples entered the land; and by this outer way also, through Cornwall and Brittany, lively contacts were maintained as far as Rome by religious organisations when Britain was in turmoil in the post-Roman period of successive invasions. Missionaries and monks such as St. Patrick travelled to and fro, and a vigorous monastic life was established which was able in due course to send out missionaries and found monasteries in northern Britain. It is significant that Ireland except the North-East (in which a late intrusive element in the population is predominant) has held to the Catholic faith, thus continuing its early Mediterranean contacts.

Ireland is part of the 'Celtic fringe' which extends through it and Wales from the Scottish Highlands to Brittany. Unlike the other members of the fringe, however, it had in the past the protection of the seas separating it from Britain and the rest of Europe. It long escaped attack or penetration from the east, and its people, left to themselves, were able in fact to develop a relatively advanced early civilisation. Ireland remained beyond the limits of the Roman Empire, and was not mastered by the English until the 17th century. The Irish language has been preserved right into modern times when its recent revival as a cultural and official medium has been an expression of the spirit of independent nationhood.

The pressure of population in Catholic Ireland upon a land that lacks mineral wealth and has but limited agricultural resources, has for over a century past enforced large-scale emigration, mainly of younger people. Similar pressure has been felt in the Scottish and the Welsh highland areas, but the migrants from these regions have readily found opportunities of settling, and have generally been absorbed in adjoining parts of their own lands or in England, all under the same governmental authority and religious institutions. Those from Ireland on the other hand, have moved mainly either to Britain where they tend to retain their Irish identity, or to the United States; or to British Commonwealth countries. Far more people of Irish descent now live in the United States alone than in Ireland itself.

This heavy emigration, entailing a continuous draining away of the younger and more vigorous elements in the population of what is now the Irish Republic, threatens to create a shortage there of agricultural labour. The land tends to be under-farmed, to be used extensively as cattle pastures rather than intensively for tillage, which means that the average farmer needs more acres to gain a livelihood. Thus under-farming leads indirectly to land hunger. The long-standing insufficiency of capital has also been a factor contributing to this situation. But steps taken through Government initiative to raise the technical level of farming have resulted in some notable recent improvements. In contrast, Northern Ireland has been little subject to the same disabilities. There the labour force has been maintained, capital is more plentiful, and the land in general is more intensively farmed than in the Republic.

THE IRISH REPUBLIC

AGRICULTURE[1]

It is well to realise at the outset that regional specialisation in Irish agriculture is not very clearly defined; it is overshadowed by the predominance of mixed farming. The majority of the farmers have some land under cultivation and a generally larger area of pasture, in proportions which vary from one region and one farm to another, and many of them, removed from means of transport, rely upon the produce of their land for the bulk of their staple food supplies, as well as of the fodder requirements of their live-stock. What can be observed is that within this overall pattern of mixed farming there is a distinct leaning in particular areas towards one or other of three branches — arable farming, the fattening of beef cattle, and dairy-farming: the first especially in the south-east and the middle central lowlands (on better drained soils); the second in the eastern central lowlands; and the last in the south-west, the north-east and in a belt round Dublin.

[1] For observations upon the influence of climatic conditions in general upon agriculture in Ireland see above pp. 136–7.

The economy of the Irish Republic is based mainly on the farming industry which supplies over three-quarters of the exports; and in that industry the rearing of live-stock is much more important than the cultivation of crops, a considerable proportion of which is in any case grown for animal fodder. The mild oceanic climate, more favourable to pasture grasses than to most field crops, is one leading cause of the preponderance of animal husbandry. Of the total area 48 per cent is

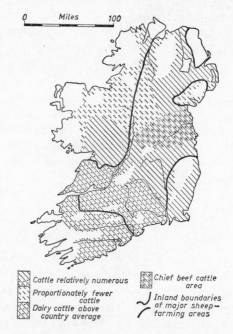

Fig. 40. The distribution of cattle and sheep in Ireland. Based on Returns by Counties for 1959, Central Statistical Office, Dublin, and Ministry of Agriculture, Northern Ireland.

under permanent pastures and only 18 per cent under tillage, compared with 9 per cent and 64 per cent respectively in Denmark. Another major cause of the concentration upon raising live-stock, especially cattle, is the indifferent means of transport by road and rail over much of the country — cattle can be moved on foot along any sort of road, or even on rough tracks.

Though the Irish Republic in the effort to be as self-sufficient as possible has increased the acreage of crops such as wheat and sugar beet, it remains nevertheless primarily a cattle country. Live animals, mainly cattle, have till recently constituted fully half the value of exports, and much more farm land is given to the production of hay (consumed mainly by cattle) than to all the field crops combined. Many of the cattle destined for export are moved as young animals from the interior plain to the rich pastures in the country behind Dublin, whence they are shipped later mainly to Britain (Fig. 40). Others are raised in the valleys of the Barrow-Nore-Suir river-system

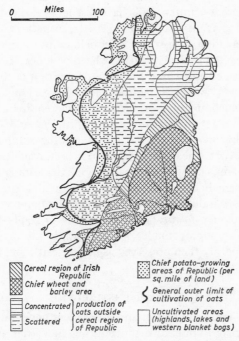

Fig. 41. The distribution of leading crops in Ireland. Based on Returns by Counties for 1958, Central Statistical Office, Dublin, and Ministry of Agriculture, Northern Ireland.

converging on Waterford, where they are an integral feature of the mixed rotation farming similar to that of the English Midlands. Others, again, are surplus stock from the cattle-farming districts in the hinterlands of Cork and Limerick; though there, especially in the Lee and Bandon valleys west of Cork and the Golden Vale east of Limerick, dairy cattle are more numerous than beef cattle. This south central Armorican region is, in fact, the chief dairy-farming area of the Republic. Sheep and pigs, both fewer in numbers than cattle, are reared now mainly for domestic consumption. The former, chiefly of rather small local breeds, are most numerous in Galway in the west, in the south-west, and on the slopes of the Wicklow Mountains. Pigs are naturally raised in largest numbers in the dairy-farming districts mentioned above; elsewhere their distribution tends to correspond with the density of rural population, for a pig or two at least are traditionally kept on almost every Irish farm. Horses are comparatively numerous in Eire. The absence of large-scale arable farming and the indifferent country roads have discouraged the development of mechanised agriculture and of motorised transport.

Excluding rotation grasses, the chief field crops in order according to the areas devoted to them are oats, wheat, potatoes, barley and root crops, which together account for about 90 per cent of the cultivated land. Two classes can be distinguished according to range of distribution: those which because of their climatic requirements are restricted in the main to the drier eastern districts, and those which being more tolerant of moisture are grown over the country in general. In the first class are wheat, barley and sugar beet, produced mainly as cash crops, i.e. for sale off the farms; whereas the leading crops of the second class, namely oats and potatoes, are commonly grown in small lots by numerous individual farmers for consumption on the farms or in the local country towns. The potatoes are a staple food of the people, and also supply fodder for pigs, while the oats, often cut before fully ripe, are then preserved as hay for cattle and horses (Fig. 41).

Manufacturing Industry. Distribution of Population

Prior to the establishment of an independent government in what is now the Irish Republic, manufacturing industries were almost entirely limited to the processing of agricultural produce at various local centres, and some specialised branches such as brewing and distilling and tobacco manufacture centred mainly in Dublin. With political independence has come the urge towards greater economic independence and, as the result of deliberate efforts directed to this end, much progress has been made in supplying the domestic market with a variety of consumer goods made in local factories. The difficulties arising from almost complete lack of coal resources have in a measure been overcome by the development of hydro-electric power. Supplies from the Shannon falls (p. 135) were first available in 1929, and current is now distributed by a grid system to all the larger centres of population from this and one or two smaller stations. Additional supplies of electricity are now generated in thermal stations fired with milled peat, mechanically extracted and prepared at large-scale works south-east of Athlone in an area which includes the Bog of Allen, and sod-peat is also extracted and prepared for thermal stations farther east in the same County Offaly (Fig. 39). As further large schemes of the same kind are in hand, supplies of electricity from this source, already some 20 per cent of the total in the Republic, are likely to expand considerably.

The earlier-established processing industries e.g. grain-milling, bacon-curing and manufactures of butter and cheese, have naturally arisen centrally in the districts that produce the primary products. The same feature applies to the newer general manufactures of leather, footwear, clothing and farm implements among others, though some that depend largely on imported raw materials are mainly concentrated in the two largest ports and centres of population, namely Dublin and Cork, e.g. textile and confectionery factories in the former, and motor car and general engineering works in the latter.

One effect of the growth of manufactures has been to add to the pre-eminence of Dublin, already assured by its commanding situation at the main gateway into Eire. The trunk lines of the railway system radiate from Dublin, making it the chief collecting and distributing centre for export and import trade, both of which are conducted mainly with Great Britain. With these advantages of situation, the capital city has attracted a number of the newer industries in addition to the established ones; and its population, now over half a million, has increased at a rate much in excess of that of the country as a whole. Other towns have shared, as noted above, in the recent industrial development, but none on a scale at all comparable with that of Dublin, except perhaps Cork.

About 40 per cent of the population of the Irish Republic is classed as urban, compared with over 80 per cent in Great Britain. Of these urban dwellers nearly half live in the Dublin metropolis, and many of the rest in a number of local ports, of which Cork, Waterford, Limerick and Galway are the largest. In the inland districts, all predominantly agricultural, population is more or less evenly spread wherever farming of some kind can be carried on. Similarly, among the numerous small inland market towns, few have acquired more than local importance, except perhaps Athlone at the main crossing of the Shannon, and Killarney the centre of a famous tourist district.

NORTHERN IRELAND

Though Northern Ireland has its share of highlands and some bogs, especially in the Erne depression and parts of the Bann valley, a large proportion of its area consists of mainly fertile drift-covered lowlands and uplands of moderate elevation. These productive lands, situated in the broad Bann-Lough Neagh depression, and in the valleys of the Foyle, Lagan and Main rivers, are in general fully utilised. The average farm is small, averaging 25 acres or less, and as such is worked intensively by modern methods in order to provide a livelihood for the occupier.

Mixed farming specialising in dairy cattle, pigs and poultry is predominant. In this small area of little over 5,000 sq. miles, there are nearly a million head of cattle which, together with the pigs and poultry, provide some surplus dairy produce, bacon and eggs for exportation mainly to the West Scotland industrial region. In several respects, in the typical small family farm, the emphasis upon dairy-farming and its adjuncts, and the export of products associated with dairy-farming, the agricultural economy of Northern Ireland resembles that of Denmark; but whereas Denmark has a large net surplus of agricultural products, Northern Ireland imports more than it exports.

The mild but rather cool oceanic climate favours the growth of pasture grasses, and is better suited to the cultivation of oats than of wheat and barley, very little of either of which is in fact grown. As in the adjoining Republic, more land is used for the hay crop than for all the field crops combined, and of the latter, oats occupy 60 per cent of the land under cultivation. The hay, of course, and much of the oats are used to feed live-stock, especially cattle. The hillside grazings on the Antrim Plateau and the Sperrin Mountains and on the upper parts of the Caledonian highlands south of the Lagan valley provide pastures for sheep, which incidentally are almost as numerous as cattle. Like the Irish Republic, Northern Ireland also produces large quantities of potatoes, some of which find their way to Great Britain when shortages arise there, thus serving as a kind of buffer stock. The most distinctive crop of Northern Ireland has been flax, grown by numerous small farmers in the Main, the lower Bann and the upper Lagan valleys; but their supply (recently dwindled to insignificance) has never been sufficient to meet the requirements of the linen mills in Belfast and neighbouring small towns.

Though manufactures play a highly important part in the economy of Northern Ireland, it remains a predominantly agricultural area. Many of the inhabitants depend directly or indirectly upon the farming industry for their livelihood, and the surplus agricultural products consigned to Great Britain help to pay for necessary imports, including foodstuffs such as wheat, and all kinds of fuel. Yet as an integral part of the United Kingdom, Northern Ireland follows the same general economic policy, i.e. that of exporting the products of its specialised industries, in order to secure maximum supplies of other products in exchange. In this its whole way of life differs from that of the Republic which is moving towards autarchy.

INDUSTRIAL DEVELOPMENT. DISTRIBUTION OF POPULATION

A special feature of the major industries, linen manufacture and shipbuilding, is that they depend almost entirely upon external supplies of primary materials; over 90 per cent of the raw flax required by the linen mills has to be imported, and all the constructional materials, as well as power fuel for the shipbuilding yards. These industries have developed on the basis of low ratio of cost of materials to value of finished products; but they are liable to be hit by adverse trade conditions, and efforts are being made to extend the range of industry, by establishing aeroplane works for example. The other manufactures of Northern Ireland, namely of tobacco, rope and cordage at Belfast, and of shirts at Londonderry, also depend entirely upon imported raw materials. Narrow in range of forms, these manufactures are also narrow in range of distribution. Outside Belfast and Londonderry there is little industry apart from bacon factories and similar works and some linen mills in small towns round Belfast — Lisburn, Lurgan and Larne among others.

The large *per capita* volume of import and export trade associated with the industrial activities and the general economic activities of Northern Ireland are handled mainly by Belfast. Like Dublin (p. 143), Belfast has been draining off population from the rural districts; nearly a quarter of all the people in Northern Ireland live within its boundaries, and one half within a radius of 30 miles of its centre. Londonderry, the second largest town, suffers from its remote border situation, part of its natural hinterland of the Foyle valley being in the Irish Republic, and also from poor facilities for shipping. Larne, the cross-channel port for the shipping connection with Stranraer in south-west Scotland, is better placed, though it is quite overshadowed by Belfast, for which it serves mainly as a ferry port.

F

Chapter 11

FRANCE: I. GENERAL SURVEY

THE most significant feature of the situation of France is that it lies astride Peninsular Europe between the northern and the Mediterranean seas. From the Bay of Biscay to the Mediterranean it is less than 250 miles wide, but it extends to 500 miles between the English Channel and the Gulf of Lions. These overland distances are small compared with that of nearly 2,000 miles by sea from the Gulf of Lions to the Channel, a route that was avoided as much as possible in early times because of the hazards of storms on the Atlantic passage. Moreover, movement within and across the French land bridge has always been facilitated by two special physical features. Rings of more or less open and interconnecting chalk or limestone form the outer zones of the Paris Basin and surround the greater part of the Central Plateau; and the river valleys are so disposed as to provide through transit routes, e.g. that following the Garonne through the Carcassonne Gap and thence along the Aude Valley to the Mediterranean coast, and that up the Saône-Rhône trough and thence over the Côte d'Or into the Seine River Basin to the English Channel, both now made into continuous waterways by the construction of canal links.

The Atlantic seas which border the northern and the western coasts of France receive the drainage of more than two-thirds of the country. Much of this drainage is carried by the three major rivers, the Seine, the Loire and the Garonne, whose basins open out fan-wise inland from the large tidal estuaries at their mouths. This feature has been of special value since the coming of the maritime age, assisting the development of overseas trade and colonial enterprise, and acting as an outward attractive force against the tendency to inward self-containment to which the inhabitants of the rich and varied agricultural lands of France are prone. France has also a window on the Mediterranean Sea, and though much less of the inhabitable territory of the country seems tributary to the Mediterranean than to the Atlantic, that sea has through the centuries been the avenue of a greater wealth of external contacts. The Rhône Valley, leading far into the country, has been a kind of conductor for the penetration of Mediterranean civilisation from Roman times; and conversely has directed the attention and efforts of the French people towards trade and other connections with Africa and the Near and Far East.

On her land borders France has good defensive barriers in the Alps and the Pyrenees, but lies open to the continental regions beyond the Rhine on the north-east and east. From these quarters successive waves of human migration have in the past reached France, where their intermixture has contributed much, it seems, to the development of the distinctive French genius. In modern times, however, especially after the consolidation of Germany into a great military power, the eastern entrances have caused France great anxiety. Dire experience has shown that fortifications are of little avail against superior armed forces. Invaded and disastrously defeated in 1870-1, France was twice invaded within 30 years in this century. Following her relative decline in economic and military strength, her best hopes for security seem to lie in promoting as a partner any kind of organisation based on the peaceful association of the countries of Western Europe, such as the European Coal and Steel Community and the Common Market (already in existence), and the eventual political federation which France favours.

PHYSICAL BUILD AND THE HUMAN ELEMENT

The structural components of France are largely the products of the Armorican-Hercynian and the Alpine phases of mountain building. The geological skeleton consists of the denuded highlands first elevated in the earlier orogenesis; their main element is the Central Plateau (Massif Central) from which two limbs branch out almost at right angles, the Armorican north-west across the Loire into Normandy and Brittany, the Hercynian north-east through the Vosges into the Hunsrück and the Ardennes. The whole system, disposed in shape like the letter Y, is more or less continuous, certainly in the north-west, for old formations of the same origin underlie the apparent breaks at Poitiers and Nantes (Fig. 42). The existing lowlands are arranged in keeping with the pattern of the older structures, the Aquitaine Basin and the Rhône-Saône trough on either side of the trunk-like Massif, and the Paris Basin in the fork between the two limbs.

The Alpine orogenesis did much to fill out the present shape of France; it raised the Alps, the Jura and the Pyrenees on the eastern and southern margins of the resistant Massif, which was re-elevated with a high eastern edge rising from the Rhône-Saône trough and with extensive outpourings of lava; and it caused the areas of the Paris and Aquitaine Basins, both of which had long been subsiding with the accumulation of marine sediments, to become dry land. Since this general transformation erosion has been active, and little has been added on balance to the make-up of the country. The Rhône delta has been built out with the waste of the highlands, and the

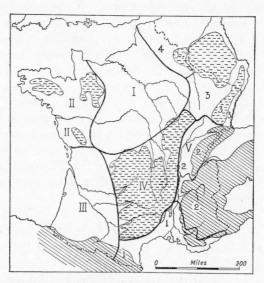

Fig. 42. Generalised geographical sub-divisions of France, as described in the next chapter. I. Paris Basin. II. Armorica–Vendée. III. Aquitaine–Charente–Western Pyrenees. IV. Massif Central. V. Eastern and S. Eastern borders: (1) Mediterranean; (2) Rhône–Saône trough, French Alps and Jura; (3) Lorraine, Vosges, Alsace; (4) Industrial North-East (French Flanders). Highlands generalised: Armorican–Hercynian in broken, Alpine in diagonal ruling.

Landes coastal strip with sand transported by rivers and blown inward from the sea, while a large north-eastern area (estimated at nearly 20,000 square miles) has been covered with deposits of limon.[1] On the other hand, land has been lost by encroachments of the sea on the English Channel coast.

Though the Central Plateau, situated towards the south of France, hardly seems to justify its title, it is the physiographical kernel of the

---

[1] Composed of weathered loess. Removal by solution of the film of calcium carbonate on the particles of loess has produced a clay-loam type of soil.

country. Round this persistent massif the major existing lowlands and the new-folded highlands have, as observed above, been built up. Parts of it seem to have been dry land from Jurassic times onwards to the Tertiary, while the surrounding areas were covered by seas. In the present age it is a negative region for human settlement set in the midst of populous lowlands, to which in recent decades it has been losing population. It is also the master element in the drainage system; its general WNW. tilt has initiated the courses followed by the three great river systems in the wide arc between Flanders and the Pyrenees, and its steep fault-bounded eastern edge defines the course of the Saône-Rhône.

A distinctive feature in the physiography of France is the ease of inter-communication between the major regions and the numerous sub-regions of which it is composed. Even the habitable highlands are with few exceptions readily accessible from the adjoining lowlands by well-marked valley routes. The compact form and the disposition of the physical elements of France have favoured social and political integration; its human geography has diversity without a leaning to separatism, which has appeared in the British Isles. This is one main condition that promoted the early formation of an organised state covering most of what is now France. The other main condition has been the nodality of Paris in the extensive and productive Paris Basin, where readily achieved consolidation became the foundation of superior strength for expansion of political power. The precocious rise of Paris has been followed by its continued absolute predominance in the administrative, economic and cultural life of France, with this disadvantage that the functioning of the country as a whole tends to be over-centralised in its over-nourished capital.

CLIMATE, NATURAL VEGETATION AND AGRICULTURE

France is favourably situated in a climatic zone transitional between North-West European and Mediterranean. It is far enough north to be in the path of depressions from the Atlantic, and yet far enough south to escape the frequent stormy weather associated with those which follow more northerly tracks. Moreover, the general westward slope of much of the country allows the Atlantic influences full play, promoting equability of temperatures and ensuring sufficient well-distributed rainfall; and the intermediate latitude and continental connection make for a high proportion of sunshine and summer heat prolonged into the autumn, especially towards the east and south.

Within this overall framework of climatic conditions, local variations are considerable in relation to the limited extension of the country in latitude and longitude. The Armorican peninsula has a typical Western Marginal climate, rather wet and unsettled in winter and relatively cool in summer. Southwards into Aquitaine, these conditions give way to less cloudy winters and distinctly hotter summers, when heavy rainfall often occurs with violent thunderstorms. The eastern parts from the Ardennes to the middle Rhône valley have a modified continental climate; they are apt to be cold in winter when snow may lie for weeks on the higher ground, and are generally hot in summer, the season there of maximum rainfall. The Central Plateau is naturally cool by reason of its elevation of 1,500 to 6,000 feet, and as its westward slope induces condensation of moisture from autumn and winter depressions, it receives precipitation over 40 inches in the upper parts, with heavy falls of snow. An enclosed south-eastern region has a distinct Mediterranean climate; its low summer rainfall is caused as much by the highlands to the west intercepting moisture drifting in from the Atlantic as by its situation on the northern margin of the Mediterranean climatic zone.

Climatic conditions in France are favourable to the growth of temperate forests which once covered most of the country other than the drier calcareous plateaux and the mountain heights, and still occupy one fifth of the total area. Moorland vegetation is less widespread than in the British Isles, though patches occur on the highlands of Brittany and on the Central Plateau. In the original forest vegetation the prevailing form was the West European deciduous, composed of oak and its associates except on sandy tracts such as the Sologne, and on the upper levels of tree growth on the Vosges, Alps and Pyrenees, where, as in neighbouring countries, coniferous trees were and are predominant. These surviving coniferous forests together with others planted in the Landes region and elsewhere cover one-third of the existing forest area. The inroads of agriculture have taken a heavy toll of the vast original hardwood forests, though numerous stretches of mainly deciduous woodland have been preserved, as well as some extensive forests on the outer escarpments of the Paris Basin and beyond them to the east.

France is a great agricultural country. The Tables of crops and live-stock (pp. 52, 56) show that it has more land devoted to the cultivation of wheat than all the other countries of North-Western Europe combined, that it leads in the areas given to barley, oats, sugar beet and maize, as well as in the number of cattle, and that in viticulture it is supreme. Alone among the countries of Western Europe, France is normally self-sufficient in wheat and other grains except maize and has a surplus of beet sugar; and unlike Britain and Western Germany, is independent of imported supplies of meat and dairy produce. The large output of French agriculture corresponds to the large proportion of productive lowlands and hillsides to total area; its remarkable variety is the outcome of the considerable range in climatic milieux outlined above. Three important cultivated plants, namely grape-vines, maize and olives,[1] and several of the more delicate fruits reach the northern limits of their general cultivation in France, and are consequently absent (except in glasshouses) from the northern lands of Western Europe; while all the leading cool temperate crops of these northern lands find congenial conditions, and are extensively cultivated within the borders of France.

As indicated by the large total stocks of cattle, pigs and poultry, mixed farming is general in the great agricultural belt that sweeps round the Central Plateau from the Belgian border to the Pyrenees. Most of the land is divided into small peasant farms; large holdings specialising in cereal cultivation or cattle-rearing are the exception. Within this belt, which extends over about the same latitudinal distance as from Land's End to Inverness, broad differences can be distinguished between (a) the cool temperate type of farming north of the Seine, in which cereals, sugar beet, fodder crops and cattle are the leading features; (b) the intermediate temperate type between the Seine and the Poitiers Gap, in which wheat is the leading crop and grape-vines make their appearance; and (c) the warm temperate type in Aquitaine, in which maize is cultivated as well as wheat, and there is much specialised production of wine from vineyards planted on south-facing valley sides.

In addition to these broad sub-divisions of the riverine lowlands four other distinctive agricultural regions can be identified: the 'bocage' country of Brittany and western Normandy; the Central Plateau; the lowlands of Provence and Languedoc; and the 'Eastern Marches' i.e. the upland and valley country east of the Paris Basin. The first, which resembles the Devon-Cornwall peninsula in structure and climate and in the hedgerows enclosing the fields, is characterised by the predominance of meadow land interspersed with fields in

[1] A fourth has recently been added, namely rice, grown on the irrigated lands of the Camargue (Rhône delta). See p. 189.

which subsistence crops and fodder crops for cattle are cultivated. The second has a complex pattern of land use corresponding with the marked and often sharply defined variations in relief and rock formation; the extensive uplands above 1,500 feet are mainly used, where herbage exists, as grazing grounds for sheep and cattle, cultivation being limited to scattered fertile patches, e.g. of weathered volcanic rocks.

The distinctive cultural landscape features of the Mediterranean region are its chestnut groves, vineyards and market gardens; it is the greatest wine-producing area of France, and also specialises where irrigation water is available in the production of 'primeurs', especially for the Paris market. The eastern provinces of Lorraine, Alsace and Burgundy, consist of a succession of partly wooded ridges and highlands, e.g. the Côtes de Meuse and Moselle, the Langres Plateau and the Vosges, separated by fertile longitudinal river valleys. Mixed farming is general, with intensive cultivation on the valley sides, viticulture on sunny slopes, especially in Burgundy and Alsace, and cattle-pasturing on the valley meadows. The marginal mountain regions of the Alps, Jura and Pyrenees form a group by themselves. Settlement is naturally restricted to valley situations where some form of agriculture is possible; the actual forms vary greatly with the marked differences in local physical conditions.

Mixed farming is in fact very general in France. Except in the Mediterranean region and other districts that specialise in the production of wine, the basic features are the cultivation of wheat and the keeping of cattle. Wheat is grown in most parts of the country, wherever possible, even on marginal lands, with greatest concentration on the fertile loams of the Paris Basin and the north-east. Cattle too are almost universal, being used for one special purpose or another in different parts of the country, chiefly however, for the production of butter and cheese. Dairy cattle are most numerous in Normandy and Brittany, in the north-east region of intensive mixed farming and on various damp riverine lowlands in the northern half of the country, e.g. in Brie in the Paris Basin. Beef cattle are raised in all the leading agricultural areas as an adjunct to mixed farming, and as a specialised branch of stock-rearing in Limousin and the Rhône delta; while in the southern parts of the country many cattle are kept as draught animals.

In other forms of agricultural production regional specialisation is most marked in the cultivation of sugar beet and of grape-vines, and in sheep-farming. For the first of these, the limon-covered region between the Seine and the Belgian border is one of the chief areas of production in Europe, having an unusual combination of favourable conditions — a climate well suited to sugar beet (p. 54), fertile soils, a diligent agricultural population and a large home market. The distribution of vineyards in France is shown in some detail in Fig. 43 and further references are made to highly specialised districts in the course of the regional surveys in the following chapters. Sheep, numbering over 8 million, are kept mainly on the Central Plateau and on the dry

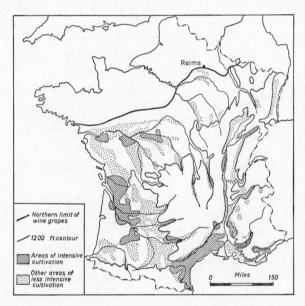

Fig. 43. Vineyards in France. Source: *Atlas de France.*

limestone and chalk plateaux to the west of it, and also on those to the east of the Paris Basin; being much less numerous in France than in Great Britain, they play a smaller part there in the forms of mixed farming on the lowlands.

MINERAL RESOURCES AND HYDRO-ELECTRIC POWER

France has large deposits of low-grade iron ore in addition to considerable resources of bauxite, salt and potash, but lacks sufficient coal, in particular of coking quality, to provide a sound industrial balance. Unfortunately also, almost all the deposits of iron ore and all those of mined salt and of potash are situated close to the eastern frontier, the two former in Lorraine and the latter in Alsace, that is, away from the main centres of population and industrial activity. The bauxite deposits likewise lie in a peripheral region, in the Var and Hérault Departments in the south-east, but this is in one way an advantage as they are near to abundant supplies of hydro-electricity for the production of aluminium.

The chief coalfield, producing about 28 million tons a year, is that of the Pas de Calais and Nord centred on the Lens-Douai-Valenciennes district of the north-east. Coal is also mined in the south-western (Moselle) section of the Saar coalfield on the French side of the border, and in various small basins round the margins of the Central Plateau, which together contribute about 9 million tons. The total French production of hard coal in 1958–9 averaged about 58 million tons, together with 2½ million tons of lignite, mainly from Provence (Fig. 51). As little of the overall insufficient coal output is of good coking quality, large supplementary supplies of coal and coke have been imported, chiefly from Saarland and the Ruhr. These, however, may decline with the further development of alternative sources of power, and the increasing use in furnace coke mixtures of specially treated French coal.

There is a small petroleum field at Péchelbronn north of Strasbourg, and another newer one on the Parentis lagoon in the Landes some 50 miles south-west of Bordeaux. Of far greater importance are the large deposits of natural gas discovered in 1954 in the Lacq district of the Western Pyrenees (Fig. 48), which are being actively developed with refineries (to remove the high sulphur content) and pipe-line distribution to industrial regions including those of Paris and Lyons.

The French production of iron ore amounts to about 49 million tons yearly, equivalent to about 19 million tons of metal. Nine-tenths of it is extracted from the Lias beds dipping westward under the Jurassic limestone of the Côtes de Moselle in a 50-mile belt which extends from Nancy into Luxembourg. These ores are low-grade phosphoric[1] similar to those of the Jurassic escarpments in England, and such as are exported go mainly to nearby lands e.g. the Saar and Belgium. For the most part they are smelted locally,[2] and the pig iron and crude steel products are sent to finishing districts, especially that

[1] Known as Minette ores, because of the low iron content (30 to 34 per cent).
[2] Largely now with coke manufactured from mixed Moselle-Saar coals, since the discovery of special processes for their treatment.

of Valenciennes, or are exported. Since the establishment of the
European Iron and Steel Community the Lorraine industry has
benefited by the freer international movement of fuels and of its semi-
finished products. Some better-grade iron ores are mined south of
Caen in Normandy and in the eastern Pyrenees. Over half the Normandy output (about $2\frac{1}{2}$ million tons) is smelted locally or sent
elsewhere in France, and the rest is exported mainly to Britain
and the Benelux countries. The small supplies from the eastern
Pyrenees are used to make special steels, in particular at Tarascon and
Alès.

Since the re-incorporation of Alsace-Lorraine in 1919, France has
had sufficient supplies of sodium and potash salts for a wide range of
chemical industries. Salt has been extracted since prehistoric times
from the Upper Triassic beds in the Saulnois east of the Moselle
and just north of the Rhine-Marne canal, and potash deposits, discovered in the Nonnenbruch Forest area just north of Mulhouse
(Mülhausen) in 1910, have been vigorously exploited since Alsace was
transferred back to France.

Though rather meagrely endowed with coal resources, France has
abundant potential supplies of water power in the Alps, the Rhône
valley, the Central Plateau and the Pyrenees, a fair proportion of
which has already been utilised. The Table, p. 26, shows that the production of hydro-electric power in France in 1958 was greater than
that of any other West European country, though not much in excess
of the outputs of either Sweden or Norway. Of this French total upwards of 60 per cent was from the Alps-Rhône-Rhine region, about 24
per cent from the Central Plateau and the balance from the Pyrenees.
In order to compensate for the shortage of coal, especially since
the formerly large supplies from Britain have declined to insignificance, vigorous efforts are being made on a national scale to increase
still further the supplies of hydro-electric power, much more of which
is needed for electrifying the railways and to feed industry.

Previous to 1940 a number of power stations, mostly small, had been
constructed in the Alps and the Pyrenees, notably in the mountain
basins of the Isère and the Garonne, utilising the steep gradients of
snow-fed streams. These supplied current for local domestic requirements and some local industries. Later large-scale projects have necessitated the construction of barrages with side canals, as at Donzère-
Mondragon on the lower Rhône, or of high dams as at Génissiat on the
Rhône below Lake Geneva, at Castillon on the Verdon tributary of

the Durance, and at several points in the upper basins of the Dordogne and the Lot, whose headwaters come from the high volcanic region of Auvergne. Various other projects, some of them very ambitious and costly, are under construction or are planned e.g. on the Rhine above Strasbourg and on the Rhône below Génissiat and near Lyons. The general long-term results of all these developments will be

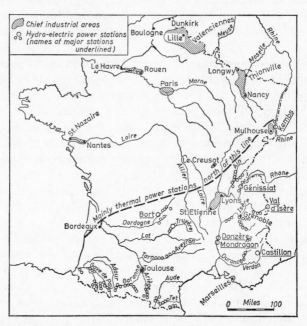

Fig. 44. Hydro-electric power stations in France, and major industrial districts. The names of the largest power stations are underlined. After A. F. A. Mutton and others.

far-reaching. All the main line railways will be electrified, as the P.L.M. has been already; manufacturing industry of special kinds, e.g. electro-chemical and electro-metallurgical, will expand in the south-east, and industry in general will tend to shift to that part of the country in dispersed rather than in concentrated distribution.

MANUFACTURING INDUSTRIES

French industry is in general both varied and decentralised, but with little on a really large scale. Much of it is carried on in many independent modest-sized establishments in numerous small towns and villages. Its diffusion springs from the traditional individual craftsmanship of the people. It has been made possible by the widespread use of electrical energy, of which by 1959 the hydro-electric output exceeded that of thermal stations. Such industrial agglomerations as exist are relatively small, none of them comparable in magnitude with that of the Ruhr or of several in Britain. France leans more, in fact, to agriculture than to industry; over 50 per cent more persons are engaged in the former than in the latter,[1] which employs less than 24 per cent of the active population, compared with 32 per cent in West Germany and nearly 40 per cent in Great Britain.

Nevertheless, modern industry is sufficiently developed for a number of specialised manufacturing regions to appear (Fig. 44). (1) The North-East region of the Pas de Calais and Nord coalfield produces some three-quarters of the cotton, woollen, linen and jute textiles, and has also substantial metallurgical and engineering industries. (2) The eastern provinces, containing the Lorraine iron ore and salt fields, produce upwards of 80 per cent of the pig iron and about two thirds of the crude steel, as well as various heavy chemicals. Upper Alsace is second in importance to the North-East in ordinary textile manufactures and produces also chemicals and dyes. (3) An area of which Lyons is the centre, reproduces on a smaller scale the diffuse nature of French industry; it specialises in manufactures of silk and artificial silk in and around Lyons, engineering products and also textiles at St. Étienne, armaments at Le Creusot, and electrical equipment at Grenoble and other places, including Lyons and St. Étienne. (4) Greater Paris, predominant in French life in other respects, has become also the chief manufacturing centre,[2] with a great variety of industries. It has long been supreme in the production of fashion and luxury articles of aesthetic quality. It leads in food processing and miscellaneous industries producing consumer goods, and it now has large motor car, aircraft and chemical and machine tool manufactures.

Apart from this regional grouping, some industrial activities are localised in particular towns, none of which is adjacent to supplies of coal. Nantes-St. Nazaire is the chief shipbuilding centre, especially for large merchant ships, and is followed by Le Havre; Marseilles is

[1] Vidal de la Blache notes a human factor here (as well as physical) in 'le tempérament obstiné agricole de la majorité de nos populations' inherited maybe from remote Danubian ancestors.

[2] The Paris-Lower Seine region now holds nearly a quarter of the total French industrial employees, followed by the Nord-Pas de Calais area with 15 to 16 per cent.

a great centre for the extraction of the oils from oilseeds imported chiefly from West Africa, and for the related manufactures of soap, as well as for refining mineral oil; Clermont–Ferrand in the Allier valley in the heart of the Central Plateau has developed large rubber and motor-tyre works; and Limoges on the edge of the granitic Limousin Plateau has long-established pottery and chinaware factories. It will be observed that with the notable exceptions of the Paris and Lyons regions, the great majority of the industrial districts and specialised manufacturing towns of France are in peripheral situations. Their integration into the economy of the country is effected by the cobweb system of railways, highways and waterways at the centre of which lies Paris. As the nerve centre of French industrial organisation, this city owes part of its disproportional growth to accretions of industry from the periphery.

It is apparent from Fig. 44 that, excepting the Lyons-St. Étienne and Toulouse areas, the major concentrations of French industry are in the northern half of the country, whereas nearly all the hydro-electric power is produced south of a line Belfort-Bordeaux. Chief among all the various physical and human factors that have contributed to the preponderance of industry in the northern parts have been the greater abundance there of coal as a source of power, and the greater agricultural resources and reserves of labour.

INLAND AND TIDAL WATERWAYS

In spite of their apparent large size, the great rivers of France form indifferent natural waterways for long-distance inland transport, although they are useful for local traffic in stretches. They all have some disabilities: tortuous meanders of the Seine, uneven flow and sandbanks on the Loire and the Garonne, rapids on the Rhône from Lyons to its unnavigable delta, and rapids and shifting channels on the Rhine above Strasbourg. Much has been done to improve the natural conditions by the construction of side canals as well as inter-connecting canals to provide continuous waterways for small craft. The two most striking examples are the Canal du Midi which links the side canals along the Garonne with another along the Aude, and the left bank Alsatian canal along the Rhine from Basle to Strasbourg. Among the numerous inter-connecting canals are those joining the Marne with the Rhine by the Saverne Gap, the Seine river system with the Loire at Orleans, and the Burgundy Canal over the Côte d'Or between the Seine system and the Saône; though the value of the first and the last of these is reduced by the numerous locks and consequent delays.

The three large Atlantic rivers end in estuaries which enable ships of limited size to proceed some distance inland, and all three provide harbourage for major ports. None of them, however, offers facilities for shipping at all comparable with those of the Thames. A proportion of the traffic of the hinterlands of the historic ports Rouen, Nantes and Bordeaux, has been diverted to outports with the increase in the size of ships. Rouen, though still an important trans-shipment port for barge traffic on the Seine to Paris, has been eclipsed by Le Havre which has grown to be one of the two leading French ports. Nantes and Bordeaux have held their own better against their outports St. Nazaire and Pauillac, the former by the construction of a ship canal along the Loire estuary, and the latter by reason of the marked tidal range on the Gironde, enabling ships of moderate size to proceed inland at high water.

FISHERIES

Although France has long sea frontages and numerous ports suitable as fishing centres, she is not a great fishing country. The landings by French craft amounting to an average of about half a million tons in 1956–8 give France sixth place (next after Denmark and Iceland) among West European countries. On the other hand, the relatively extensive fresh water fisheries provide France with supplies to supplement the harvest of the sea. The main fishing ports are in two groups; on the north-east coast, where Boulogne and Dieppe are the chief centres, and in Brittany (p. 171). The Mediterranean fisheries worked from Sète and other places on the lagoon coast of Languedoc are of comparatively small importance. Of all the French fishing ports Boulogne is the leading centre, now that most of the vessels operating in Newfoundland and Icelandic waters (some of them formerly from Breton ports) are stationed there.

THE FRENCH ECONOMY

Notwithstanding the fairly generous endowment of natural resources and the intelligence and industry of the people, the average income per head in France is comparatively low. A century ago France was more prosperous than any other European country except Great Britain. Her relative decline set in after 1870 and has increased since the beginning of the present century. Neither agriculture nor industry in France has kept pace with developments in neighbouring lands of North-Western Europe; the yields of farm produce per acre and per man-hour are lower, and the modern forms of industry, using high proportions of capital resources to labour, have made slower progress.[1]

Great as is the output of the French agricultural industry, a large and increasing deficit in the trade 'balance alimentaire' has been apparent in recent years; the production of wines has been unequal to consumption in terms of money values. In parts, in fact, it seems that the land has become partially exhausted for lack of sufficient fertilisers. The relative technical backwardness of French agriculture may be largely the outcome of the widespread sub-division of the land into uneconomically small holdings. There are over $4\frac{1}{2}$ million farms of less than 25 acres, on which it is generally impossible to find profitable use for modern mechanical equipment; many operations are still commonly performed in simple old-fashioned ways costly of labour, so that agriculture in general needs substantial protective duties. Thus a considerable labour force is immobilised in agriculture, which otherwise might have been available for the expansion of industry.

With some notable exceptions French industry has presented a somewhat similar picture. The French people excel in various branches of artistic expression and in individual craftsmanship — in forms of production that are neither adapted to exploit the economies of heavily capitalised manufactures nor are able to find a growing demand in the present-day world. Though the French have produced great scientists, they seem hitherto in general to have lacked the flair for technical developments based on the application of discoveries and inventions to industry. Because of this, and contributing further to relative inertia, French investors have been inclined to neglect domestic industry in placing their funds. Behind it all there has been the physical handicap of an overall shortage of coal in what was a coal-using age.

The material damage inflicted on France in two great wars was the less readily made good, because the general fall in the West European birth-rate began earlier in France than in other countries and had proceeded farther there. The resulting shortage of labour has led to the importation of several millions of permanent and seasonal workers,

[1] *Overseas Economic Surveys*, France, 1953; *Economic Survey of Europe*, Ch. VII, United Nations, 1955; *Annales de Géographie*, LXVII, No. 360, 1958; *Economist*, 14/1/56, 'France in the economic race'.

mainly from Italy and Spain. The loss too of considerable parts of a large colonial empire and the costs of the Algerian war have thrown further strains on the French economy.

However, as in past critical situations, the French people have shown remarkable recuperative powers, so indications of surprising economic recovery have been apparent since 1959. Annual rates of growth of population, stimulated by devaluation of the franc in 1958 and bumper harvests, have been among the highest in Europe; exchange reserves, almost exhausted in 1957, have increased to an enormous figure following upon some restrictions on domestic consumption and marked expansion of both agricultural and industrial production and exports; population seems to be on the increase; great works for the further development of hydro-electric power are in hand or are planned (cf p. 156), and the Saharan oil, as well as the domestic natural gas (p. 154), is being vigorously exploited. France should be in a strong position in this electricity- and hydrocarbon-fuel-using age; and is likely to derive substantial benefits from the trade facilities afforded by her membership of the European Common Market and especially of the Coal and Steel Community.

Chapter 12

FRANCE: II. THE PARIS BASIN AND ARMORICA

Two large lowland regions, the Paris and the Aquitaine Basins, and two old highland areas, the Central Plateau and Armorica, fill the greater part of France. The rest, in the form of an eastern arc extending from the Straits of Dover to the Mediterranean Sea and the eastern Pyrenees, is composed of various distinctive regions of which three, namely the industrial belt of Flanders, Lorraine and the Mediterranean area, are of special interest and importance. The four major regions, each several times the size of Belgium or the Netherlands, all comprise various sub-regions or *pays*, of sufficient individuality in their physical and human geography to be distinguished under separate names, as for example, Brie and Beauce in the Paris Basin, and Limousin and Auvergne in the Central Plateau. Though the regional types are commonly extensive in keeping with the size of France, it contains a great variety of land forms, reflecting differences mainly in geological structure and relief, with corresponding diversity of the human element.

I. The Paris Basin

Viewed in a broad structural sense, the Paris Basin is the large saucer-shaped area, the outer edges of which are marked by the discontinuous ring of old highlands — Ardennes, Vosges, Central Plateau and Armorica. In this basin sedimentary rocks, ranging in age from Triassic to Tertiary, have been laid down from the foothills of the Vosges to the English Channel, and from Flanders to beyond the bend of the Loire. But from the standpoint of human geography, the Paris Basin is less than this whole basin of sedimentation. It consists primarily of the area that is integrated by the convergent drainage of the Seine and its tributaries; together with the 'heels' of the horseshoe ring of chalk uplands drained to the English Channel by other short rivers such as the Somme, as well as the lowlands in the middle course of the Loire which once continued north to join the Seine.

The northward flow of the Meuse and the Moselle helps to give Lorraine physical individuality, reinforced by its mineral deposits and industrial activities. Like the Flanders industrial belt (marked off by the Artois ridge), Lorraine is peripheral to the core basin. Less these marginal lands, the Paris Basin is a flagon-shaped area opening on to the English Channel and having a broad base aligned along the north-western borders of the Massif Central. It covers an area of some 50,000 sq. miles, equal to that of England.

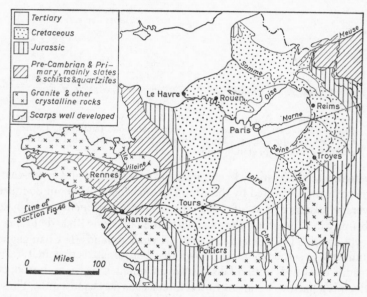

Fig. 45. Northern France: geological structure.

A common geological history gives physical unity to the basin as a whole, as the dominating influence of Paris does to much of its human geography. Prolonged subsidence, most pronounced towards the central region, has caused the whole area to be covered with extensive beds of marine sediments, the oldest being now exposed on the outer margins, and the youngest surviving in an elliptical area, near the geometrical centre of which lies Paris (Fig. 45). The youngest rocks, consisting mainly of Tertiary sands and clays, formerly covered a much larger area; they have been almost completely stripped by erosion from a wide belt round the existing central ellipse, thus exposing the geologically older rocks, mainly chalk. In an extensive east

and south-east segment the Cretaceous beds have likewise been removed, to expose the Jurassic series in which compact limestones
form the uppermost strata.

The most distinctive part of the Basin is approximately co-terminous with the drainage·system of the River Seine, the pivotal point of
which is Paris; upon it the Oise, Marne, Yonne and Loing flow
convergently with the Seine. Outwards from that city a series of
concentric escarpments, pierced by the radial rivers of the Seine

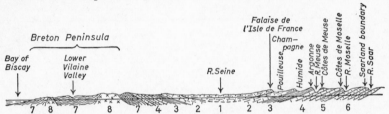

Fig. 46. Geological section on line W.S.W. to E.N.E. through northern
France (Fig. 45). 1. Tertiary. 2. Upper Cretaceous (chalk). 3. Lower
Cretaceous. 4. Jurassic. 5. Lias. 6. Triassic. 7, 8. Metamorphic Palaeozoic
and older rocks, with granitic ridges.

system, rise successively in elevation towards the east and south-east,
the parts most affected by the Alpine disturbances. At about 80 miles
average distance east of Paris the Tertiary sediments terminate
abruptly in a limestone scarp known as the Falaise de l'Isle de France,
beyond which lies a belt of dry and bare chalk uplands (la Champagne
Pouilleuse), some 40 miles in width. This unattractive belt rises
steadily eastwards until it falls away in an indented scarp, at the foot of
which is a narrower zone of Lower Cretaceous clays and sands. These
beds form what is known as the Champagne Humide, being retentive
of moisture in contrast with the dry Champagne Pouilleuse. They are
succeeded eastwards by a broad arc of Jurassic rocks which rise to
over 1,000 feet in places towards the Hercynian blocks, in the re-
elevation of which they have shared.

West and north-west of Paris the sedimentary rocks of the Basin
flatten out to nearly horizontal, but with an upward tilt against the
Armorican massif, where Jurassic rocks outcrop along a belt from
west of Caen to Maine, and where the Perche anticline brings lower
Cretaceous sandstone to the surface. With these exceptions and that
of the Bray anticline with its small Jurassic outcrop between the Seine
and the Somme, the Tertiaries west and north of Paris are surrounded
by a broad belt of chalk plains and platforms from Touraine to Picardy,

covered with clay-with-flints or, as in the northern parts, with limon.

The alternations of outcrop of the various types of rock that compose the Basin, especially in the eastern section, together with the diverse derived or transported surface deposits such as clay-with-flints, limon and alluvium, have given rise to a great variety of landscape forms (*pays*) known by distinctive local names. In this long-settled region the forms of land use are closely adjusted to local conditions and vary accordingly from one *pays* to another. Thus Brie between the Marne

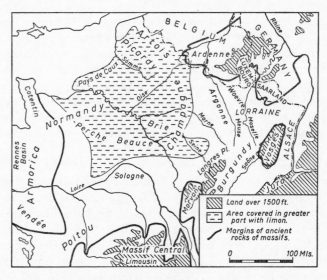

Fig. 47. The Paris Basin and surrounding parts: Limon deposits, *pays*.

and the Seine, having considerable areas of clayey soils better suited to pastures than cultivation, specialises in dairy farming, though it produces a variety of crops on the limon-covered stretches; Beauce, between the Seine and the Loire bend, a level limon-covered lime-stone plain, is one of the chief grain-growing districts of France; Touraine, a district of rich alluvial soils deposited by the Loire and its convergent tributaries, is known as the garden of France; the Cham-pagne Humide, the fertile Cretaceous belt mentioned above, not only produces a variety of crops, but also carries considerable numbers of cattle; and the champagne wine-producing district at the base of the Falaise de l'Isle de France, which owes its fertility to the mixed waste material washed down from the escarpment behind it, has gained a far-famed reputation for its chief product.

The references made in this selection of productive *pays* by no means cover the wide variety of specialised forms of agricultural land-use in the Paris Basin, of which among others the following are further examples. Picardy and the north-eastern parts generally resemble East Anglia in their cultivation of wheat and sugar beet as key crops combined with cattle-keeping. The *Pays Normand* is noted for the attention given to dairy-farming and the quality of its products, especially butter, and some districts near Paris, in particular Hurepoix with deep loam soils retentive of moisture, are devoted to intensive market gardening (cultures maraîchères) in which the French excel.

Some of the *pays* of the Basin, on the other hand, are distinguished rather by the comparative poverty of their soils; among them the Argonne sandstone ridge, mainly under forest; the Champagne Pouilleuse, of little use except for sheep-farming; the Sologne, a region of ill-drained clays in the angle between the Loire and the Cher; and the dry limestone uplands of the Langres Plateau, where settlement is confined to the deeper valleys floored with softer rocks.

DISTRIBUTION OF POPULATION. TOWNS

Owing to the magnet force of Greater Paris, which has drawn a population of over 5 millions to itself, two-thirds of the 13 million inhabitants of the twenty Departments of the Paris Basin are concentrated in the four Seine Departments. The geographical, historical and modern social-economic factors that have contributed to the growth of Paris itself have been referred to in the previous chapter. Opportunities for sharing in its vigorous many-sided life, and also the facilities offered by well-developed communications along the Seine artery, have attracted people and industries into and adjacent to the city and along the north bank of the river. Le Havre and Rouen, for example, have grown in modern times, not only as ports serving the capital, but also as centres of industry; both have shipbuilding yards and oil refineries, and Rouen manufactures cotton textiles.

Outside this limited area, the population is predominantly rural, varying in density with the productiveness of the different *pays*. Within a radius of 75 miles of Paris, no towns of more than purely local importance have arisen, except Beauvais, an old religious centre. At about that radial distance, however, four larger and several smaller towns of some importance have come into existence, each by reason of special features of its site. Amiens at a convenient crossing of the Somme has textile manufactures, originally using wool from the neighbouring chalk uplands, but now working mainly on cotton and linen; Reims situated at the entrance to a gap in the Tertiary 'Falaise' has long been an important centre both of trade between diverse *pays* and of manufactures of wool obtained from the dry Champagne, and is now also the chief commercial centre of the champagne wine district; Troyes in the wide gap cut by the Seine in the chalk plateau, followed by the trunk railway from Paris to Alsace and Switzerland, is an important route centre and also has textile manufactures; and Orléans on the Loire where it bends nearest to Paris, is the bridge town for roads and railways connecting the Seine basin with that of the middle Loire and thence with Aquitaine. Of the smaller towns, Épernay on the Marne, a little south from Reims, is likewise a gap town and a centre of the champagne wine belt; and Dieppe, in a gash in the chalk plateau cut by a small river, is a cross-Channel port for traffic between Paris and London.

As the distance from Paris increases to over 120 miles, towns in favourable situations are able to develop independent functions and to grow larger than those nearer. Thus Boulogne, besides being the leading fishing centre (p. 159), is a major cross-Channel port; Tours at the Cher-Loire confluence and Le Mans in the middle Sarthe valley have both developed as regional centres of productive districts, rich in historical buildings — the so-called château country; Caen in Normandy on the Orne river, though small, has some importance as the port for the export of agricultural produce from the Pays de Caen and also in recent years of iron ore; it has perhaps greater importance through its historical associations, for at Falaise not far away William the Conqueror was born, and on the beaches close by the Allied landings were made in 1944, followed by battles in the course of which Caen and its early medieval churches suffered much damage.

Though lacking basic minerals except the Caen iron ore (p. 155), the Paris Basin contains a great variety of building stones and materials, which have been used to erect public and other buildings of striking architectural designs all over the land — cathedrals, churches, palaces, hôtels de ville and châteaux. The rich and varied agriculture of the region has been its main source of wealth. Endowed with a high proportion of fertile land, it has withal an almost ideal climate for agriculture, a moderate and reliable rainfall averaging about 30 inches, warm and sunny summers, and winters seldom unduly cold. Agriculture in its various forms dominates the landscape except on the wooded sandstone and limestone ridges and uplands. The greater part of the whole area consists of fully cultivated land: on the nearly level plains such as those of Beauce, Touraine and Picardy, or on the low Tertiary and Cretaceous platforms generally intersected by numerous valleys with strings of villages and small market towns at intervals, or on the middle and lower slopes of the scarp faces where springs have given rise to similar lines of nucleated settlements.

II. ARMORICA

This region comprises the Brittany and Cotentin peninsulas, part of western Normandy and the Vendée district south of the Loire. Its eastern boundary with the Paris Basin lies roughly along the upper course of the Orne in Normandy, thence a little west of the Sarthe River to the Loire near Angers, and along the eastern edge of the Gâtine heights to the Poitiers Gap. In contrast with the adjoining Paris Basin, it is composed of hard, slaty Palaeozoic shales, with ridges and dissected plateaux of granites, gneiss and quartzites. These are the remnants of the much denuded Armorican folds aligned mostly W.–E. in the north and curving round to NW.–SE. in the south, the main axis of the former being marked by the Monts d'Arrée and the Alençon Hills, and of the latter by the Montagne Noire and the Gâtine Heights.

Prolonged erosion subsequent to the Armorican folding reduced the mountain system to a peneplain, which at a later stage became partially submerged as in the Ille-Vilaine depression. Throughout the Secondary geological era and on into the Tertiary during which thick beds of limestones, chalk and sandstones were laid down in the sea covering the Paris Basin, the greater part of this western region remained dry land and was probably continuous with the British Armorican highland region. Slight uplift in the Alpine orogenesis caused some rejuvenation of the drainage system and remodelling of the landscape features, since which another phase of partial submergence[1] has led to the formation of rias and the detachment of resistant fragments as islands, e.g. the Channel Islands and the Sept Îsles. The long-established larger rivers have worked down towards a new base level in generally wide valleys in their lower courses and their head-streams have cut numerous gaps in the ridges. The region as a whole is, in fact, once more approaching a state of peneplanation: the general level of the residual dissected plateaux is under 600 feet, and the three highest points, those in the Alençon Hills, the Monts d'Arrée and the

[1] By the positive (eustatic) rise of the general sea-level at the close of the Ice Age.

Montagne Noire, rise to not much more than 1,000 feet. Two valley depressions cut right across the region, that of the Ille and the Vilaine rivers between St. Malo and Nantes, and that of the lower Loire. Thus what remains of the massif is divided into three residual highland sections: (i) Western Brittany, (ii) the Cotentin Peninsula and the uplands south of it to the Loire, and (iii) the Hauteurs de Gâtine south of that river. Between the first and the second of these divisions, the broad and fertile valley of the Vilaine known as the Rennes Basin forms a fourth sub-division.

The pronounced Atlantic climate of this Armorican region, especially in the two peninsulas, reinforces the contrasts in structure and relief features between it and the adjoining parts of France. Brittany resembles Cornwall in the rainfall of over 40 inches distributed throughout the year, the relatively high winter temperatures carried forward to give precocious spring growth of plants, and the frequent strong winds in all exposed places. The natural vegetation throughout the whole region except in windswept situations seems to have been deciduous forest or bushy heath, but these forms have now been replaced by moorlands, meadows and cultivated fields. The fields, whether meadow land or cultivated, are enclosed either by stone walls banked with earth, as in parts of Cornwall and Devon, or more commonly by hedgerows with trees. Both kinds of enclosure provide shelter for cattle from the frequent strong winds, and the lopped limbs of the trees furnish supplies of domestic fuel. This Breton type of country composed of chess-board pattern of fields with tree-lined boundaries, known in France as bocage,[1] prevails eastwards into Normandy and Maine to the limits of the Armorican region.

The people also of Brittany differ in their origins, their native speech and their ways of life from those of the rest of France. The region was settled, it seems, from Wales and Ireland by 'Britons' of Celtic speech, which has persisted as the language of the ordinary people — to the exclusion of French in some parts. Having come by sea from sea-girt lands, the people clung to the coastlands, at all events in Brittany, avoiding the wild and unattractive interior. There they supplemented the resources of the land by fishing and seafaring activities, for which the highly indented coasts with numerous sheltered bays and rias gave

---

[1] This term, literally meaning grove, is applied by the French to the Armorican type of rural landscape, owing to the impression it gives of parkland as seen from the ground or a detached height — in contrast with the open agricultural landscape of the plains, where trees are rare except in the wooded parts and in avenues along the highways.

special opportunities, as they do at the present time. Breton fishing
fleets are active in both the Biscayan and Channel waters, and have
been, as far away as Iceland and islands in the Gulf of St. Lawrence;
and the French navy and mercantile marine draw heavily upon Bretons to man their ships. In religion these Bretons are more devoutly
Catholic than the majority of their fellow French, and in politics
strongly conservative. In the course of time the damp valleys of the
interior were settled by people of the same stock, but till recent improvements in transport were made, these remained isolated and
largely self-contained, whence their marked traditionalism.

Brittany occupies a considerable and the most typical part of
Armorica. In this peninsula the distinction between the moderately
fertile coastlands and the less attractive dissected upland core is very
marked in human as well as in physical geography. The former, called
Ar-mor, the land of the sea, offers a variety of means of livelihood, is
densely populated and contains numerous ports, some of them fair-
sized towns, e.g. Brest, Lorient and St. Malo. The latter, called
Ar-coet, the land in the woods (because of the former forests), is wet
and misty, and is broken up by ridges and stumps of hard ancient
rocks; settlement there is confined to the network of rather damp
valleys, and is generally in the form of isolated farms, except in the
few wide valleys floored with softer rocks in which towns such as
Rennes and Châteaulin have arisen.

Though Brittany is the archetype section of Armorica, others including western Normandy, Maine, the lower Loire valley and the
Vendée, together cover a larger area. The first two of these are transitional in the racial composition of the inhabitants, and in human
geography between Brittany to the west and the lowlands to the east,
from both of which settlement has penetrated. In them the dicho-
tomy between Ar-mor and Ar-coet is blurred, if not lost, though the
bocage landscape persists. The nearer to the eastern border in Normandy and Maine, the less is seen of the Breton type in the population,
and the more the outlook and the ways of life of the people conform to
the general French pattern. The growth of means of transport has
been a powerful factor in this process of assimilation, the main railways and river valleys serving as filaments of attachment. Cherbourg
on the northern extremity of the Cotentin Peninsula is now a transatlantic port of Paris; and similarly Nantes and St. Nazaire have
developed as national ports and centres of shipbuilding, overshadow-
ing their functions as ports for local trade. The Vendée district on the

other hand, situated between the Gâtine barrier and the sea, remains somewhat isolated and tends to preserve much of its individuality.

FARMING, FISHING AND CENTRES OF POPULATION

Farming of one kind or another is the major means of livelihood, especially in the eastern districts mentioned above, where wheat and other cereals are cultivated. Brittany is in general too wet for wheat, and there the staple food grains were rye and buckwheat in former times when the inhabitants had to rely mainly on local resources; but with the improvements in transport the tendency now is to substitute cattle forage crops for the inferior food grains, and to draw supplies of wheat from the adjoining parts of the Paris Basin. Cattle-keeping, mainly for the production of milk, is now a leading form of farming from Normandy into Brittany. It has been assisted by the improved transport system, which provides means of sending dairy produce speedily to Paris, or to England, and of distributing supplies of fertilisers and other requirements to the farms. Modern means of transport have also furthered the development of a large market-garden industry on the coastlands of Brittany, especially the northern, the produce being despatched to Paris when the Mediterranean supplies are coming to an end, and at times also to England. Access to shell sand for treating the ground and to seaweed for fertiliser has been an important factor in the growth of this industry, which rests primarily on the relatively early return of spring weather conditions. Cider-apple orchards are a common feature of the countryside in Normandy and parts of eastern Brittany, as in some districts in south-west England, where climatic conditions are broadly similar (p. 71). Throughout northern Armorica cider is a common substitute for wine or beer, neither of which can well be produced locally.

Fishing has remained a mainstay of the Ar-mor Bretons, since they first settled in Brittany. It is now operated on a commercial scale, supplying the inland regions with lobsters from the rocky coves, sardines and tunny from Biscayan waters, and inshore and deep-sea fish landed at the northern ports. Among the more important fishing centres are St. Malo and Paimpol on the northern coast and Lorient and Douarnenez on the southern. The largest coastal town in Brittany is Brest, on a magnificent harbour which is the chief French Atlantic naval base, but of little importance either for commercial shipping or for fishing. The chief commercial port in the whole of Armorica is Nantes, the hinterland of which extends far beyond the limits of the region to include Paris for some traffic. Of the inland towns only Rennes has more than 100,000 inhabitants. Situated at the intersection of the central Finisterre route with the N.–S. route from St. Malo to Nantes and in a fertile basin covered in parts with Tertiary sediments, it has become the chief commercial and administrative centre of Brittany. Other inland towns such as Alençon and Châteaulin are much smaller, little else in fact, than local market towns.

Chapter 13

FRANCE: III. THE AQUITAINE BASIN, THE WESTERN AND CENTRAL PYRENEES AND THE MASSIF CENTRAL

THE Aquitaine Basin fills the wide angle between the Pyrenees and the Massif Central. Triangular in shape, it is bounded on the north by the Vendée extension of Armorica, is open on the west to the Atlantic, and reaches inland to the Carcassone gap where its south-eastern corner meets the western angle of the Mediterranean region in Languedoc. Its eastern boundary with the Massif may be taken as the contour of 300 metres (approximately 1,000 feet), which marks in the lower valleys of the main rivers. With this basin the western and central Pyrenees may properly be included, for these mountains have contributed much to its structural development, and are closely bound up with it in their human geography.

During long periods of gradual subsidence, beds of Jurassic limestones and Cretaceous rocks were laid down in this area, as in that of the Paris Basin to the north-east. The elevation of the Pyrenees by folding movements and the block uplift of the Massif Central in the Alpine orogenesis caused the basin to assume its existing concave form, with an outer rim of Jurassic limestones followed by an inner incomplete outcrop zone of Cretaceous beds. Both of these appear in the northern front of the Pyrenees, the Jurassic limestones along the western borders of the Massif, partially incorporated with it by differential upthrusts, and the Cretaceous series in the Charente Departments north of the Gironde. Apart from the latter, the whole of the lower-lying parts of the basin is covered with Tertiary and Recent glacial and alluvial deposits derived from the waste of the bordering highlands. Much of this material has been swept down from the Pyrenees, the demolition of which began in the middle Tertiary and reached a climax in the Ice Age. A great triangular area north of the Pyrenees, not less than 10,000 sq. miles, has been covered with molasse, consisting of beds of loose sandstones, clays and thin limestones, deposited in a shallow sea, and overlaid in the south with

gravels and other coarse materials of glacial origin. Since the close of
the Ice Age, rivers have been active in removing further waste from
the highlands, excavating flat-bottomed, alluvium-strewn valleys in
the weak molasse, and carrying loads of sandy sediment to the Biscayan coast, thus contributing to the formation of the extensive dune
belt of the Landes.

The greater part of the basin is drained by the fan-shaped Garonne

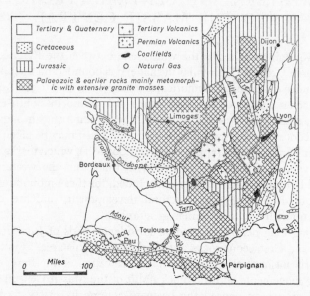

Fig. 48. Southern France (Massif Central, Aquitaine, Pyrenees):
Geological structure. The three eastern coalfields from N. to S. are those
of Le Creusot, St. Étienne and Alès, and the two west of the Allier, those of
Commentry and Decazeville.

river system. The main river rises in the lofty central Pyrenees, collecting the waters of the Ariège and various other Pyrenean tributaries in
its great circular sweep. On its right bank it receives the drainage of a
considerable part of the Massif, carried by such rivers as the Tarn, the
Lot and the Dordogne. The convergence of the Garonne system on
the Gironde leaves the areas on either side of that exit to be drained
independently — by the Charente to the north, and the Adour in the
extreme south; while the indeterminate drainage of the Landes is
largely by percolation.

The prevailing landscape features both of the Tertiary molasse area

and of the Landes are unusually monotonous. The former consists of
rolling country broken only by successions of low rounded hills and
open valleys with gently sloping sides. The latter is composed of an
endless series of sand dunes, active and high on the coast, dead and
lower inland; a string of lagoons lies behind the line of coastal dunes,
and elsewhere marshes are common in the depressions, where an
impervious ferrous hard-pan sub-stratum is liable to be formed. North

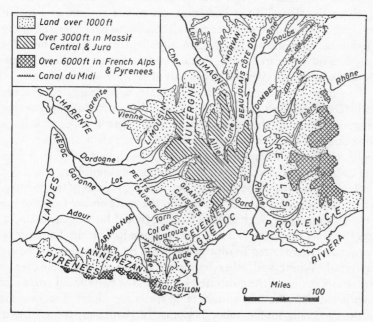

Fig. 49. Southern France: physical regions and drainage systems.

of the Gironde the landscape is again rather monotonous. Shallow
valleys, often dry, intersect the low Cretaceous platform, and only the
longer streams have cut down to the underlying less pervious marls,
so forming fertile valleys with abundant surface water. In contrast
with these somewhat tame lowland forms, the stony Lannemezan
outwash fan below the Pyrenees, is deeply dissected by the numerous
turbulent mountain feeders of the Garonne, some of which have worn
down to the molasse sub-strata; the commonly narrow intervening
ridges are chilly, bare and windswept, and altogether this plateau
section of the basin is distinctly inhospitable. Above the Lannemezan

the central Pyrenean rivers and streams have cut deep gorges through the foreland limestone belt between their partly habitable upper valleys and the plateau.

CLIMATE AND LAND USE

The climate of Aquitaine is dominated by the Atlantic from which depressions travel eastwards, especially in winter. The rainfall, which in most parts is upwards of 30 inches per annum (twice as much on the slopes of the Pyrenees), shows late autumn and spring maxima. The negative summer rainfall conditions characteristic of the Mediterranean region to the east are only slightly in evidence here, for heavy rains associated with thunderstorms occur in the summer months when moist Atlantic air spreads in over the heated ground.

The relatively equable warm temperate, semi-maritime climate, with rare incidence of frost on the lowlands, ensures a long growing season which, together with the generally fertile soils, enables a wide range of crops to be cultivated. This is the chief maize-growing region of France, where the crop is mainly used, both as green fodder and as ripe grain to feed live-stock, including large numbers of draught cattle. It is also one of the chief wine-producing regions of the country. The vineyards are generally planted on the south-facing banks of the west-flowing rivers, such as the Charente (noted for Cognac brandy), and the Dordogne, the Lot and the Garonne itself from Toulouse to Bordeaux, where noted Bordeaux wines e.g. Sauternes and Médoc are produced. Wheat and other temperate cereals occupy, however, a larger proportion of the cultivated land than the two special crops just mentioned. In addition, considerable tracts are under meadows for cattle, especially in the valley bottoms. In particular, the Charente area north of the Gironde specialises in the fattening of cattle brought down from the indifferent pastures of the granitic Limousin Plateau (p. 181).

These generally intensive forms of agriculture are pursued more especially in the lowland region of Aquitaine proper. The marginal zones of calcareous formations abutting the Massif, of outwash fans rising to the Pyrenees, and of the Landes, are much less suited to close settlement and fully developed agriculture. In the first and second of these, cultivation is restricted to the river valleys, and the intervening uplands provide only rough grazings used mainly as sheep walks. The Landes are a distinctive region, the most extensive of their kind in the world. There opportunities for agricultural settlement are limited to patches of drained marshland. The systematic planting of pine trees, partly to impede the drift of sand inland, now provides the chief forms of industry, in the care of the forests, the cutting and transport of timber and the collection of turpentine.

The ravined western, and the still wilder, loftier central Pyrenees, harsh in climate and rain-drenched, naturally support little population except on the valley platforms, especially those developed by longitudinal rivers in the Cretaceous and Jurassic belts. Yet in three ways they furnish resources of value in the economy of Aquitaine: additional labour is provided by mountaineers who regularly come down to assist in the autumn grape harvest; a string of tourist and other resorts e.g. Oléron, Lourdes, Bagnères de Bigorre, has arisen in the foothills, frequented by visitors from all over France and beyond, who bring some income to a population whose land is poor in resources for sustenance: and hydro-electric power has been developed on the fast, snow-fed mountain rivers, for transmission to such lowland centres as Toulouse.

In spite of the general uniformity of landscape features over several of the major regional sections of Aquitaine, there is sufficient variety of physical forms, geological structure and land use within the area as a whole to justify the recognition by the inhabitants of a number of *pays*, as in the Paris Basin (p. 165). In addition to the Lannemezan and the Landes already mentioned, other districts with distinctive characteristics are the Médoc peninsula west of the Gironde, and Saintonge in the Cretaceous belt north of it, specialising in the production of wine and corn respectively; Périgord and Quercy, transitional in structure and land use between the fertile champagne of the lowlands and the bare karst of the western Massif; Armagnac, lying between the Lannemezan Plateau and the bend of the Garonne, another important wine-producing area; and Lauraguais, east of Toulouse, a rather dry and thinly populated upland and valley district, which, however, includes the important corridor over the Col de Naurouze leading from Toulouse to Carcassonne, and thus connecting Aquitaine with Languedoc.

COMMERCE, COMMUNICATIONS AND TOWNS

The commercial and industrial activities of Aquitaine are concentrated largely in the two cities Bordeaux and Toulouse, situated towards either extremity of the medial axis of the region lying approximately along the course of the Garonne. Both are regional centres, Bordeaux at the head of ocean navigation and lowest bridging of the Garonne, and Toulouse at the intersection of the route followed by the Canal du Midi with those connecting the southern Massif with the Pyrenees via the Tarn and upper Garonne valleys, and southern France with north-east Spain by the Ariège valley.

Bordeaux is the commercial centre not only of the wine-producing districts of its immediate hinterland in lower Aquitaine, but also (in like manner with Paris) of the whole region of convergent valleys of the Garonne system. Its chief industries are shipbuilding and those connected with its distinctive trade — conditioning and preparing wines for export and distribution, and treating imported wines for marketing. Bordeaux ranks among the major ports of France, special-ising in trade with transatlantic countries and North Africa. Though like London, it has the advantage of a considerable tidal range on its river, the increasing size of ships and volume of shipping has entailed the construction of outports on the Gironde estuary at Pauillac, and more recently at Le Verdon near the open sea. The regional nodality and facilities for handling larger ships at Bordeaux with its outports has enabled it to outstrip the Charente ports La Rochelle and Rochefort. These have long been used as naval stations, but as com-mercial ports depend now mainly on the trade of their limited local hinterlands. Toulouse has for centuries been a leading cultural and communications centre of the French Midi, but the recent rapid increase of its population to nearly 350,000[1] has been the result of the growth of engineering and chemical industries (utilising hydro-electric power from the Pyrenees), in addition to the processing of agricultural products.

In this predominantly agricultural region of Aquitaine, population tends to be dispersed, rather than concentrated in urban centres, its rural density outside the two main cities varying with the fertility of the soil. Thus country towns are as a rule simply small local market centres. The one exception is Angoulême situated on the upper Charente at the crossing of the main road and rail routes from Paris to Bordeaux. For the rest, a distinctive feature of the distribution of most of the larger towns is their arrangement at intervals along three lines in sites of limited nodality: along the Garonne valley between Bordeaux and Toulouse, e.g. Agen; at points where rivers from the Massif enter upon their lowland courses, e.g. Périgueux, Cahors and

[1] Toulouse is now the fourth largest town in France, having surpassed Bordeaux in population.

Montauban; and on the outer fringes of the Pyrenees on rivers whose valleys lead into the highlands, e.g. Bayonne, Pau and Tarbes.

IV. THE MASSIF CENTRAL[1]

The limits of this plateau region are distinctly marked by boundary faults on the east and south-east, where it rises steeply from the Rhône-Saône trough, but are somewhat indeterminate elsewhere. On the west and north-west, where the plateau falls away gradually into the plains, the contour of 300 metres (nearly 1,000 feet), taken above as separating off Aquitaine, is a sinuous line bulging round the spurs between the trenched river valleys. On the other hand, the trough-faulted valleys of the Allier and a section of the Loire, though below 1,000 feet in their lower parts, are generally taken as belonging to the plateau region, since they are in the main structural, not erosional features. Broadly defined, the Massif consists of a large central plateau area tilted westward from its upthrust eastern edge, with a northern limb in the Morvan block, and another limb in the south extending (in the Montagne Noire) towards the Pyrenees.

As the outcome of various episodes in the long geological history of this region, its structure is complex. First elevated with some volcanic activity (in the Beaujolais north-west of Lyon) in the post-Carboniferous Armorican-Hercynian orogenesis, the highlands were reduced to a peneplain which was later submerged and covered with thick beds of Jurassic limestone, overlaid with less substantial deposits of early Tertiary clays. The re-elevation of the area in the Alpine orogenesis was unequal, being greatest in the parts nearest the Alpine storm centre. It was accompanied by marked dislocations, especially in the north where differential vertical movements of several thousand feet resulted in the formation of the Allier trough (the Limagne) with a side pocket in the Loire Valley; and also in the south where large blocks of the Jurassic limestone sank and have been preserved in the Causse regions. Associated with these violent movements, prolonged volcanic activity developed along fractures west of, and parallel with, the Limagne trough. Huge volcanoes and many smaller crater summits arose, and great streams of lava and masses of volcanic debris were discharged, not only on a broad belt of the Auvergne plateau extending south nearly to the Causses in the Monts

---

[1] General references have been made to the Massif in earlier chapters (pp. 149 and 151). The features already described are mentioned only incidentally here.

d'Aubrac, but also on the Tertiary beds of the upper Limagne adjacent to the great volcanoes.

These upheavals initiated a vigorous new cycle of erosion. The Tertiary capping has been removed except in the trough valleys and where it has been protected by lava flows. The Jurassic limestone has likewise gone but for the Causses, thus exposing over the greater part of the plateau the basal crystalline rocks. The old peneplaned surface composed of granites and schists has, in fact, been exhumed. This later erosion cycle is still in full progress; it has demolished the upper parts of the earlier great volcanoes, has planed off the crystalline rocks and the Causse limestones to a more or less even surface, and enabled the rivers to cut deep gorges on their steep courses on the margins of, and well into, the plateau.

The existing plateau averages upwards of 3,000 feet in height. It rises to about 5,000 feet along its eastern escarpment, from which it falls away into the great basins on its western and north-western borders. This downward slope is interrupted by the volcanic masses of Auvergne which rise to over 6,000 feet in their highest points, and by the other less imposing volcanic masses south and south-east of them. The high elevation and exposure to storms from the Atlantic cause the upper highland climate to be uninviting. The rainfall is well over 40 inches, and the region in general is windswept and misty. The soils in most parts are no better than the climate. Those derived from the crystalline rocks are characteristically thin, siliceous and deficient in mineral constituents; and such as have formed on the permeable Karst-like Causses lack moisture, in spite of apparently generous rainfall. Though there are some modest exceptions to these prevailing disabilities, in climate and soil, the Massif as a whole is a region of low agricultural productivity.

Other resources are also limited. There are hardly any metallic ores, in spite of the violent dislocations which in some other old highlands of similar age, have given rise to mineral-bearing intrusions. The only significant industrial resources are the small coalfields and the fairly abundant supplies of water-power. The former, preserved in minor tectonic basins, all in marginal situations, are worked at Le Creusot, St. Étienne, Alès (Alais) and Decazeville. Water-power has been already developed in the upper valleys of the Allier, Dordogne and Lot, and further projects are in hand; but the current is distributed mainly to places outside the whole region.

The area of the Massif is given as 31,000 sq. miles, over one-seventh of that of France, and its population at about 4 millions, less than one-tenth of that of the entire country. Its density of population is therefore well below the French average, and were it not for the considerable concentrations in the industrial districts of Clermont-Ferrand, St. Étienne, Le Creusot and Limoges, its overall density of population would be much lower.

The Massif is in fact an area of dispersion, the 'Pole répulsif' as de Martonne calls it, not only in the drainage system of France, but also in its human geography. The peoples of its diverse marginal areas, each group separated from the others by physical obstacles, are linked in their modes of life with their adjoining lowlands — those of Limousin with the Charente country, those of the south-west with Aquitaine, of the Cévennes with Languedoc and of the Allier-Loire troughs with the Paris Basin. The more intensive life of the respective lowlands exercises a gravitational pull on the populations of the highlands, following the lie of the relief. The agricultural areas of the Massif where life is in general hard, are understandably losing population to other parts that offer better opportunities. Though the Massif appears as a unit in a broad survey of the physical geography of France, this disparate feature in the external relationships of physically diverse parts suggests a sectional treatment of the human geography. The region falls in this respect into four main sub-divisions: Limousin, Causses and Cévennes, Auvergne including Limagne, and the Lyonnais-Morvan north-eastern limb.

Limousin is a granite tableland which, standing at about 1,000 feet on its outer margins, rises gradually eastwards to an inner highland area, several thousand feet in height, strewn with tors and marshy hollows. The tableland itself is an old peneplaned surface, on the margins of which the radial rivers of the present cycle of erosion have excavated gorge-like valleys similar to those on the outer borders of Dartmoor. Up to about 1,800 feet the climate is suitable for ordinary temperate agriculture, and the soils, though siliceous, respond to treatment with lime available from the limestone fringe round the plateau. Wheat and barley are grown at lower elevations, where also there are fairly rich meadows and numerous chestnut plantations. These parts resemble the bocage country of Armorica (p. 169), and are famed for the red-coated cattle raised there, whence the local name, Plateau des Millevaches. Higher up, rye and buckwheat take the place of wheat, and the pastures are naturally poorer and more scattered.

The main focus of the life of the whole area is Limoges in the upper valley of the Vienne, where the main railway and road from Paris to Toulouse cross the river. Its remarkably nodal situation has enabled it to overshadow completely other centres such as Argenton and St. Yrieix, which are merely peripheral market towns. Limoges has added to its regional functions a high-class pottery industry specialising in artistic chinaware, for the production of which kaolin is obtained from the decayed granites of the area.

The Causses and the Cévennes. The Causses are composed of two areas of massive limestone, separated by a southern extension of the crystalline rocks, into the Grands Causses to the east standing at 4,000 to 5,000 feet, and the Petits Causses, or Causses de Quercy, to the west a couple of thousand feet lower down. East of the former, a ridge of crystalline rocks, broken only by a single gap, forms the Cévennes escarpment (Fig. 48). The Grands Causses, known by various names in different sections, are thus almost entirely surrounded by the crystalline formations, except for the gap just mentioned, where the Jurassic limestones extend into the semi-arid belt of the Garrigues at the foot of the escarpment.

The Grands Causses plateaux offer little to attract human settlement. They are pitted with dolines (swallow holes); the bare rock projects in many jagged patches; and the scanty vegetation is limited to xerophilous shrubs, with some herbage in the hollows. The subterranean drainage of these parts finds its way into the Tarn and the Lot which with their tributary streams have cut deep gorges in the limestone. The only use of this country is as rough grazings for sheep, from the ewes' milk of which Roquefort cheese, named after a place in this area, is made. Permanent settlement is restricted to the valleys of the larger rivers, the most favourable sites being the places where these rivers open out and have cut down to the marls and clays of the Lias underlying the limestone. The chief centre is Millau in the upper Tarn valley which has some woollen manufactures. The Petits Causses are similar in surface forms to their higher counterparts, but they contain some broader valleys and consequently carry a greater population.

The Cévennes, rising steeply from the Garrigues, have been sculptured into numerous ravines by the headstreams of the Ardèche, Gard and Hérault. Here the climate is Mediterranean, and settlements have been established wherever terraces occur on benches in the steep courses of these streams. In the ascent of several thousand feet a distinct zoning appears of both cultivated and indigenous plants; the vine-olive-wheat cultivation of the lower levels gives place to the chestnut economy higher up, and to the sheep pastoral economy of the topmost parts. Here we have one of the most striking examples of transhumance. For centuries past sheep have been regularly driven up by well-defined tracks (*drailles*) from the Mediterranean lowlands in late spring when the summer drought sets in there, to where the melting of winter snows on the mountain heights allows fresh green grass to spring up.

The mainstay of the comparatively small population of the southern Massif is some form of agriculture. The only mineral deposits of importance are two small coalfields; one at Alès which extends up the Gard valley towards Bessèges and produces about 2½ million tons per annum, and another in a small basin in the crystalline rocks at Decazeville in the middle Lot valley. The iron ore previously worked in the Alès district and the coal of coking quality have given rise to metallurgical industries there to which chemical manufactures have been added.

Auvergne including Limagne. These, as seen above, are geologically complementary to each other. The convulsions that caused the two-pronged Allier-Loire block subsidence were preceded and accompanied by immense volcanic activity in a zone lying west and south-west of the Limagne, with an outlier at the head of the Loire. In addition to the now largely demolished huge volcanoes such as the Puy de Dôme, Mt. Dore and Cantal, swarms of *puys*, i.e. volcanic cones with more or less intact craters, and great flows of basaltic lava, remain as evidence of prolonged outbursts. Some of these lava flows reach the Limagne in the upper Allier valley covering the Tertiary sediments, and subsequent erosion has carved this area into a series of valleys, leaving a number of picturesque hills and ridges capped with basalt.

Both on the plateau and in the upper Limagne human settlement is much influenced by the disposition of the lava flows, for round their margins springs are numerous and the soils have been enriched by minerals derived from the decay of the basalt. Villages and even small towns, e.g. Aurillac, have arisen in such situations on the plateau; while in the Limagne the towns and larger settlements all cling to the valley sides along the spring lines below the basalt cornice, avoiding the damp soils of the main valley floor; good examples of these are seen in the situations of Clermont-Ferrand, Thiers, and Vichy.

Above about 3,000 feet on the plateau, cultivation even of such crops as rye and potatoes becomes impracticable, because of the long winter snows and the short frost-free season. But good summer pastures are available at still higher levels on the *planaises*, the weathered wedge-shaped masses of lava between the ravines cut by radial streams flowing from the old volcanoes.

The largest town and the capital of Auvergne is Clermont-Ferrand on the western edge of the Limagne almost under the shadow of the Puy de Dôme. As the main agricultural centre of Auvergne it has developed food-processing industries, e.g. fruit-preserving, and also leather manufactures. Its career as an important industrial centre began with the establishment of the Michelin rubber tyre works, and now that hydro-electric power is available in plenty from the upper Allier, its future industrial expansion is assured. Almost opposite Clermont-Ferrand, on the other side of the Limagne, is Thiers, which like Sheffield and Solingen has a long-established reputation for cutlery. Some 30 miles lower down the valley lies Vichy, one of the most famous spas in Europe. The lingering aftermaths of violent crustal disturbances in this region have given rise to mineralised springs exploited for medicinal purposes. Still lower down the Limagne valley, on the Loire near where it enters the Paris Basin, Nevers has grown as a transport centre and a minor iron-manufacturing town.

Lyonnais and Morvan. These horsts together with the upper Loire valley and the limestone escarpment of the Côte d'Or form the north-eastern extension of the Massif. It has been described as a mosaic of faulted blocks; not only do N.–S. boundary faults mark its eastern and parts of its western edges, but diagonal faults of NE.–SW. Hercynian trend also divide it into a series of upthrust blocks — Lyonnais, Beaujolais and Morvan — with intervening down-faulted basins such as those of the St. Étienne and Le Creusot coalfields. Situated in the area of intersection of earlier Armorican and Hercynian folds (Fig. 1), this north-eastern section of the Massif was more readily rent by the Alpine convulsions, not only by diagonal faults, but also notably in the formation of the Saône, Loire and Allier troughs — counterparts of the Rhine Rift Valley. The upland blocks are all composed of crystalline rocks, and settlements on them are mostly confined to the margins and the small lateral valleys. The chief populous districts are the two small coalfields, the scarp slopes from the Côte d'Or to Lyons and the upper Loire Valley.

The four to five million tons of coal per annum from the coalfields, supplemented nowadays with hydro-electric power, have given rise to industrial activities in three separate districts. The most important is the St. Étienne Basin, where the older silk and ribbon manufactures are now outstripped by the expanding metallurgical group of industries. A little to the north of this is the depression followed by road and railway from Lyons to Roanne. Utilising the local supplies of relatively cheap labour, numerous textile factories have been established along this route, producing silk near Lyons, and cotton and woollen fabrics towards and including Roanne. In the depression south of the Morvan horst, Le Creusot has been developed for strategic reasons as an armaments manufacturing centre away from the eastern frontier.

The Beaujolais escarpment of the Massif and the Côte d'Or are noted for their wines, e.g. Burgundy brands. Being nearer the climatic limits of the grape-vine than Languedoc, they are able to produce wines superior in flavour to the vin ordinaire of that region. The Côte d'Or is, in fact, a southern extension of the limestone uplands of the Langres Plateau which here forms the outermost edge of the Paris Basin; yet, though it is an extraneous element of the Massif, it has become involved in the intense faulting of the Morvan region which has resulted in its scarp face, and it partakes more of the character of the Massif than of the Paris Basin.

Chapter 14

FRANCE: IV. THE MEDITERRANEAN, EASTERN AND NORTH-EASTERN REGIONS

1. THE MEDITERRANEAN REGION AND THE EASTERN PYRENEES

DISTINCTIVE features of climate, vegetation and landscape mark off the area round the Gulf of Lyons from the rest of France. The indigenous olive, now widely cultivated, is often taken as the criterion of the bounds of this Mediterranean region, which, however, extends climatically on to arid tracts and up mountain sides where the olive cannot survive. The valley limits are clear enough: on the west up the Aude as far as its bend at Carcassonne; up the Rhône Valley as far as Montélimar; and shorter distances up the valleys of other rivers such as the Durance, Hérault and Tet. The mountain-side boundaries are less obvious; but for practical purposes all parts may be included that have the characteristic rainfall and temperature regimes as distinct from the mountain types. Thus in addition to the olive-defined lowlands Mediterranean France embraces the inhabited parts of the eastern Pyrenees, the lower slopes and valleys of the Cévennes and the Alps, and the eastern coastlands as far inland as a line from the lower Durance curving round on the 1,600-foot contour of the Alpes Maritimes to the Italian border.

The historic names Provence and Languedoc are in common use to distinguish the areas east and west of the Rhône, areas which differ in their geographical forms, their economic structure and the character of their inhabitants. As seen on a map, one appears as the counterpart of the other. They share the Rhône Valley lowlands, both are backed by mountains into which the valleys lead from the lowlands, and both have important coastwise extensions, Provence in the Riviera east of Toulon, and Languedoc in the Plain of Roussillon south of Narbonne. Yet Languedoc and Provence differ essentially in their physical build. The belt of lowlands which in the former is nearly continuous between the mountains and the sea, is almost non-existent in the latter east of Marseilles; and there is all the difference in the world between the succession of sand-spits shutting off lagoons on the regular coast of Languedoc and the jagged Riviera coast broken by projecting low spurs of the mountains in numerous rocky promontories.

The eastern Pyrenees and the Plain of Roussillon form a distinct unit among the sub-regions of Mediterranean France. East of the Ariège the Pyrenees are broader and much drier than their central and western parts. The fractured blocks of ancient rocks of which they are composed, are flanked by others such as the Corbières rising out of the belt of limestones continued from the west. Thus the rivers east of the

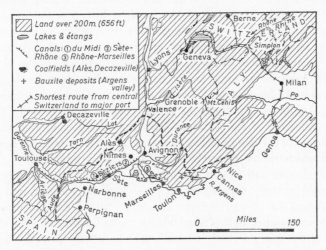

Fig. 50. S.E. France and neighbouring parts. The broken line indicates the approximate limits of the Mediterranean region of France.

upper Aude flow longitudinally to the Mediterranean, and it is in the mountain-girt tectonic basins, situated at intervals in the courses of these rivers, that the upland population is concentrated. In this area including the Plain of Roussillon, all life depends on supplies of water, none too plentiful because of the pronounced Mediterranean climate. The mountains and even parts of the lowlands away from the rivers carry little or no vegetation of use except scattered cork oaks; but wherever water is available by irrigation in the valleys or on the terraced hillsides, the land is intensively cultivated, chiefly under vine-yards from which strong types of wine, e.g. Banyuls, are produced. The commercial centre of the whole area is Perpignan, the only large town, in a markedly nodal situation on the River Tet.

Though the French Mediterranean region has attracted settlement from the earliest times, its productive resources are distinctively restricted by features of relief, structure and climate. Except for the narrow Rhône and Aude inland exit valleys, it is hemmed in by mountains which, composed of limestones or crystalline rocks, have lost much of their soil cover since the early destruction of the forests by man. In parts they present a desolate appearance scorched in the fierce summer heat. The bare rock is often exposed and, except on the shady north-facing (ubac) slopes, all that contrives to find roothold in crevices or where some soil is left, is a degenerate, stunted secondary growth (maquis) of drought-resisting fleshy-leaved or thorny shrubs in scattered formation or dense thickets, with some coarse herbage plants. Nor are the lowlands by any means uniformly productive. They are interrupted by ridges of calcareous rocks such as the Alpilles east of Arles, by residual highlands of crystalline rocks such as the Maures and Esterel east of Toulon and by the Corbières mentioned above. In the riverine tracts the pebble-covered wilderness of Crau at the confluence of the Durance with the Rhône, and the marshy Camargue of the Rhône delta, have both required extensive reclamation works to render even selected parts of them productive.

The climate with a high proportion of sunshine, dry summer heat and mild winter temperatures, is physiologically pleasant and even stimulating to human beings, especially those of Mediterranean origin, accustomed to this type. But the rainfall regime and the visitations of the cold northerly mistral[1] make severe demands by way of adaptation upon the natural vegetation and the forms of cultivation practised by the inhabitants. The characteristic trees and shrubs, e.g. evergreen and cork oaks, olives, cypress pines, brooms and juniper, all have glaucous or needle-shaped leaves, which they retain during the winter, in contrast with the soft-foliage deciduous natural vegetation of northern France. Those and other protective devices are essential for plants to survive in a climate in which a hectic spring growing season is followed by a flaming summer when absolute droughts lasting five or six weeks or even longer enforce rest for plants except for seeding and fruiting.

The staple cultivated plants are grape-vines, olives and wheat, all of

[1] In the rear of depressions passing over the Mediterranean, cold air is drawn from the north, which blows with special violence down the funnel of the Rhône Valley and is apt to have a withering effect upon tender crops, and the new foliage and flower buds of other vegetation in early spring.

which, especially olives, are tolerant of hot dry weather. Vegetables, small fruits and similar leafy plants generally require irrigation, and wheat as well in the drier parts. Much attention has been given to the construction of irrigation works, in particular along the lower valleys of the Rhône, Durance and Aude, and of the Tet and other rivers in the Plain of Roussillon. Throughout Languedoc a very large proportion of the cultivated land is given to vineyards. Quantitatively this is the greatest wine-producing region not only of France, but probably also of the whole world; but, as experience has shown, that form of monoculture has been pushed to dangerous limits for the financial security of the producers and the preservation of balance in the soil.

The indigenous olive tree (the main source of fats in the diet of the ordinary people in this region unsuited to dairy cattle) is ubiquitous. It is grown in groves on hillsides difficult to cultivate, which it shares with the sweet chestnut, another native tree, providing a staple article of diet for the peasants; it is also grown in avenues on roadsides and boundary lines, as well as scattered singly over the fields. In contrast with these marginal forms of land use is the intensive cultivation of *primeurs* for the Paris and northern markets, which has expanded greatly in recent times with the increase in the areas of irrigated land and the speeding-up of rail transport. For this specialised industry the region has the great advantage of being early in the field, but those tender crops require protection, provided by planting wind-breaks of cypress and other close-growing plants, from the fierce Mistral of the Rhône Valley. A relatively new crop of growing importance on the irrigated lands of the delta area is rice, the production of which increased from an average of 46,000 tons in 1948–52 to 100,000 tons in 1956.

Apart from the commerce and industry of the Marseilles area and the Riviera tourist traffic, the mainstays of the region are agriculture, viticulture and horticulture. The summer drought, which parches the herbage, especially on the numerous limestone outcrops, restricts the keeping of live-stock. Some goats browse on the hillsides, some herds of cattle roam the marshes of the Camargue, and sheep-farming on a limited scale is made possible by the regular practice of transhumance to the highlands of the Cévennes (p. 183). The mineral resources do not give rise to any extensive local industries. Bauxite (named after Les Baux near Arles where it was first worked) is quarried in the Argens valley north of Toulon (Fig. 50) and transported elsewhere for extraction of the aluminium; there is a small output of lignite from a district north-east of Marseilles (Fig. 51) and sea salt is obtained by evaporation from the lagoons along the coast of Languedoc.

Settlement of the region by civilised Mediterranean peoples dates back some 3,000 years. Phoenicians and Greeks established themselves in succession at Marseilles in the first millenium B.C. Then came the Romans who occupied the whole area east of the Rhône as their base for the control of Gaul, naming it their transalpine province, whence the name Provence. Under their rule urban life developed at Arles, Avignon, Nîmes and other places round the Rhône delta, as well as at Marseilles, then as now the major port of entry. These inland towns are no longer such active centres of life as in Roman times, but they contain striking architectural remains of the centuries of their Roman past. In what is now Languedoc the ancient port of Aiguesmortes has been choked to partial extinction by the growth of the Rhône delta several miles beyond its site; but the arc of old towns — Nîmes, Montpellier, Béziers and Narbonne — inside the lagoon fringe, survive as centres of the populous zone of intensive viticulture behind them.

From the time of the Greek colony Marseilles has been a focus of commerce and travel between the Mediterranean and the regions to the north via the Rhône corridor. The old harbour was the small inlet just north of a west-projecting promontory. In order to accommodate the expanding shipping trade with North Africa, the East through Suez, and the Americas and West Africa through the Straits of Gibraltar, extensive dock basins have been constructed behind a four-mile breakwater parallel with the shore, built for protection against the storms of the Gulf of Lyons. Round the Étang de Berre a canal has been constructed which links the new harbour with the Rhône above the delta (Fig. 51). Handling large quantities of imported petroleum and tropical produce, Marseilles has added to its commercial activities oil-refining (on the Étang de Berre), besides the extraction of vegetable oils from groundnuts, copra etc., and large-scale soap manufactures. Its population numbering upward of 800,000 in 1962 places it first in size by a wide margin among French provincial cities.

East of Marseilles, Toulon has a better natural rock-basin harbour, but poorer access to the Rhône Valley. Its well protected situation convenient for defence, has been the main reason for its choice as a great naval station and arsenal. Beyond Toulon, where the N.-E. trending discordant coast offers various sheltered inlets suitable as harbours, remoteness from the main centres of economic activity has debarred the rise of any important commercial port. Along this south-facing Riviera coast broken into a succession of picturesque bays and coves by jagged headlands, a great 'tourist' industry has been built up. It is most active in winter and early spring when sunshine and warmth are at a premium for West Europeans, and becomes quieter in summer. Hence has arisen the regular practice of hôteliers to migrate with their staffs to and fro between the Riviera and the Channel seaside resorts, according to the seasons.

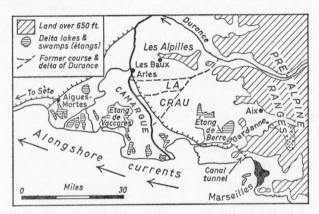

Fig. 51. The Rhône delta and the situation of Marseilles. The dotted area N.E. of Marseilles is the Provence lignite field.

Much the largest centre of this artificial life built round luxury hotels and casinos is Nice, with Monte Carlo not far away. Expansion of the built-up area has reached its limits there, and the hotel industry has had to find sites to the west in places such as Antibes and Cannes for its continued development. Except by way of providing a local market for fresh produce, the Riviera is a kind of excrescence upon the Mediterranean region. Much of its population is of the floating kind, composed of persons who come and go, having their domiciles elsewhere in France or abroad.

2. The French Alps and Jura and the Rhône-Saône Valley

The Rhône-Saône tectonic trough, constituting the main artery of drainage and of communications in this composite area, is structurally related to the folded mountains as a down-faulted zone formed in association with their uplift. In the asymmetric cross-section profile of the Rhône Valley, the fault scarps of its western wall rise at a steeper angle than the mountain slopes generally do on the eastern side. The large loads of waste material deposited by the mountain rivers, and in the past by ice, have pushed the Rhône, and the Saône likewise to some extent, up against the Massif, and have also contributed, by infilling and obliteration of overthrusts, to a grading of the slopes on the eastern side of the trough valley. A more important result of erosion by the Alpine-Jura rivers is the ready access provided by their incised, ice-deepened valleys far back into the mountains, the human settlement of which is thus closely linked with the arterial valley. In spite of marked contrasts in relief forms, physical geography has given a large measure of unity to the life of the whole area.

The foreland zone of the French Alps in the Dauphiné and Savoy is composed of massive Cretaceous beds and Jurassic limestones (which continue northward without break into the Jura). These are intersected by the valleys of the main consequent rivers, the Isère, Drôme and Durance, which divide them into a series of mountain blocks, e.g. Vercors and Grande Chartreuse. Behind these blocks, in the line of junction between the limestones and the crystalline rocks of the high massifs from Mt. Blanc to Pelvoux, subsequent valleys have been excavated, thus forming a nearly continuous longitudinal trench followed by the Route des Alpes from Albertville on the upper Isère to near Marseilles.

The Jura, lower in elevation, more homogeneous in rock composition and situated some distance from the former Alpine ice-cap, have suffered less dissection by ice than the Alps. In the south, where the highland has the characteristic structure of a series of parallel anticlines and synclines, the ridges are broken here and there by transverse river gorges called *cluses*, while the valleys are followed by the main longitudinal rivers such as the Ain. In the north on the French side they form a plateau, the drainage of which is mainly subterranean, though there too, the Doubs combines in its tortuous upper course the Jura surface-drainage features of synclinal valley stretches constricted here and there, and transverse breaks through *cluses*.

The Saône Valley, upwards of 50 miles in average width, has a generally fertile overlay of glacial drift and alluvium. An exception occurs in the Dombes district in the south between the Saône and the Ain, which being covered with coarse glacial deposits strewn with lake-filled clay hollows, large and small, is naturally unproductive. It

is better suited as an abode of fish and wild fowl than for agriculture
or horticulture, though parts near Lyons have been reclaimed for
market gardening to supply the city. The Rhône Valley between
Lyons and Montélimar, the northern limit of the Mediterranean
region (p. 186), varies in width from about 10 miles at Valence to
almost nil in the defiles formed by several projecting Alpine spurs in
the stretch below Lyons. It is far from being a typical alluvial valley
and is of limited agricultural value, however great its importance as a
highway corridor. Nor is the river itself of much use for transport in
its unimproved state owing to turbulent swiftness in places; though
its defects in this respect are being remedied by the construction of
side canals provided with locks, in conjunction with the development
of hydro-electric power, as at Donzère-Mondragon above Montélimar,
already completed, and at other places planned.

In the Alpine area, permanent settlements are naturally restricted
to lower elevations, mainly in the river valleys and on terraces and
benches similar in origin and form to the *alpen* or *mayen* of Switzerland. The chief concentrations of population are in the valleys of the
upper Rhône above Lyons, and of the Isère and its left-bank tributary
the Drac. The inner crystalline zone, with its lofty ice-clad peaks and
no passes below 6,000 feet, is almost uninhabited during the winter
months, though its magnificent scenery attracts tourists and those
who provide for their needs in the summer season. The various blocks
of the calcareous foreland are likewise mostly too high and cold to
attract more than a scanty scattered population. Even the valleys,
especially those deeply incised in the mountain recesses, e.g. of the
upper Isère and its tributaries, are uncongenial in climate, wet and
sunless, misty and cold most of the year.

The traditional mainstays of the inhabitants of these Alpine valleys
are dairy farming, supplemented by some domestic handicraft industries, and the seasonal tourist trade in popular scenic centres. New life
has come to a number of valleys with the recent rapid increase in the
development of hydro-electric power, particularly on the Rhône
below Lake Geneva, the Isère above Grenoble, and the upper
Durance (Fig. 44). Age-long sleepy villages have become busy industrial towns, still mostly small and scattered; while the larger towns
such as Grenoble and Chambéry, commanding exits from the
Longitudinal Trench, and Annecy on Lake Annecy in upper Savoy,
which have long been centres of trade and transport, have added
manufactures to their other activities. The older branches of industry,

namely paper and glove manufactures in the Isère Valley round
Grenoble, remain, but much more prominent now are the widespread
new developments based on cheap electrical power, in plants producing steel and aluminium alloys, chemicals, electrical equipment, and
textiles (in the valleys near Lyons). The regional centre of all these old
and new activities except the last is Grenoble which, with a population
approaching 120,000, is second to Lyons among the towns of this
whole south-eastern mountain and trough valley region.

Apart from the northern karst plateau, the Jura ridge and valley
country is less inhospitable than the greater part of the French Alps.
Like the Alps, the Jura have been covered with ice-sheets which have
left patches of clay moraine on the forested limestone ridges and in the
combes at various levels on their flanks; and it is on these water-
retentive patches that most of the highland settlements are situated,
the inhabitants combining summer farming with forestry in the
winters, when snow may lie for months. The valleys are much richer
wherever the rivers have cut down through the limestone to the Lias
marls. Green meadows with dairy cattle, cultivated fields, orchards,
and even vineyards (in the south), and villages at intervals, extend in
succession along their floors. Such towns as exist are mostly transport
and market centres at the entrances to the *cluses*, through which the
transverse railways and roads thread their ways.

Along the north-western edge of the Jura, where the Lias marls
outcrop in a band from beneath the limestone escarpment, and springs
are therefore plentiful, a belt of close settlement extends for nearly 100
miles south of Bésançon. This belt is really tributary to the Saône
Valley, which it overlooks and adjoins. Bésançon has grown to a
medium-sized town of about 75,000 inhabitants, not only as a focus of
important routes between the Saône Valley and the upper Rhine by
the Belfort Gap, but also as *the* centre of the long-established watch-
making industry of the French Jura. It has become a university
town and a kind of regional capital of the northern Jura and Saône
Valley.

The Alps and the Jura lie athwart the main railway routes connecting northern France and the British Isles with Switzerland and Italy;
and no serviceable break exists between the two ranges, the zig-zag
passage of the Rhône being beset with deep gorges. Taking advantage
of the *cluses* in the Jura, several lines cross that mountain zone with
the help of tunnels through the ridges, in particular the direct route
Dijon-Lausanne via Vallorbe, connecting Paris with Milan. The only

through route from France to Italy across the French Alps is that from Chambéry to Turin by the Arc valley and the Mt. Cenis tunnel; though several other lines penetrate by the Isère and Durance Valleys into the heart of the mountains, and a railway has been built along the Longitudinal Trench all the way from Chambéry to Aix-en-Provence. The total population of the 10 Departments from Haute Saône to Drôme is just over 3 millions, of whom one-sixth live in Lyons, the third largest city of France. Situated midway down the Rhône-Saône Valley and at the confluence of the two rivers, it commands the traffic on the great highway along the valley, and is a focus of intercourse and trade for all the French territory to the east of the highway. The advantages of its situation were recognised by the Romans, who selected it as the capital of Gaul. Its career as an industrial town has been associated with silk manufacture, greatly advanced by the introduction in the late eighteenth century of the Jacquard loom, named after the inventor, a native of the city. The industry arose on locally produced raw silk, but in modern times supplies have been mostly imported from Italy and the Far East. Nowadays the real-silk factories have been dispersed in the neighbouring small towns of the Lyonnais (p. 185) and the Alpine foreland. Lyons itself has turned more to artificial silk, though it continues as the business centre of the whole industry. In this and in its increasing development of miscellaneous engineering, chemical and metallurgical industries, it has followed in the steps of Manchester in England.

3. Lorraine, Vosges, Alsace

The easternmost section of France lying beyond the outer margin of the Seine drainage basin, comprises three distinct types of structure and relief: the ridge and valley country of Lorraine, the Vosges highlands, and the western half of the Rhine Rift Valley in Alsace. The Vosges, uplifted in association with the formation of the rift valley, are the master element in the physical structure of the area as a whole. They have imparted the general N.-S. alignment to the Jurassic escarpments in Lorraine, and indirectly also to that of the two main rivers, the Meuse and the Moselle, which have developed from former subsequents upon the softer strata interbedded with the Jurassic limestones (Figs. 46, 47). Though the outward-facing escarpments characteristic of the Paris Basin continue eastwards from it into Lorraine beyond the Moselle, the N.-S. Rhenish influence is dominant in this eastern area, and this feature, together with the industrial developments based on the iron ores of the Jurassic series and the salt-beds of the Trias farther east, mark it off as a separate region. It is distinguished also by reason of its frontier situation, open on the east to the Rhine Valley and Germany by the Moselle Valley and the Saverne and Belfort Gaps, which has caused it to figure much in the defensive strategy of France in her attempts to achieve security.

The frontier character of these eastern marches is borne out by the fact that the crest of the Vosges is the general linguistic boundary between the French-speaking people of Lorraine and the German-speaking of Alsace; though some of the latter have migrated across the boundary, planting industries in the midst of the French agricultural population. The Alsatians, in spite of their German origins, have had no desire to be incorporated in Germany, as they were forcibly from 1871 to 1918; on the contrary, they remain ardently French, many of them being familiar with the French language as well as with German.

The varied geological structure of this frontier region has given rise to a succession of different land forms from the Meuse to the Rhine. East of the Argonne sandstone ridge a series of escarpments (côtes) and vales has been developed from the upturned edges of the Jurassic beds. These are followed by a broad belt of less disturbed Triassic marls and sandstones, the latter of which extend over the northern Vosges to the edge of the Rift Valley, but have been largely denuded from the upper parts of the high southern Vosges. Thus the crystalline core is exposed over a belt some 25 miles wide by 35 miles in length, characterised by rounded granitic summits (*ballons*), which rise to over 4,500 feet in the Ballon de Guebwiller. Sharply contrasted with these highlands in genesis and land forms are the lowlands of Alsace. Here the down-faulted older rocks were covered while slowly sinking, with thick Tertiary beds deposited in the seas which long extended across this part of Western Europe; and in the late glacial period these strata were overlaid with pebble-beds and alluvium on the lower levels, and a band of loess higher up.

The above-mentioned and other special structural features have contributed to a marked differentiation in the physical and the human geography of the various parts, similar to the distinctive *pays* of the Paris Basin. Between the Côtes de Meuse and the Côtes de Moselle lies the comparatively level Woëvre plain, covered with impermeable clays and given more to forests and meadows than to field crops. Beyond the Moselle where the Trias reach the surface, the somewhat infertile Saulnois plain is cultivated only in patches, being more important for the salt-deposits worked from prehistoric times. On the eastern boundary of this plain are the sandstone Vosges, distinguished from the southern High Vosges, not only by their lower elevation, but also by their tabular blocks separated by deep ravines, and their pine forests, in contrast with the rounded forms, the glaciated valleys, the

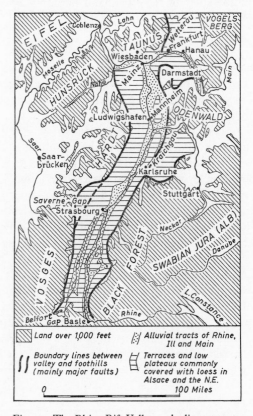

Fig. 52. The Rhine Rift Valley and adjacent parts.

scattered woods and highland meadows of the latter. Variety of landscape extends also to the Alsatian trough, where complex step-faulting has resulted in the formation of longitudinal terraces of successively lower elevation away from the Vosges down to the alluvial tract called the Ried, bordering the Rhine, the lowest terrace being separated from the middle by another alluvial belt along the River Ill parallel with the Rhine. The valley also slopes from south to north, from the Sandgau platform on the Swiss border to the riverine plain below Strasbourg (Figs. 52, 64A). Throughout the ages the middle loess-covered, well-drained longitudinal terrace has always been sought for settlement; since Roman times at least it has been marked by a string of villages, and has been followed by the main highway. The Ried belt, on the other hand, swampy in parts and liable to flooding by the meandering Rhine, is thinly populated.

CLIMATIC CONDITIONS, AGRICULTURE

The climate in general is more continental than elsewhere in France. In Lorraine and on the Vosges the winters are severe, and snow lies long on the higher ground. Summer temperatures are correspondingly high, and the continuance of warm weather into the autumn season is favourable to the cultivation of wine grapes on sunny slopes, especially in Alsace, where over half a million acres are given to vineyards. The considerable differences in elevation — between escarpment and valley in Lorraine, between mountain heights and deeply-cut valleys in the Vosges, and even in Alsace between the upper and the lower fault steps, naturally give rise to contrasts in local climates. There is also a marked regional contrast between the exposed western and the sheltered eastern sides of the Vosges, for these mountains are high enough to form a climatic barrier. The Alsatian valley has less than half the rainfall, and is consequently much more sunny, and warmer because of that and of its lower elevation, than the upland country of Lorraine.

Agricultural productivity varies greatly in accordance with the physical conditions. Some parts, such as the loess terrace of Alsace and the Lias marls outcropping at the base of the Côtes in Lorraine, are unusually fertile and intensively cultivated with a great variety of crops. The limestone Côtes, the Trias of the Saulnois, and the valleys and western slopes of the Vosges are cultivated in pockets and patches. Other parts, including the upper levels of the northern and southern Vosges, and the gravel stretches in the Rift Valley, are of little use for farming, except for meadows here and there. In general, the pattern of cultivation and settlement is selective in keeping with the sharp contrasts in relief and geological formation. Ribbons and patches of farmland along the valleys and the lower slopes are interspersed with large stretches of forest on the uplands and the poorer soils, inhabited solely by woodcutters.

MINERALS AND MANUFACTURES

The forests of the limestone Côtes and of the northern and southern Vosges constitute, in fact, one of the main resources of the region. But more important resources of rising relative importance have been found in the mineral deposits. The yearly output of iron ore extracted from the Lias beds of the Côtes de Moselle between Nancy and the Luxembourg border is nearly 40 million tons; of salt from the

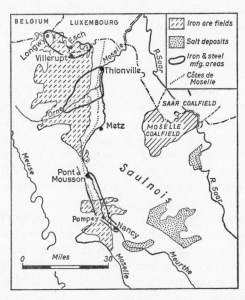

Fig. 53. Lorraine: iron ore and salt deposits; iron and steel works. Of the iron and steel manufacturing areas the Thionville–Orne valley is the most important, producing upwards of two-thirds of the Lorraine output of pig iron and over half the total French output. After Nistri and Prêcheur, *La Région du Nord et du Nord-Est*, 1959.

Saulnois north-east of Nancy, over 2 million tons; of coal from the Lorraine (Moselle) section of the Saar coalfield, some 15 million tons; and of potash salts from Upper Alsace near Mulhouse, about a million tons.

These mineral resources provide the material basis for considerable industrial activities in two areas, one of which extends along the left bank of the Moselle, following the iron ore belt northwards from Nancy, and the other is situated in and around Mulhouse. In the former, the major seat of French heavy industry (p. 154), the blast furnaces and steel works are located in three main groups: Longwy-Villerupt; Thionville-Orne Valley; Nancy-Pont à Mousson (Fig. 53). In the latter also, large chemical industries based on salt from the Saulnois have arisen in and around Nancy. In the Mulhouse district the discovery of potash deposits (p. 155) has given birth to chemical works, producing in particular fertilisers for the great agricultural regions of France. Apart from these developments based essentially on mineral resources, textile manufactures have long been important in Upper Alsace at Mulhouse, Colmar and neighbouring places, whence they spread after the Franco-Prussian war to Épinal on the Moselle and other valley towns of the western Vosges.

COMMUNICATIONS AND TOWNS

Two major routes between France and the Rhine Valley traverse this region; one through Nancy and the Saverne gap (cut by a river through the low northern Vosges) to Strasbourg, and the other through the Belfort gap (Gate of Burgundy) between the Vosges and the Jura to Mulhouse, meeting in these towns the Alsatian highway running parallel with the Rhine. Strasbourg and Mulhouse are accordingly important centres of transport and trade. But other factors have contributed to their growth to towns of over 200,000 and 100,000 inhabitants respectively. Strasbourg is a leading Rhine port,[1] at the head of effective navigation on the river, where goods destined for places farther upstream are transferred to barges operating on the lateral canal, and vice versa. Mulhouse is the capital of Upper Alsace, as well as being an important centre of textile, chemical and engineering industries.

Belfort is a fine example of a gap town, formerly, before the return of Alsace to France, a leading fortress. It is naturally an important route centre for railways connecting France with the upper Rhine and Danube Valleys and with Switzerland. Its situation has contributed to the development of manufactures of textiles and (more recently) of electrical machinery. Colmar, situated near midway between Mulhouse and Strasbourg, is the third leading regional centre in Alsace, besides being an important textile town.

Of the industrial towns along the iron ore belt in Lorraine, Nancy is much the largest, having the advantage of situation at the point where

[1] Strasbourg is on the River Ill, but is connected with the Rhine by a short canal, by which barge traffic moves into and from the Alsatian lateral canal, constructed to circumvent rapids on the main river.

the main railway route from Paris to the middle Rhine and lands beyond, and also the Rhine-Marne Canal, intersect the route following the Moselle. Formerly the capital of the duchy of Lorraine, it is now the chief administrative and commercial centre of the region, and has a variety of manufactures besides those of steel and steel products. Metz, situated lower down the Moselle, and nearer the geographical centre of the iron ore belt, has had little share in the recent industrial developments, but it retains some importance as a military post on the route by the Moselle from Germany. Two other historic frontier towns in Lorraine are Verdun and Toul, the former situated on the Meuse, and the latter on the Moselle at the gap through which the upper Moselle once flowed to join the Meuse. Both suffered great damage in the 1914–18 war, and neither has become an important centre of industry.

4. FRENCH FLANDERS: THE INDUSTRIAL NORTH-EAST

A line running south-east from Boulogne to St. Quentin follows the axis of the low Boulonnais[1]-Artois anticline, from which the headstreams of the Scheldt system and the Sambre flow north-eastwards away from the Paris Basin. This line, continued east to the Meuse at Charleville-Mézières, is the approximate interior boundary of the French north-east region, the human geography of which is marked by a wide range of highly-developed manufactures superimposed on the overall intensive agriculture. Its northern boundary is the Belgian border, an irregular, purely artificial line of historical origin, which in turn cuts across the low coastal plain, inner Flanders and the south-western Ardennes, as well as the upper courses of the north-east flowing rivers.

The Artois saddle, sinking gradually south-east from the Straits of Dover, is the French continuation of the Weald anticline. The chalk strata that compose it soon dip north-east under the Tertiary clays and sands of the Flanders Basin, as the North Downs similarly do into the counterpart London Basin. Several times invaded by the sea, the inner Flanders Plain has a thin topmost sandy stratum underlaid by clays, and though its soils are none too fertile, water is as a rule easily obtainable from the shallow wells.[2] The coastal plain, 15 to 20 miles

---

[1] The name given to the westernmost section of the anticline behind Boulogne, from the crest of which the Cretaceous beds have been denuded exposing Jurassic rocks.

[2] From artesian wells; the English term has come from the name Artois.

in width, is quite different. It is covered with highly fertile clays deposited during submergence in late glacial times (the so-called Flandrian transgression), is fringed with sand dunes, and being very flat and little above sea-level, has required an elaborate system of artificial drainage and dykes for its effective use. This coastal plain of French Flanders, extending from Calais to the Belgian border, is the south-west part of a belt which runs the whole length of the Belgian

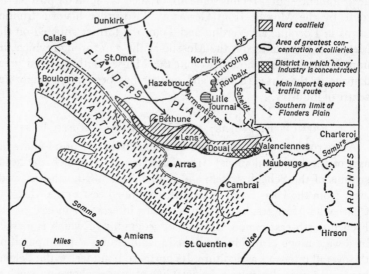

Fig. 54. French Flanders and the industrial belt of Le Nord. Upwards of 90 per cent of the textile manufactures of the Nord are concentrated in the Lille bay, and 60 per cent of the iron and steel works in the Valenciennes basin, the rest mainly in a coastal group at places near Dunkirk, Boulogne and St. Omer.

coast (see p. 285), and continues thence into the polderlands of Holland.

The Flanders Plain ends eastward near the Sambre Valley, which marks approximately the transition from the comparatively recent deposits to the primary rocks of the Ardennes, flanked on the south by a wedge of the Jurassic series (Fig. 45). This hilly, partly wooded country, intersected by incised river valleys, contrasts with the open, rather featureless plain to the west. Associated with the primary rocks of the Ardennes are the coal-measures of the Carboniferous cordon on their northern edge in Belgium. These sink gradually under the Cretaceous and newer rocks as they swing westward in France; from them some

29 million tons of coal are raised per annum (equivalent to approximately 50 per cent of the total French output), which provide the fuel and power basis of the various manufactures of the industrial belt from the Meuse to the upper Lys.

The coal seams of this northern field are difficult and costly to work, being thin and badly faulted. Moreover, the coals are mainly bituminous and little of them is usable for metallurgical coke. Extraction began near Valenciennes, but has gradually migrated west following the seams to Lens and Douai, and on towards Béthune (Fig. 54).

AGRICULTURE

The dense and diligent population of Flanders[1] and the whole North-East has made the utmost use of the commonly mediocre soils by unremitting labour. On the generally small holdings intensive mixed farming is the rule. Incidentally, the so-called agricultural revolution in Western Europe originated from technical improvements in rotation farming made in Flanders (cf. p. 289). The basis is cattle-farming and the growing of fodder crops for their upkeep. These animals together with pigs associated with dairying, have supplied the manures (now supplemented by artificial fertilisers) for the cultivation of a variety of cash crops, in particular flax and hemp, wheat and sugar beet. Sheep, less productive in terms of fodder consumption than either cattle or pigs, are uncommon now except on the coastal sand-dune belt.

MANUFACTURES

Agriculture alone could not support a dense population in this area. Thus the people of Franco-Belgian Flanders, profiting by their situation at the cross-roads of trade by land and sea in Western Europe, turned early to manufactures; at first chiefly of linens and woollens from local raw materials, to which those of cotton, jute and artificial silk have since been added. On the French side of the border the district comprising Lille, Roubaix and Tourcoing, with an extension west to Armentières, is the main seat of the textile industries. Lille, with a variety of manufactures besides textiles, is the commercial capital of this group, while Roubaix and Tourcoing specialise in

[1] The two Departments of Pas de Calais and Nord contain 3·4 million inhabitants, i.e. over 700 per sq. mile; while the Belgian Provinces of West and East Flanders have an overall average density of 950 to 1,000 per sq. mile. In both the high density is the outcome of intensive agriculture as well as considerable industrial activities.

woollens, and Armentières in linens. Another less concentrated area of textile manufactures lies along the base of the eastern extension of the Artois anticline in a belt from Hirson to Cambrai. The Flemish textile industry in its various branches has a long tradition behind it, and has throughout been adaptable to changes in the market conditions both for raw materials and the finished articles.

The iron, steel and engineering industries of the North-East date in their modern substantial forms from the application of the Thomas-Gilchrist process to the treatment of phosphoric ores of Lorraine. Blast furnaces exist in the neighbourhood of Valenciennes, but the North-East region as a whole, because of the unsuitability of its coal for smelting, concentrates upon the finishing and engineering branches of the heavy industry, obtaining its major supplies of pig iron and crude steel from Lorraine. Heavy machinery and constructional steel of various kinds are manufactured in the Valenciennes district on the older eastern part of the coalfield, and also in the western section beyond Douai, while textile machinery and locomotives are produced around Lille.

Another modern form of industry in this area is the chemical group; works for the production of heavy chemicals and fertilisers, for the distillation of bituminous coal and the manufacture of plastics have been established at various places along the canal and railway routes between Douai and Dunkirk. In addition to the three leading forms of secondary industries — textile, engineering and chemical — the North-East has developed miscellaneous manufactures, in particular of glass and common pottery (in the Lille district), for which it is the chief area of France; and of industrial alcohol among those using raw materials of agricultural origin.

TRANSPORT AND TRADE

The highly developed productive economy of the region involves extensive movements of goods in both internal and foreign commerce. Means of transport for the heavy traffic have been fully provided by canals as well as by railways. The main axis of the transport system lies parallel with, and not far from the Belgian border. It links up the string of towns situated at short intervals all the way from the Meuse to Dunkirk which, with its commodious artificial harbour, serves as the commercial port of the whole region. Direct links also between the heavily industrialised central section and Paris have been supplied by railways through Amiens and St. Quentin, and three canals converging on the navigable lower Oise. A network of railways provides close connections with Belgian Flanders from which tens of thousands of work-people travel daily to French factories, especially in the embayments of Lille and Valenciennes. The textile and the steel and engineering groups of manufactures in the North-East, of which these two towns are the leading centres, have close historical and industrial connections with their counterparts in Belgium over the border — with the long-established textile manufactures of Belgian Flanders on the one hand, and with the steel and engineering industries of the Sambre-Meuse Valley on the other. In France both have spread from the border centres, textiles south as far as Amiens in the Somme Valley, and the heavy industries north-west beyond Douai and Lens towards the coast, crossing and combining with the textiles in the Lille-Béthune area.

5. SAARLAND

Wedged into German territory on the eastern border of Lorraine, the Saarland has for centuries been under the control of one external authority after another. In the general settlement of 1815 it was assigned to Prussia, and remained so until 1918, when it was placed in charge of a League of Nations Commission for 15 years. The episodes of its recent political history are the outcome of the contention between France and Germany for control of the territory. It was absorbed into the German Reich in 1935, and was included in the French Customs Union from 1947 until 1959, when finally, following upon a Franco-German agreement, it was completely integrated with West Germany as one of its *Länder*. Though much of the trade of Saarland is with France, its people, unlike the Alsatians, have preferred to align themselves politically with Germany.

Little less than 1,000 sq. miles in area, Saarland has gained importance out of proportion to its size, owing to its valuable coalfield adjoining French Lorraine, which has abundant supplies of iron ore, but no coal other than the extension of the Saar coalfield into it (Fig. 53). Saarland produces over 16 million tons of coal per annum, of which nearly half is sent to France or to other parts of Germany, much of the rest being consumed in the local iron, steel-engineering and chemical works. The economy of this small territory which is hilly and forested in parts, and has limited agricultural resources, and yet supports about 1,000 inhabitants per sq. mile, is based upon a complex system of exchange trade, mainly with France and with other parts of Germany. It depends on Lorraine for supplies of iron (which it lacks) and of foodstuffs, of which it cannot produce enough; and on the Ruhr for coke to mix with the local coal in the smelting processes; in exchange it exports coal, steel and timber. The heavy metallurgical industry with an annual output of 3 million tons of steel, together with coal-mining, employs a third of the active population. Saarland clearly stands to gain much through the agency of the European Coal and Steel Community, by the free inter-Community movement of the materials it uses and sells.

Most of the Saarlanders live either in the valley of the Saar, or on the coalfield which continues north-east from Lorraine. The chief town, Saarbrücken, is situated near the Lorraine border at the angle of intersection of the coalfield by the river.

Chapter 15

SWITZERLAND AND AUSTRIA

THE massive Alpine ranges dominate the physical geography of both Switzerland and Austria, occupying 60 per cent of the area of the former, and of the latter 70 per cent. They have been built up by intense pressures from the south, which in Switzerland have forced great bodies of rocks northwards by successive overthrusts from an

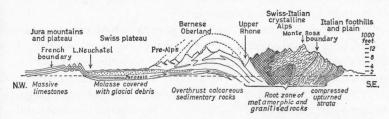

Fig. 55. Geological section N.W.–S.E. through Switzerland (Fig. 57) showing structural elements. The Pre-Alps, apparently driven over en masse from far south, do not appear east of Lake Thun. After R. Staub, *Der Bau der Alpen*, Blatt 2 (simplified).

inner root zone along the Swiss-Italian border. There both the granitic rocks of the crystalline core and the highly metamorphic primary rocks flanking the core on the south were squeezed up almost vertically; while those of the broad northern arc consisting mainly of limestones and sandstones were pushed out more or less horizontally in great recumbent folds (Fig. 55). These now form the outer mountain groups, e.g. the Bernese Oberland, the average height of which, in spite of severe erosion of their relatively soft rocks, is not much short of that of the crystalline zone.

This two-fold structure of the Swiss Alpine system has had a marked influence upon the development of the drainage pattern. The line of junction between the crystalline and the northern sedimentary zones is followed by the long upper courses of the Rhône, the Rhine and the Inn; and as the forces of erosion have attacked the relatively less resistant rocks of the northern sedimentary arcs more effectively than those of the southern crystalline zone, these rivers have escaped north, so that the main watershed, which in general is followed by the Swiss-Italian boundary, lies well to the south of the whole mountain system.

East of the Swiss border, the crystalline zone is flanked on the south (as well as on the north) by a broad sedimentary girdle which links up with the Dinaric ranges east of the Adriatic. Here also these lines of junction between the sedimentary and the crystalline zones are followed on either side of the latter by longitudinal rivers, in particular the Dráva for over 120 miles on the south, and also by the Inn and the Enns in their mountain courses on the north. Here too, the main watershed, that between the Danube system and the Adriatic rivers, lies for the most part well to the south, and being taken as the international boundary, gives Austria like Switzerland a large assignment of unproductive mountain territory.

The limited resources of the Alpine regions of both countries have indeed been turned to account by the inhabitants, more, however, by the Swiss than the Austrians. Most of the carefully-tended forests, covering 4,000 sq. miles in Switzerland and nearly 12,000 sq. miles in Austria, are on the slopes and valley sides of the mountain ranges; similarly, the great bulk of the output of hydro-electric power amounting by 1960–1 to over 18,000 million kwh per annum in Switzerland, and over 11,000 million kwh in Austria, is generated in the Alps, where the physical conditions in many places are ideal; and the scenic attractions of the high mountain regions, furrowed and rendered accessible by deep penetrating valleys, have enabled both the Swiss and the Austrians, notably the former, to establish valuable tourist industries. On the other hand, in common with most other mountain ranges of similar age in Europe, the Alps and Jura have scanty deposits of useful minerals; none of importance except some salt in the northern Jura has been discovered in Switzerland, nor are the iron ore of Styria, the salt of Salzburg and the scattered lignite deposits of the Austrian Alps sufficient basis for the development of any large-scale industries.

The permanent population of these Alpine regions is small compared with that of their borderlands. Neither the forests nor the hydro-electric power resources require large labour forces on the spot, and the tourist industries become progressively more seasonal, the higher the resorts, apart from a limited number favoured for winter sports. Farming pursuits are restricted to the valley floors and to the summer pastures of the *mayen* or *alpen* on the mountain terraces above them. Altogether the hard life which the harsh winter climate and the general niggardliness of nature enforces upon the inhabitants of these mountain regions, repels rather than attracts population. Above the towns situated here and there at the exits of the mountain valleys, and partaking in the life of the borderlands, settlements are seldom more than small villages strung out along the valley floors.

Nevertheless, it was the mountain redoubt of the forest cantons that was the birthplace of the Swiss nation. Round the independent nucleus established there late in the thirteenth century, the other cantons composing the Swiss Federation acceded at intervals between 1332 and 1815. The hardy mountaineer spirit of independence and self-reliance, of making the most of slender resources by careful organisation and persistent effort, has been infused into the way of life of the people throughout; it provides the unifying force that welds the 25 cantons, each legally a sovereign state, into a nation. The Swiss Alps, situated at an important cross-roads of communications in Western Europe[1] but poor in natural resources, have had a profound influence upon the external relations and commerce of the people who, though inhabiting a poor inland country, have developed a world-wide outlook. Their scanty endowment of natural resources has forced them to seek supplies of food and raw materials outside their territory, and to sell the products of their skill and sound workmanship, and their financial services, in the world market. Because their economy is vulnerable to disturbances in the free flow of trade, their interests and their efforts in the international sphere lie in promoting peace; and because the bulk of their import and export trade is with their near neighbours and with oversea countries reached therefrom, they are thrust into alignment with the West.

On the other hand, the Alpine environmental influence has been small in the life and outlook of the Austrians and of their development as a nation. With them the Danubian lands have been the master attraction and determining geographical force. Austria began as the Ostmark established to defend the Danube gateway against Turkish expansion farther west. In those early times the Alpine region formed

---

[1] Those connecting the Rhine Valley and northern Europe with the Mediterranean by the Alpine passes and the railways tunnelled under them, and those following the northern edge of the foothills between the Rhône and the Danube Valleys. Switzerland lies astride the Alps, physically by extending almost into the Italian plain in Canton Ticino, strategically by controlling two major north-south routes, those of the Simplon and St. Gotthard railways.

a kind of rampart against which the Ostmark could lean for refuge if need be. With the repulse of the Turks, the Ostmark was able to expand eastward, turning its back upon the uninviting mountains. Thus the Austrian empire developed from a nucleus in the lowlands (round the north-east fringe of the Alps centred on Vienna) into the middle Danube lands, which were more attractive as fields of political and commercial expansion than the upper Danube region, where other Germans were strongly entrenched. In contrast with the Swiss, whose national spirit is based on the hardy virtues of the mountaineer, the Austrians have been a 'Herrenvolk' basking in the splendours of imperial power, now departed, leaving in Vienna symbols of its bygone glories.

SWITZERLAND

Switzerland is a small country, a little less than 16,000 sq. miles in area, which contains a population numbering approximately $5\frac{1}{4}$ millions (1959). Of these about 73 per cent are of German speech, 21 per cent French, 5 per cent Italian (in Ticino) and 1 per cent Romansh (in the Alpine valleys of Grisons [Graubünden]). German-speaking people form the great majority of the inhabitants in the rectangle bounded west by a line between Bern and Fribourg, and south by the front range of the high Alps; the French-speaking are concentrated mainly in the south-western cantons round Lake Geneva and in the southern Jura. The Alps and the Jura occupy about two-thirds of the country, leaving little more than 5,000 sq. miles of plateau in the depression between them, which holds upwards of three-quarters of the population with the high average density of 700 to the square mile (Fig. 56).

The Swiss Jura, wider in the north than in the south, are composed of parallel limestone ridges with intervening synclinal valleys, like the southern French Jura (p. 194). As on the French side, there is a marked contrast in landscape features and human occupation between the partially forested, thinly populated ridges and the generally fertile, fully-settled valleys; and as in France, gorges (*cluses*) here and there through the ridges, supplemented by railway tunnels, provide routes for means of communication which link both one valley with another and also the Jura valleys as a whole with the plateau region. These Jura valleys are utilised for mixed farming based on dairy cattle, but much more important for the Swiss economy nowadays is the highly-specialised watch-making industry. This is carried on in numerous villages, and in various towns from which, as the centres of technology and the manufacture of parts, the whole industry is organised — among them La Chaux de Fonds, Le Locle and St. Imier in the valleys, and Geneva, Neuchâtel and Biel along the base of the Jura.[1]

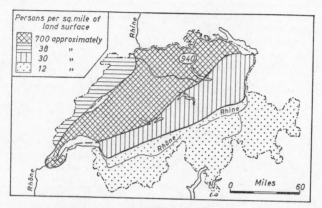

Fig. 56. The distribution of population in Switzerland. In the Plateau area (average density 700 per sq. mile) the five northern cantonal divisions, marked off on the map, have the remarkably high average density shown by the circled figure. Based on the officially estimated populations of the separate Cantons 1958.

The plateau region, extending from Lake Geneva to Lake Constance (Bodensee),[2] about 170 miles long by an average width upwards of 30 miles, though less varied and spectacular in scenery than the Alps or the Jura, is the essential element of Switzerland; it contributes even greater proportions to the aggregates of both agricultural and industrial production than it contains of the population.

The plateau rises from about 1,200 feet along the Rhine above Basle to 3,000 feet at the foot of the Alps. The general north-westerly slope

[1] Swiss watches are composed of anything between 123 and 200 parts. Though the manufacturing side has been largely standardised, the high quality of the finished product depends much upon the skilful accuracy of artisan craftsmen on the assembly side, many of whom work in small establishments in the towns and villages.

[2] As noted above, either German or French is spoken by the majority of the Swiss, hough many of course are familiar with both. The names of a number of places accordingly have alternative French or German forms. The general rule to be followed is to use the spelling of the language current in the area, except for the names of a few well-known places which have been quite anglicised, e.g. Geneva, or for which the French form has been traditional in English usage, e.g. Lucerne.

is followed by the rivers, in particular by the Aar and its tributaries, which drain almost all the region except the north-east and south-west corners round Lake Constance and Lake Geneva. The plateau occupies a trough between the Alps and the Jura, the floor of which was raised in the course of the uplift of those mountains, and was covered

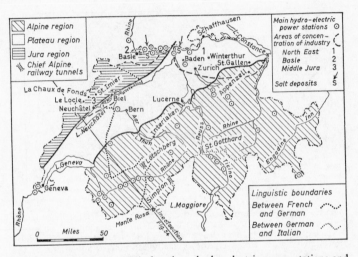

Fig. 57. Switzerland: physical regions, hydro-electric power stations and chief industrial areas. After A. F. A. Mutton and others, and *Carte Linguistique de la Suisse*.

with river-borne sediments (molasse) and later with glacial deposits (p. 23). Its topographical features bear the marks of comparatively recent glaciation. The surface is far from level, being broken by ridges and low hills in the stretches between ice-deepened hollows occupied by lakes, some quite large, e.g. Constance, Geneva, Neuchâtel, Lucerne and Zürich. The soils accordingly are moderate to poor in fertility, except where alluvium has been deposited by the sorting action of rivers since the Ice Age. The glacial ridges, consisting of poor gravel soils, are commonly wooded, and the agricultural output of the region as a whole is insufficient, except in dairy produce and wine, to supply the requirements of the dense population.

CLIMATE

The continental situation, the high general relief, the sharp contrasts in the elevation of adjacent parts with consequent differences in

vertical temperatures and in exposure to moisture-bearing air currents, and the position of the country towards the southern margin of
the Transitional climatic province, are all factors in the make-up of
the Swiss climates. Above about 4,000 feet on the northern side of the
Alps and on the Jura, and above 5,000 feet on the southern-facing
valley slopes, permanent habitation generally ceases owing to the
adverse climatic conditions. A marked feature of the distribution of
settlements in deep valleys aligned across the meridian, e.g. that of the
upper Rhône, is that they are more numerous and extend higher up
the slopes on the northern sunny, than on the southern shaded side;
they are distinguished by the Provençal French terms *adret* for the
former and *ubac* for the latter.

Another special climatic feature influencing the distribution of
settlement in the Alps is the Föhn[1] wind. This is experienced on an
average of 40 days in the year in the northern Swiss valleys, especially
those that widen out at lower levels, and compensates in some measure for their situation. These warm dry winds, drawn in over the
mountains as depressions pass on tracks north of the Alps, cause
marked rises in temperatures as long as they last, and thereby afford
some relief from the generally cold and sunless winter weather of
these valleys. Their abnormally high temperatures arise from the fact
that such air-currents, if originally moist, gain the heat liberated by
condensation on rising, the loss of heat through expansion in ascent
being offset by the gain *pro rata* in descent. The net gain may be as
much as 20° F.

The continental situation is reflected in the moderately wide range
of temperatures, which at each of three representative plateau stations
— Basle, Lucerne, Geneva — is 34° F., compared with 22° F. in
London. Their mean January temperatures are about or below freezing point, but in July they are several degrees warmer than London.
The mean annual precipitation at these same stations is 30 to 40 per
cent greater than the London average owing to air-lift against the
neighbouring high Alps, yet they get considerably longer hours of
sunshine per annum. On the whole the climate of the plateau and the
south-east slope of the Jura is fairly well suited to ordinary temperate
agriculture; but these parts are apt to be damp and misty in winter and
subject at intervals to a fierce north-easterly wind (the Bise), when bitterly cold air from the Eurasian High is drawn through the wind tunnel

[1] A German-Swiss term, of Romansh origin; from Latin Favonius, the west wind
favourable to the growth of plants.

between the Alps and the Jura by depressions travelling east over the Mediterranean.

LAND UTILISATION: AGRICULTURE AND FORESTRY

Switzerland has been scantily endowed with productive agricultural land. Of the total area, excluding water surfaces, only 11 per cent was under cultivation in the period 1953–6, of which little more than half was given to crops for direct human consumption, namely cereals, potatoes, vines and vegetables. The percentages are very little short of the maxima which a Council of the Federal Government has deemed economically possible. It is true that in addition 40 per cent of the land area is classed as meadows, but much of this is on poor sandy soils and on mountain ledges and slopes and is of very limited use. Less than 17 per cent of the entire working population is engaged in farming pursuits, compared with over 40 per cent in industry and handicrafts. Nearly all the sugar, and over half the cereals, besides large quantities of butter, poultry products and animal fodders consumed in the country are imported. Against these items, the only agricultural product exported in quantity is cheese,[1] but that represents no more than about 2 per cent of the value of all exports. During the 1939–45 war, although agricultural production was strained to the utmost, severe rationing of foodstuffs became necessary.

The chief crop is wheat, which occupies upwards of half the arable land, mostly that of better quality on the plateau, followed in importance by potatoes, which succeed on the sandy soils when treated with fertilisers. Smaller quantities of oats and barley, and very small amounts of sugar beet are also grown in the mixed rotation farming, in which the raising of cattle for dairy produce, and of pigs, together with the production of some fodder crops for these animals, are the main objects. Though the migratory form of cattle-farming between the floors of Alpine valleys and the summer pastures (*alpen*) on the ledges[2] above them, has attracted attention because of its picturesque adaptation to physical conditions, it is very limited in scope; the great majority of the Swiss cattle remain permanently on the Plateau farms where most of the Swiss cheese including Gruyère (named after a place near Lake Geneva) is made. In general also, the cattle both on the

---

[1] An example of the characteristic Swiss specialisation in quality products. The exports of cheese more than cover the cost of such imported butter as could be made locally from the same quantity of milk.

[2] Resembling river terraces, but cut out of the solid rocks partly or mainly by ice in the earlier of the several Alpine glaciations.

Plateau and in the Alpine valleys are kept in barns and are stall-fed, except for the period between the last hay harvest and the onset of winter, when they feed on the late growth of grass.

The manufacture of condensed milk, of which the Nestlé firm of Vevey near Lausanne was pioneer, has declined in relative importance owing mainly to the contraction of supplies of surplus milk. The population of Switzerland has more than doubled in the last 100 years, and is still increasing more rapidly than that of most Western European countries, without a corresponding increase in the number of dairy cattle being possible. The present production of milk is barely sufficient to cover domestic consumption of dairy products as a whole, for that which goes into the cheese exported is more than offset by what would be needed to make good the butter imported. Switzerland is not, and cannot be a great dairying country; it has only 32 cattle all told per 100 of the population, compared with 40 in France, 72 in Denmark and 280 in New Zealand. Some supplementary supplies of milk are, however, obtained from goats which number 150,000 in all. One or more of these animals, well adapted to rough conditions of terrain and pastures, make up the live-stock complement of many small mountain-valley farms.

The relatively high summer and autumn temperatures of the semi-continental climate, and the intense insolation on south-facing slopes, are favourable to the cultivation of grape-vines in south-west Switzerland. About 34,000 acres are planted as vineyards, chiefly in Ticino, in Valais (the Rhône Valley region), the north side of Lake Geneva and the south-eastern face of the Jura, which normally produce enough to cover the Swiss demand for ordinary wines.

Woods and forests composed largely of coniferous trees of indigenous and introduced species cover a quarter of the area of Switzerland in parts unsuited to agriculture on the plateau as well as on the mountainsides. They reach up to the summits of the Jura, and up to about 6,000 feet on the Alps where they occupy discontinuous belts between the valley farmlands and the limits of tree vegetation above. The maintenance of the forests is generally under the control and supervision of public authorities which regulate the cutting and re-planting operations; for in addition to supplying timber, the forests serve the important purpose of arresting soil erosion on steep slopes, especially of preventing destructive avalanches from sweeping down into the inhabited Alpine valleys. In spite of the relatively large proportion of the total area under forests, heavy imports of timber and wood cellulose are needed to meet Switzerland's ordinary domestic and industrial requirements.

HYDRO-ELECTRIC POWER AND MANUFACTURES

Switzerland has great water-power resources which are being rapidly developed and compensate in large measure for the complete absence of mineral fuels. The output of hydro-electric current nearly doubled between 1938 and 1954, and small as Switzerland is, it now stands fourth in hydro-electric power capacity among Western European countries (cf. Table p. 26). The majority of the larger stations are in three groups: in the Rhône Valley above Lake Geneva; along the Rhine between Lake Constance and Basle; and in the valleys in a broad belt along the northern front of the Alps (Fig. 57). In addition, medium-sized to small stations are widely distributed, e.g. in the Ticino Valley, and along the various rivers of the Aar system. The railways are now completely electrified, and industry is well supplied with motive power; nevertheless considerable quantities of coal have to be imported, mainly from the Ruhr, for the extensive metallurgical industries.

The development of manufactures of world-wide repute for the quality of their products, in a country that has no coal nor industrial raw materials besides some rock salt and a little iron ore,[1] is a tribute to the practical genius, steady persistence and organising ability of the Swiss people. Their success, it has been said, is the result of a double tradition, the artisan and the scientific. This tradition has been applied with equally remarkable results to each of the three main groups of modern industry, metallurgical and engineering, chemical, and textile which together supply 45 per cent of the total exports, in addition to the highly-specialised watch-making industry, which contributes a further 18 to 20 per cent of the exports. Concentration upon high quality and adaptability to changing external market conditions have been enforced upon the Swiss, who must import the great bulk of the materials they use, and sell their products in the world market in competition with others better endowed with resources. Yet these characteristics owe much to the instinctive craftsmanship and diligence of a happily blended people, who in their social organisation

---

[1] Most of the pig iron and crude steel used in the metallurgical industries is imported. Very little wool is produced in Switzerland, which has only 200,000 sheep all told, and all the raw cotton and silk and non-ferrous metals are obtained from external sources.

and industrial activities furnish an example to be followed by other countries of North-Western Europe, if they are to survive in a world changing to their disadvantage.

A salient feature of Swiss industry is its wide dispersal throughout the inhabitable parts, conditioned by the diffusion of waterpower resources and the flexibility of hydro-electric power transmission, in combination with the quest for supplies of labour. Though manufactures of one kind or another have been established in many towns and villages, even in the recesses of the Alpine valleys, some broad regional groupings can be discerned: metallurgical industries and general engineering are located in the North-East, where the chief centres are Zürich, Winterthur and Baden, as well as in several smaller towns round Basle; the high-quality cotton and silk textiles in which Switzerland specialises, are also produced in the North-East, especially at Zürich, St. Gallen, Appenzell and Glarus, and also at Basle itself; chemicals, dyes and pharmaceutical products are manufactured at Basle and the surrounding places; and watches and parts are made in the group of towns in and at the foot of the Jura, referred to above.

The most striking advances have been made in the engineering group, which in the middle 1950's furnished nearly a quarter of all exports. The products cover everything from giant turbines to machine tools and the most delicate precision instruments. The notable expansion of the electro-technical branch under the leadership of great firms such as Brown-Boveri of Baden and Oerlikon is understandable in view of the extensive development of hydro-electricity within the country, but it is also evidence of the Swiss instinct for specialising in response to anticipated growth in world demand.

Towns and Communications

It is apparent from the above survey that Zürich and Basle, both in German-speaking Switzerland, hold dominant positions in the industrial activities of the country; and it is not surprising that these two towns with populations of over 430,000 and 207,000 respectively in 1960 should have outdistanced all others in size.[1] The shift in the balance of population and economic weight away from the French-speaking south-western sector round Lake Geneva and the neighbouring parts, to the north-eastern zone, is a disturbing feature, because its continuance is liable to upset the traditional cantonal

[1] Three of these had more than 100,000 inhabitants at the 1960 Census, namely Geneva (169,100), Bern (164,200), and Lausanne (126,000).

balance in this profoundly democratic community of peoples. The
rise of Zürich as the leading industrial, financial and even cultural
centre is largely the outcome of its rôle as the commercial capital of an
area which has specialised to meet the requirements of a world that
prefers capital goods to articles of refinement.

Bern, the Federal capital, is mainly an administrative and residential city, of importance also because it is the focal point of the Swiss
railway system in its connections with the great international railway
route from Paris through the Lötschberg and Simplon tunnels to

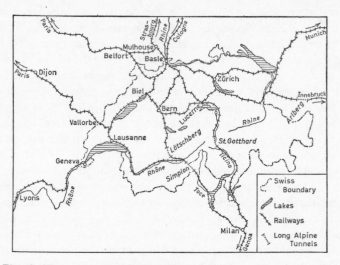

Fig. 58. The main railways and railway centres of Switzerland, and
international connections.

Milan and Rome. Geneva has a much less favourable situation in the
extreme south-western pocket of Switzerland, but it has achieved
fame and importance out of all proportion to its size and its association
with the Jura watch industry, in the higher fields of human endeavour.
It has a strong religious tradition as the scene of John Calvin's
reforms in the sixteenth century, and it has been chosen as the headquarters of several international organisations based on a will to
peaceful co-operation. On the sheltered south-facing slope overlooking Lake Geneva, which has a Riviera-like climate, Lausanne has
grown as an important railway centre, favoured also as a residential
town and cultural centre.

Among the smaller towns, besides those of the Jura and the North-East already mentioned, others owe their growth to the highly developed tourist industry, in which upwards of 100,000 persons are employed. Of these Lucerne on the northern bay of Lake Lucerne is the largest, being an important transport as well as tourist centre. It is situated at the main middle gateway to the Alps, where the St. Gotthard railway linking Basle with Milan begins to enter upon its mountain tract up the Reuss Valley and under the pass that leads by the Ticino Valley into Italy. Typical examples of tourist centres, some quite small, but noted for the scenery and facilities for winter sports of their surroundings, are Interlaken between Lakes Thun and Brienz, Kandersteg and Grindelwald in the Bernese Oberland, Zermatt near the Matterhorn, and Davos and St. Moritz in the upper Engadine. The Swiss have turned their wonderful scenery to account; the balance of the receipts from tourists, after payment has been made for the additional supplies of food materials imported for the requirements of the hotel industry, represents an important item of invisible exports.

The International Position of Switzerland

In spite of the large exports of high-quality industrial products, the visible trade balance of Switzerland shows a considerable deficit, made good by receipts from banking, insurance and other international services, as well as from the tourist industry. Fortunate in having escaped direct involvement in two great wars, Switzerland has been a centre of financial stability, its economy saved from the worst of the shocks that have shaken the surrounding countries. Yet the Swiss economy rests upon a somewhat fragile basis; the people have to find markets for the products of their skills and intensive efforts in a tariff-ridden world market, in order to pay for food and raw material essentials their land cannot provide. This demands a large measure of adaptability and the weeding out of inefficiency by allowing competition full play. Switzerland has stood out of the limited group of the six European Common Market countries but would probably be willing to consider any proposal that might lead towards the eventual establishment of a free market throughout the countries (including Italy) of Western and Central Europe.

This small country has been a source of inspiration and activities for the advancement of European civilisation. It has been a champion of religious toleration and political freedom, from which it has gained the material benefits of receiving refugees skilled in crafts and industry. It has made great contributions in the field of industrial technology, of banking and exchange, and of natural and social science. Above all, it has been an example to the world of the synthesis into a well-balanced society of elements diverse in racial affinities, outlooks and interests. Such a country is a fitting home for international organisations based upon the principle of co-operation among the peoples of the world.

AUSTRIA

Austria is the residual Succession State of the former Austro-Hungarian Empire, that of the territory inhabited by people of German affinities and language. Fully two-thirds of its area is occupied by the Alps which completely fill the elongated western province called the Tyrol, and extend eastward almost to the boundary with Hungary. North-east of the Tyrol Austria widens out to include various parts of lower elevation, namely the southern slopes of the Bohemian Plateau, a section of the Danube Valley above Vienna, the Vienna Basin and the eastern foothill and valley belt including the wide valleys of the Mur and the Dráva. All these peripheral areas are fertile in parts, and between them contain upwards of two-thirds of the entire population. Not only is the population unevenly distributed over the country as a whole, but also among these outer areas. Vienna and the surrounding districts of Lower Austria, which include a small section of the Hungarian Plain, hold 3 millions of the 7 million Austrians; three-sevenths of them are concentrated on less than one-seventh of the total area.

As delimited on an ethnic basis in 1919 after the first Great War, Austria has been described as having a head without a body. Vienna the former imperial capital, was deprived of control of natural resources sufficient to maintain its healthy existence. The shrunken Austrian territory was relatively poor in both agricultural and mineral resources, and there was little industrial development apart from some manufactures of luxury articles in Vienna. Since 1919 progress has been made towards remedying these distorted conditions, though the country is still economically weak. In order to help make ends meet, the proportion of cultivated land has been increased to about 22 per cent of the whole area (compared with 11 per cent in Switzerland), but even so the produce must be supplemented by imported supplies; considerable strides have been made with the development of hydro-electric power, used in an increasing range of light engineering and textile manufactures in addition to the luxury industries of Vienna; modern iron and steel works are in operation at Graz supplied with ore from Eisenerz; and efforts have been made to expand the tourist traffic.

Austria is also deficient in mineral fuels. It has no hard coal, and the outputs of lignite and petroleum are together quite inadequate to support the much-needed expansion of industry, without considerably increased development of hydro-electric power. Other natural resources besides those mentioned are the forests which cover nearly

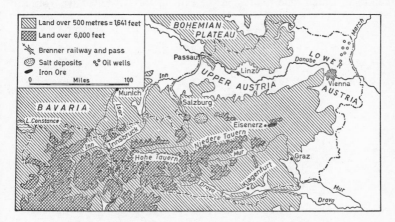

Fig. 59. Austria: relief features and mineral deposits.

40 per cent of the total area, high-grade graphite and small deposits of salt. Any increase in manufactures is likely to lead, as it has done in other countries utilising hydro-electric power, to a further concentration of population in the larger more prosperous centres, in spite of some decentralisation.

Vienna, situated in the gateway from Western into South-Eastern Europe, and at the crossroads where the transcontinental N.–S. route intersects that by the Danube Valley, has survived as a great city and cultural centre, though hampered in its trade connections by the restrictive policies of neighbouring Succession States. Innsbruck on the Inn in the Tyrol, is situated like Vienna at a vital point on a main continental N.–S. route, that between Munich and Verona, across the Alps by the Brenner Pass. This pass, long used for trade and traffic between the Mediterranean and North-Western Europe, especially when the Italian cities controlled the trade with the Orient, is the lowest of all over the Alps (4,494 feet); the Brenner railway has been constructed without a long summit tunnel as on the St. Gotthard, Simplon and Mt. Cenis lines.

Innsbruck in the Tyrol and Klagenfurt on the upper Dráva are within the Alpine region. Both are naturally in river valleys, but so also are all the other larger provincial towns — Salzburg on the Salzach, Linz on the Danube and Graz on the Mur, among others. In a country composed largely of mountains and uplands the river valleys are the chief lines of communication and internal trade, focal points in which tend to arise at the exits of the larger valleys from the highlands.

Chapter 16

GERMANY AND ITS EASTERN
BORDERLANDS: I

IN this intermediate section of the Continent, Central Europe merges eastwards into the Polish-Russian plains, and south-eastwards into the Danubian lands. The eastern political boundaries have for centuries past been as unstable as any in the world, with the to and fro swings of predominance of German or Slav in a zone of weakly defined geographical features and interlocking of these two groups of people. The German territory as it existed prior to 1944–5 is at all events to be included in Central Europe and geographically also the extension of the North German Plain into the Vistula Basin, and of the Hercynian highlands into Bohemia. The following account deals mainly with pre-war Germany, giving special attention to the present West and East German Republics, and making only selective references to the borderland areas in Central Poland and Bohemia-Moravia.

The Germany of the period 1870 to 1940 covered the transition from West to East in Central Europe, which was apparent in a zone a little east of Berlin. The West, economically more advanced with its greater variety of terrain and resources than the mainly agricultural East, became increasingly industrialised; and under the forceful leadership of Prussia, these naturally complementary elements were welded into an integrated economic unit. After the extraordinarily rapid transformation from a predominantly agricultural to an advanced industrial country, accomplished within thirty-five years after 1870, Janus-headed Germany was strong enough to exploit both the inner continental and the outer maritime avenues of expansion. Commercial penetration into the immature regions of the Austro-Hungarian Empire and of the Balkan lands led to dreams of political expansion symbolised in the projected Berlin to Baghdad railway; and the development of extensive oversea trade was later accompanied by vigorous efforts to build up a strong navy and a colonial empire. In both directions the outward movements were backed by shows of force, which aroused hostility and suspicions in the Great Powers affected, and eventually to the 1914–18 War. The disasters that befell Germany as the outcome of that war and the still greater disasters that overtook the German people in the 1939–45 War are both causally related to the geographical factor of two-way orientation. In neither conflict were the German forces, though unquestionably powerful, able to cope with the tasks forced upon them in waging warfare on two fronts at once.

Fig. 60. The physical regions of Germany, Bohemia and western Poland.
Land over 200 metres (656 ft.) shaded.

The advance of the western boundary of Poland to the Oder-Neisse line has deprived Germany not only of valuable agricultural lands in Pomerania, East Prussia and Silesia, but also of control of the Eastern Baltic through the two former, and of access by the Moravian Gate to the Danubian lands through the latter. The present territorial arrangements may not last in this zone of oft-changed boundaries; but as long as they do last, Germany is shorn of a considerable slice of eastward-orientated territory swallowed into the Slav bloc. The separation of East Germany from the rest of the former Reich has completed this process of amputation, excluding West Germany from the whole Elbe basin except the lowermost part and a sector of Berlin, and from the Baltic coast except in Schleswig-Holstein. The more or less closed boundary between the two Germanys detaches West Germany from Eastern Europe and forces her economy into association with the West and with overseas countries through the North Sea ports.[1]

PHYSICAL BUILD

The area comprising pre-war Germany together with western Poland and the Bohemian block is one of extraordinarily varied geological structure and land forms. In broad outline it is made up of five structural elements: (1) the northern glaciated plain and its southern embayments; (2) the outer Hercynian blocks including (a) the middle Rhine highlands and (b) the Harz and the Thüringer Wald, together with the intervening wedge of Triassic uplands and basins; (3) the inner Hercynian blocks, namely the Black Forest and the Odenwald bordering the Rhine Valley, and the Bohemian plateau with its peripheral highlands; (4) the triangular area of the South German Scarplands bounded east and west by these inner Hercynian blocks and by the Danube in the south; and (5) the Danube Valley, the Alpine Foreland and a short section of the northern zone of the Alps (Figs. 60, 61). Each of these, including the extensive northern plain, contains within itself considerable variety of surface forms, soil types and land utilisation, which has contributed to a highly complex pattern in the human geography of the German-Bohemian area both in its several regions and as a whole.

I. THE NORTH GERMAN PLAIN

The northern plain was subject during the Ice Age to repeated glaciations, the southern limit of the maximum advance of which was an irregular line following the northern slopes of the central highlands and the inner edges of the several bays (Fig. 61). The last advance of the ice-sheets, which halted on a curved front through western Denmark and a little south of Berlin, has naturally had the most marked effects upon the surface topography and the character of the soils, especially in a wide belt inland from the Baltic coast. This and earlier invasions of the Scandinavian ice-sheets resulted in the deposition, during their periods of rest in retreat, of a series of concentric terminal moraines, composed of sand, clay and gravel in extremely

[1] This is examined at some length below, pp. 265–6.

varied proportions, e.g. the lake-strewn Baltic Heights, left by the last (the Vistula) glaciation, and the long arc of older moraines of the Lüneburger, Altmark, Fläming and Niederlausitz Heaths (Fig. 61). In contrast with these commonly infertile ridges, a belt of fertile ground moraine 20 to 50 miles wide, was deposited along the Baltic coast by the last ice-sheet.

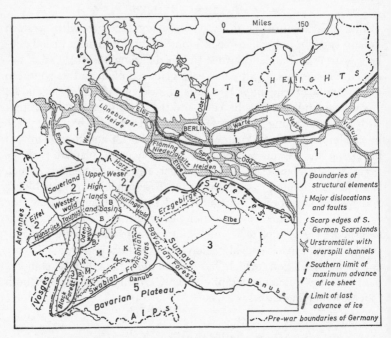

Fig. 61. Germany, Bohemia and western Poland: limits of glaciation, Urstromtäler, heaths and highlands. Urstromtäler after Woldstedt and Charlesworth. Major structural elements: (1) Northern glaciated plain; (2) Outer Hercynian blocks; (3) Inner Hercynian blocks; (4) S. German scarplands; (5) Danube valley, Alpine Foreland and Bavarian Alps. In the Triassic scarpland area B=Bunter sandstone, M=Muschelkalk, K=Keuper marls. (See Fig. 64B.)

The successive advances of the ice-sheets forced the ordinary drainage north-west along their fronts towards the present lower Elbe: and as the ice retreated, vast quantities of melt-water were added to the flow of the diverted rivers. Thus between the concentric morainic ridges broad valleys were formed, which are now followed in parts by the rivers (in the subsequent sections of their zig-zag courses), but which are deprived of flowing water in other parts, owing to headward erosion captures by youthful post-glacial Baltic rivers, e.g. the lower Oder and lower Vistula. The most conspicuous example of the late glacial continuous lower river valleys[1] is that marked by the lower Elbe, the Havel lakes and the Warte-Netze tributaries of the Oder. The low gradients of the Urstromtäler, since partly filled with sands, gravels and clays, causes them to be rather waterlogged, whether they

Fig. 62. The river waterways and canals of Germany. The figures indicate vessel tonnage capacity. Based on Ravenstein's *Organisationskarte . . . Deutschlands* No. 78, 1950.

are occupied by sections of the existing rivers or not, and though they are on the whole of low agricultural value, they are eminently suitable or the construction of canals linking the present main river waterways (Fig. 62).

The north-west section of the Plain in the lower basins of the Ems and Weser, which was subject to the earlier glaciations but escaped the

[1] Called Urstromtäler in Germany, i.e. ancient river valleys; where they have not been abandoned by the rivers, they are often disproportionately large for the existing 'misfit' rivers.

last, differs in character from the younger forms of glaciated country east of the Elbe. Its generally subdued relief causes the drainage to be sluggish and uncertain, and the damp and misty climate restricts the rate of evaporation. A common element of the landscape is what is known as Geest. This consists of stretches of outwash sands and gravels and morainic ridges of similar materials, which are covered in their natural state with moorland vegetation interspersed with smaller or larger patches of bog in the hollows. Reclamation of the Geest as well as of the once extensive marshy tracts on the lower ground else-where has long been in progress and has recently been speeded up, so much of this area, apart from the Lüneburger Heath, is utilised for farming, especially dairy-farming.

The northern and the southern margins of the North German Plain show special features as the sequels of glaciation. The rise of the sea-level consequent upon the melting of the ice caused parts of the Baltic coastlands to be submerged. East of Rügen Island large shallow bays (Haffs) occupy depressions in the glaciated surface, now more or less closed off by long sandy spits (Nehrungen) formed of material removed from the headlands and carried eastwards by shore currents; in the Schleswig-Holstein isthmus a number of coastal valleys of glacial origin (p. 305) have been invaded by the sea as V-shaped inlets (Förden); on the North Sea coast a belt of tidal flats (Watten) forms the seaward continuation of low but naturally fertile 'fens' (Marschen) extending up the river valleys and now largely reclaimed (Fig. 68). On the southern margin of the plain, outblowing winds from the retreat-ing ice-sheets have deposited a somewhat broken belt of fertile loess (Fig. 69) in the openings between and on the slopes of northward projections of the Hercynian highlands — in the Cologne, Münster, Lower Saxony-Magdeburg, Leipzig-Halle and Silesian bays. The middle sections, which are almost continuous, form what is known as the Börde zone.

II. The Outer Hercynian Zone

The outer Hercynian highlands comprise the large dissected block of old metamorphic rocks of the middle Rhine (Rheinisches Schiefer-gebirge), as well as the Harz and Thuringian Mountains, likewise composed basically of metamorphic Palaeozoic rocks, the former separated from the latter by a wedge of Triassic sandstone uplands drained by the Weser headstreams. All of them contain some intrusive masses of volcanic rocks, notably the Vogelsberg and the Rhön in the sandstone area, at various places in the Eifel, and even in the Rhine Gorge, e.g. the Sieben Gebirge near Bonn. A general NE.–SW. Hercynian trend of the rock formations runs through the Rhine Highlands and Saarland. It appears in the major boundary fault along the southern face of the Rhine Highlands and in the quartzite ridges of the plateaux, as well as in the zones of weaker rocks followed by the incised Moselle and Lahn Rivers, which with the Rhine itself divide

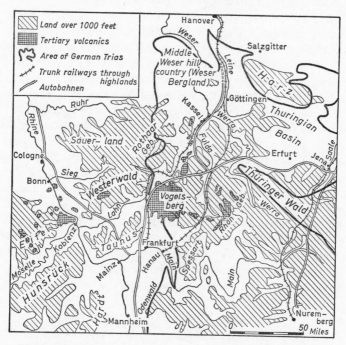

Fig. 63. The Mittelgebirge region of Germany and adjoining lands.

the German Rhine Highlands into four quadrants — Sauerland-Westerwald and Taunus east of the Rhine, and Eifel and Hunsrück west of it.

The gorge cut by the Rhine is both picturesque in scenery and interesting in its origin. Initiated by a river antecedent to the elevation of the Rhine Highlands, it became later the overflow channel of waters impounded in the lower part of the Rift Valley. The existing full-grown Rhine is the result of a complicated series of earth movements connected with the elevation of the Alps. Earlier the drainage of the rising Alps escaped through the Belfort Gap southwards via the Saône-Rhône trough until, with a rise in the Gap area relative to the level of the Rift Valley floor, that exit was closed and the drainage reversed. By the close of the Ice Age the Rhineland river (now the Rhine below Bingen) had completed the downward cutting of the gorge through the re-elevated Hercynian plateau, thenceforward enabling the glacier-fed Alpine waters, laden with debris, to flow unhindered to the Netherlands and the North Sea.

The Harz and the Thuringian Forest on the other hand, are good examples of horsts.[1] They are bounded by upthrow faults on their western sides, aligned NW.-SE., from which they are tilted downwards to the north-east. Faults such as these, and extensive dislocations such as the Wetterau depression north of Frankfurt, combined with the incised valleys of the Rhine and Weser systems, have broken up this whole outer Hercynian highland arc (known as the Mittelgebirge[2] in Germany) into a complex pattern of plateaux, mountains and hills separated from one another by numerous, often winding valleys. Through these valleys, especially those of the Weser and its headstreams the Werra and the Fulda, the lines of communication, linking north with south Germany, thread their ways. The main railways diverge southwards through the several valleys from Hanover on the northern margin of the uplands, to converge later from either side of the Vogelsberg upon Frankfurt, the main distributive point in the transport system in south Germany. In an intermediate position in the basin of convergence of the Fulda and the Werra, Kassel has grown as an important railway transport and engineering centre.

III. The Inner Hercynian Zone

The widely separated inner Hercynian highlands east of the Rhine, namely the Black Forest and the Bohemian massif, are both bounded by major faults on their western sides, the latter by double faults, the outer of which separates the Bavarian Forest upthrust from the Bohemian Forest continuous with the main plateau. From both highlands erosion has removed much of the former sedimentary cover, thus exposing the basal ancient crystalline rocks, mainly granites and gneiss. Both the Black Forest and the Bohemian Forest blocks are tilted downwards towards the north-east from their western boundary

---

[1] A German word (eyrie or crag), first applied in the physiographical sense by German geomorphologists to land forms such as these in their country.

[2] So called because intermediate in both height and situation.

faults; the granitic uplands of the Black Forest fall away in that direction under a belt of Triassic sandstones, and those of the Bohemian Plateau into a basin filled with Cretaceous rocks, covered in parts with Tertiaries, which is bounded on the north-east and the north-west by the fault-escarpments of the uplifted border zones — the Lausitz (Lužické) ridge of the Sudeten on the north-east, and the Erzgebirge (Krušne Hory) on the north-west.

In contrast with the fault-riven Bohemian Plateau, packed in its whole northern half with diverse formations, the Black Forest is simple in build. It bears a close resemblance to its counterpart the Vosges (cf. pp. 196–7), with which it was once continuous. On its eastern slopes the Neckar rises and eventually joins the Rhine, as does the Moselle from the Vosges; but the southern section of its granitic crest is a continental watershed, sending short torrents into the Rift Valley, and the source waters of the Danube on their long journey eastwards. The ravined slopes of the Black Forest, of little use for agriculture, and covered largely with dark pine woods (whence the German name Schwarzwald) are picturesque enough to give rise to a modest tourist industry which, with the limited farming possible, supplements the basic forestry occupations and the associated wood-carving crafts, as means of livelihood for the scattered population.

The Black Forest is but the southern section of the eastern wall of the Rhine Rift Valley, which on the right bank of the river extends its whole length of nearly 200 miles in German territory. North of the Black Forest this eastern wall sinks somewhat in the Kraichgau depression, where the relatively soft rocks of the Triassic series of the Neckar-Main Basins reach west to the Rift Valley, but it rises again in the Odenwald, similar in structure to the Black Forest. These great faults marking the eastern boundary of the Rift Valley continue northwards beyond the Mainz-Frankfurt Basin to form the Wetterau depression which is in reality an extension of the Rift Valley (Fig. 52).

The Rhine Rift Valley is of unusual geographical interest, not only as a fine example of its kind of structure, but also because of the part it plays and has played in human activities. The terraces and slopes on either side formed by complex step-faulting (cf. Alsace p. 197) are intensively cultivated; and this valley, like the Rhône-Saône corridor, with which it is connected through the Belfort Gap, has long been the route followed by a main link in the chain of communications between the Mediterranean lands and Northern Europe.

The Bohemian Plateau is a composite area, the product of a series of differential vertical movements. The peripheral and southern interior parts consist of tilted upthrust crystalline blocks which like the Black Forest formations are of little use apart from forestry, except in some valley basins. The great bulk of the farming, mining and industrial activities, and consequently also of the population, is concentrated in three down-faulted depressions: the Cretaceous Elbe Plain, the Carboniferous inlier drained by the Berounka River of the Elbe system, and the Ohře trough on the inner side of the Erzgebirge. The first and the largest of these is the main agricultural area of Bohemia, the second contains some scattered coalfields of value for industrial purposes e.g. at Pilsen, and the Ohře valley produces in

Fig. 64A. Generalised geological section across the Vosges, the Rift Valley and the Black Forest. Vertical scale = horizontal × 14. 1. River alluvium and gravel. 2. Tertiary. 3. Triassic. 4. Granite. 5. Gneiss. 6. Down-faulted Mesozoic beds.

addition to abundant supplies of lignite, both uranium ores and kaolin. These contiguous regions together form the heart region of Bohemia and of Czech national life. They are situated in the upper basin of the Elbe-Vltava river system which is navigable up to Prague, and was till after the Second World War the main highway for Czech commerce with the outside world (via Hamburg). See Fig. 69.

This basin-shaped, mountain-girt region of the Hercynian highlands together with the Moravian tectonic depression adjoining it on the south-east, has become the home of a gifted and vigorous people of Slav origin, who to their disadvantage have as a racial outpost been surrounded by others none too friendly, mainly of German origin. The Czechs have been unable to safeguard their independence in their enclave, in spite of the defensive barriers of the mountain walls. After their release from Austro-German domination in 1918, they looked to the West for trade and political support. In this, as events have shown, they were disappointed, because of their situation deep in Central Europe encircled by the German Hitlerite power. The only course open to them now, and that which seems to offer the best

promise of security, lies in association with other Slav peoples under
the leadership of the Russian Soviet Union.

IV. The South German Scarplands

The convergent lines of the Black Forest-Odenwald horsts on the
west and of the Bohemian-Thuringian fronts on the east frame an
area composed of sedimentary rocks ranging in age from the Lower
Triassic in the north to Tertiary and Recent south of the Danube.
The whole series has been uplifted under the impact of Alpine pressures, and north of the Danube has been thrust forward, with upturn-
ing of the outer strike edges of the successive strata, in escarpment

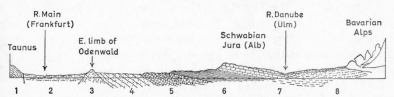

Fig. 64B. Generalised geological section on line N.W.–S.E. from the Taunus through
Frankfurt and Ulm to the Alps. Vertical scale = horizontal × 20. 1. Palaeozoic.
2. Tertiary. 3. Crystalline. 4. Bunter sandstone. 5. Muschelkalk. 6. Keuper marls.
7. Jurassic limestone. 8. Tertiary with overlying waste deposits.

formations dipping south-east. The most pronounced of these is the
broad limestone and sandstone arc of the Swabian and the Franconian
Jura, the bare and waterless uplands of which, several thousand feet in
height and raw of climate, are known as the Alb or Rauhe Alb in
Germany.

North of the Jurassic escarpments a large triangular area, the apex
of which extends into the region of the upper Weser, is covered with
massive beds of Triassic rocks, which dip south-east from subdued
escarpments, towards and finally under the Jurassic arc (Fig. 64B).
In this German area three distinct series are all well represented;
these are, in order of age and of outcrop from north to south, Bunter
sandstones, Muschelkalk and Keuper marls.[1] The first of these, the
brightly coloured and generally rather barren sandstones, similar to
those of the northern Vosges region of Lorraine and originally continuous with them, cover much of the upper Weser Basin and the

---

[1] The term Trias to denote the series of rocks intermediate in age between
Permian and Jurassic was first suggested and applied by a German geologist over a
century ago in keeping with the threefold division recognised by him in central
Germany. One or more of the three series so apparent there, is often missing in
other countries, e.g. the Muschelkalk in England.

eastern slopes of the Odenwald and the Black Forest; the second, consisting of shelly limestone, form a broken intermediate belt of irregular width; and the red Keuper marls fill an extensive area in the upper basins of the Main and the Neckar on the northern edge of the 'Alb' zone. Because the soils formed from the Muschelkalk and the Keuper marls are in general fertile in contrast with those on the sandstones, the distribution of the several types of Triassic rocks is a key to the forms of land-use for agricultural purposes.

V. THE DANUBE VALLEY,
THE ALPINE FORELAND AND THE BAVARIAN ALPS

The valley of the Danube in Germany marks a sharp transition from escarpments to Alpine Foreland, which is similar in origin to, but differs in surface features from the Swiss Plateau, of which it is the eastward continuation. Here a great apron of material has been built up in a former pre-Alpine trough with thick deposits of molasse derived from the waste of the rising Alps, overlaid with masses of coarse glacial debris in the south, and with patches of loess near the Danube. The plateau so formed rises from a height of over 1,000 feet along the river (Ulm 1,570 feet, Regensburg 1,152 feet) to between 3,000 and 4,000 feet at the foot of the Alps. The swift Alpine rivers such as the Iller, Lech and Isar, have cut wide valleys in the coarse waste down to the underlying molasse in places and, loaded with sediment deposited in their lower courses, have pushed the Danube against the dip-slope of the Jurassic escarpments and the wall of the Bavarian Forest, leaving stretches of marsh at intervals between the patches of loess (Fig. 10) along the southern bank of the river.

The upper parts of the plateau are uninviting. The river valleys are marshy in places and their courses are strewn with lakes; while the coarse soils and raw climate of the high interfluves render them of little use except as indifferent pasture lands. The scattered population consists of peasant farmers whose livelihood depends largely upon cattle, including dairy cattle. The few large settlements of upper Bavaria are situated in the better-drained sections of the valley floors. In the whole Foreland region only two really large towns have arisen, namely Munich and Augsburg, but both of these are located lower down at elevations well under 2,000 feet, on the outer margin of the inhospitable Alpine apron.

The intermediate zone between the Danube marshes and the high Foreland has been a transit passage from pre-historic times (see p. 44).

It is intersected almost midway by the north-south route over the lowest and easiest of all crossings of the Alps, that by the Adige valley from Verona, the Brenner Pass and Innsbruck; and at points of intersection of this route with the earlier lines of movement and traffic, the two historic cities just mentioned are situated, Munich on the Isar, and Augsburg on the Lech. Both have been and are important centres of commerce and traffic, and both have developed manufacturing industries fostered by hydro-electric power from the Alpine rivers.

The German share of the Alps is small and of little account except for water-power resources and for a few tourist resorts which, like many of those in Switzerland, provide for winter sports as well as summer residence. Of greater importance in some ways is the Danube waterway on the northern margin of the Foreland region. Navigable up to Ulm for small craft and up to Regensburg by larger vessels, this river gives Germany a doorway into the heart of Austria and into the Danubian lands beyond.

In a broad survey of the central and southern highland areas of Germany some general groupings can be observed. In the Mittelgebirge region the sporadic dislocations associated with the Alpine orogenesis have resulted in a complex and not readily disentangled pattern of upthrust blocks and troughs, with basins of more or less undisturbed rocks. The uplifted masses may, however, be classified in three groups: (a) the rectangular middle Rhine plateau divided by river valleys into its five major sections — Eifel, Hunsrück, Sauerland, Westerwald and Taunus; (b) the Thuringian Forest (with the outlying Harz) and the Erzgebirge, radiating north-west and north-east from the Fichtel knot; and (c) the middle and upper Weser uplands. The highland pattern in south Germany is simpler. Between the Bohemian and the Rift Valley upthrust blocks lies an extensive sedimentary zone. North of the Danube this has been thrown into monoclinal folds carved into scarplands. South of the river the land rises via the Alpine Foreland to the great overthrust of the Bavarian Alps.

Most of these German highlands are more widely utilised for forestry than for perennial agriculture, both of which give way in places to summer pastures and stretches of open moorland at higher levels. The forested and moorland areas of the highlands as well as the moors, bogs and barren outwash stretches of the glaciated northern plain are virtual blanks in the distributional pattern of German agriculture, pushed throughout to the margins of economic utilisation with the help of man-made improvements.

CLIMATE AND AGRICULTURE: FORESTRY

Apart from the general features of increasing ranges in seasonal temperatures and of higher proportions of summer rainfall from west to east, and of an overall rise in lowland temperatures from north to south, the most significant conditions affecting the climate in various parts of Germany are the special maritime influence in the north-west and along the Baltic coast, and the local topography in the central and southern regions. Though naturally weaker well inland, the stabilising Atlantic influence extends throughout, producing general reliability of climate favourable to well-developed agriculture. No part of the whole area has more than 15 per cent variability in rainfall, and north-west Germany has less than 10 per cent. In the determination of winter temperatures, however, the Atlantic influence yields gradually eastwards (less so southwards) to the continental. Mean temperatures below freezing point last less than one month in western Germany, but for over three months in East Prussia and Poland, where the duration of snow cover and freezing of static water surfaces averages 80 days per annum.

The mean annual rainfall over the German-Polish area is in the range of 28 to 30 inches, more on the North Sea coastlands and ex-posed slopes, several inches less on the eastern part of the plain, and down to a little over 20 inches on some sheltered interior basins and valleys. But as in general, especially to the east and the south, some two-thirds of the annual total falls in the six months May to September, when most needed by plants for their growth, and the melting of winter snows provides some carry-over stored in the ground, the available supplies of moisture are sufficient for meadow grasses and a wide variety of temperate crops according to soil and location. South of the northern plain the generally broken relief gives rise to marked local variations in climate. In the Mittelgebirge region of Germany and in northern Bohemia valleys and depressions, sheltered by adjacent highlands which receive the brunt of the rain-storms, are exceptionally dry and warm; equally striking is the contrast in climate between the Rhine Rift Valley, where the rainfall is less than 25 inches, and the Vosges-Black Forest Mountains, which in parts get more than twice as much.

Neither Germany nor the eastern borderlands have a generous

endowment of first-class land in proportion to total area. In Germany itself really fertile soils are limited to the loess tracts, some valley bottoms and the reclaimed Marschen; the predominant types, especially those derived from the glacial mantles in the north and on the Alpine Foreland, are medium to poor in quality. Within the limits set by indifferent soil fertility, German agriculture is intensive, employing large labour resources in proportion to land. The same

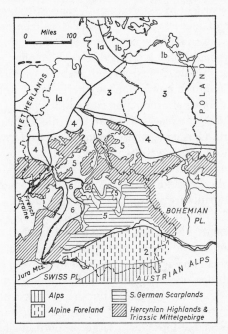

Fig. 65. The agricultural regions of Germany. Land over 1,000 ft. shaded. Regions numbered as in the text. After R. E. Dickinson.

holds true of Czech agriculture, but not of Polish. In pre-war Germany there were nearly two million small farms of between 5 and 50 acres in size, the great majority worked by owner-occupiers on a family basis. Mixed farming is the general rule, though the relative importance of the two main sources of income, live-stock and cash crops, varies from one region to another according to differences in soil, climate and market conditions.

On the basis of these variables Germany and its eastern borderlands may be divided into six agricultural regions, as shown in Fig. 65: (1a) the relatively cool and humid north-west lowlands, which specialise in live-stock (cattle and pigs), being better suited owing to considerable rainfall during the summer months to pastures and fodder crops than to cereals; (1*b*) the Baltic coastlands, somewhat drier and warmer in summer than 1*a*, and covered largely with boulder clay, are noted for their production of grain, especially wheat; (2) the Alpine Foreland and some scattered unforested parts of other uplands, where the climate is likewise cool and humid, and which also specialise in live-stock, mainly dairy cattle; (3) the central lowland wedge of medium to poor glacial soils, the rye-oats-potato belt, where the mixed farming concentrates more on these crops than on live-stock, though some are raised, especially pigs; (4) the fertile loess belt of highly-developed mixed arable farming with heavy concentration upon the cultivation of wheat, barley and sugar beet, akin to which in forms of production is the Elbe Plain of Bohemia; (5) the valley lowlands interspersed throughout the highland regions of central and south Germany, where intensive mixed farming, producing both live-stock and cereals (wheat and barley) is the general rule; (6) the sheltered and relatively warm Rhine Rift and Moselle valleys and hillsides, where in addition to the staple crops wheat and barley, wine grapes and fruits are grown in favoured situations.

In several of its characteristic features German agriculture differs from that prevalent in France or England. In them the rye-potato pattern, so common on the sandy soils of northern Germany, is hardly ever seen. Further, very few sheep are kept in the whole of Germany to the Polish border, about 3 million in all, compared with nearly 25 million in the United Kingdom;[1] but many more pigs, some 23 million against under 14 million in France and the United Kingdom combined. The staple foods of a large proportion of the German people are rye and wheat bread, potatoes, dairy produce and pig-meat from which sausages are made in great variety; and the national beverage is beer, brewed from home-grown as well as imported barley, and hops cultivated chiefly in Bavaria and Württemberg in the south.

Deprived of large primarily agricultural areas in the east by the advance of the Polish border to the Oder-Neisse line, Germany as a whole, and West Germany in particular have become food-deficient areas. The Federal Republic is quite unable to furnish from its limited resources of productive land enough food for its 55 million inhabi-

---

[1] The German uplands (and those of Bohemia) are utilised principally to grow timber, not for sheep walks, as commonly in the United Kingdom.

tants,[1] either directly as cereals for example, or indirectly as fodder for its live-stock. It now imports some 2½ million tons of wheat per annum, besides large quantities of maize, oil-seeds and other materials used mainly or partly as stock feed, and is exceeded only by the United Kingdom in its dependence upon external sources for supplies of these agricultural products.

FORESTRY

In spite of selective clearance during 2,000 years of human settlement, forests still cover over 28 per cent of the area of Germany and of Bohemia-Moravia and over 33 per cent of that of Poland. Much of the relatively large proportions in the first two countries is accounted for by the Hercynian highlands, which like the Scandinavian uplands are of little use for agriculture, and are characteristically forest-clad, as they have been from time immemorial. The German descriptive epithet *Wald* which appears so often in the names of these highlands, and the age-long association of German folk-lore and fairy-tales with dark pine-woods, are significant indicators of their most striking feature.

Whereas the upland forests are predominantly coniferous, Scots pine for the most part, with spruce at higher elevations, those which have been left or planted on the less fertile stretches of the northern plain are mixed in character according to soil and drainage; beech woods occur in places, but the commonest trees are oaks, often associated with hornbeam, birch or pines; while coniferous trees have been planted in parts of Germany where the glacial sands cannot well be otherwise turned to account, among them the silver pine (Tanne), an indigenous tree which grows in lower-level belts on the highlands.

German forestry is operated on scientific lines, mainly under the supervision of special public authorities which control the regeneration, cutting and replanting. Elaborate precautions are enforced to prevent damage by fire or otherwise. Each section of the forests is in the care of a ranger (Förster) and has its *Schönung* or nursery where young trees are raised in readiness for planting out as vacancies arise through cutting. The timber and pulp wood, of which the annual cut is about 25 million cubic metres in West Germany alone, are clearly valuable contributions to the supplies of raw materials for industry and handicrafts, as well as for the constructional trades.

[1] Including since late 1959 over a million in Saarland.

MINERAL RESOURCES

The considerable mineral resources of Germany and Bohemia-Moravia, especially in respect of coal and lignite, have been of immense significance in the industrial and general economic development of both. Germany has in addition to abundant solid fuels, supplemented by water-power in the south, exceptionally large deposits of potash salts and rock salt, and smaller ones of mineral oil, zinc and copper. Though post-war Germany has lost the whole of the two Silesian coalfields to Poland, West Germany is left with the Ruhr coalfield, the richest in Europe, and East Germany has the most productive lignite field in the whole world in the Saxony-Anhalt-Niederlausitz area. The exploitation of these various mineral resources, which is associated largely with manufacturing industries, is described in the following chapter.

Note on spelling of names in Germany and its eastern borderlands. The general rule is to adopt the spelling of the people of the country or region, unless the names have current anglicised forms, e.g. Cologne, Nuremberg, Munich, Prague. In the regions east of the Oder now in Polish territory, many places are more readily recognised by their erstwhile German names, and the same applies, though less generally, to places in Bohemia, formerly in Austrian territory. Wherever any obscurity is likely to arise through using the new Polish or Czech names, the traditional German form is added in brackets, e.g. Wroclaw (Breslau).

Chapter 17

GERMANY AND ITS EASTERN BORDERLANDS: II INDUSTRIAL AREAS; WEST GERMANY

THE variegated pattern of the physical framework of Germany and its eastern borderlands, and the corresponding variety in farming and forestry, form a geographical background superimposed on which is another simpler pattern of industrial areas, each containing one or more large urban centres. Four major areas of urban constellation form, namely Ruhr-Rhineland, Hanover-Brunswick, Saxony-Anhalt (Mitteldeutschland) and the Polish-Czech Upper Silesian coalfield district, lie in a belt on the northern border of the Hercynian highlands. Two others, the Middle Rhine and northern Bohemia, though situated within the highland zone, both have connections by river highways with the outer belt and thence with the sea, the Middle Rhine with the Ruhr and northern Bohemia with Mitteldeutschland (Fig. 66).

These industrial areas, situated at intervals in a zone which extends in an arc from the Netherlands-Belgian borders across central Germany into southern Poland, owe their rise mainly to the deposits of coal, lignite, salt and metallic ores on or within the northern margins of the Hercynian highlands. They have had the further advantage of obtaining food supplies for their increasing populations from the rich agricultural lands of the loess belt, largely coincident with that of the coal and lignite fields on which most of them lie.

In addition to the concentrations in these urban groups, industry has developed in and around a number of single larger towns, already important as centres of transport and trade. Two of them, Hamburg and Bremen, are leading seaports whose notable trading activities date from Hansa times; two others in the northern plain, pre-war Berlin and Warsaw, have developed various industries furthered by their roles as capital cities and as nodes in the systems of inland transport; while in South Germany such leading historic towns as Nuremberg,

I

Munich, Stuttgart and Karlsruhe have in modern times become centres of various specialised manufactures in the lines of the traditions of their earlier crafts.

The economic separation between West and East Germany that has accompanied the post-war political division has destroyed the former bonds of industrial integration between them. Based primarily on the

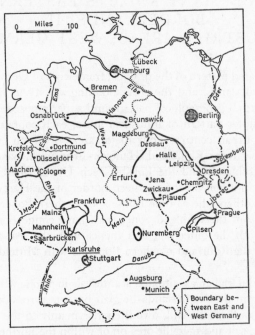

Fig. 66. Germany and Bohemia: chief industrial areas (ringed), and detached centres of industry (underlined).

location of mineral deposits, these ties were amplified by the development of regional specialisation in the production especially of semi-finished materials, and by the movement of both these and raw materials from one region to another. Thus for example the Saxony-Anhalt industrial region of highly developed finishing manufactures, having little or no coking coal, but plenty of lignite, drew upon the Ruhr for hard coal and semi-finished steel; the great chemical industries of the Middle Rhine area depended in no small measure upon supplies of potash and common salts drawn from what is now East German territory; and the anomalous position of Berlin has broken up an integrated economic unit which was able to obtain from all quarters of Germany the materials required for its varied manufactures. On the whole, West Germany has come off much better than East Germany n its assignment of the basic factors for the pursuit of industry. It has not only the immense asset of the Ruhr coalfield, but also the internal highway of the Rhine waterway and, through the terminals of that waterway in the Low Countries as well as its own North Sea ports, facilities for maritime expansion and for trade with all lands overseas.

The Rhine waterway, which with the Ruhr-Ems canal and river extension, in effect spans the whole distance from Emden on the North Sea to Kehl (opposite Strasbourg) well up the Rift Valley, is of singular value as an artery of transport in the elongated territory of West Germany (Fig. 62). With lateral feeders, it serves most of the more populous parts of the Federal Republic; the two main canals of the Ruhr area, the Lippe-Seiten and the Rhine-Herne, connected by the southern section of the Dortmund-Ems with the Mittelland Canal, link up the whole industrial belt from the Rhine to the East German border beyond Brunswick, with the Rhine navigation; the Moselle, though not naturally serviceable as a waterway owing to its numerous incised meanders, provides in its valley a useful railway route between the Ruhr and the Lorraine iron-ore field; the Main is navigable up to Bamberg, whence the Ludwig Canal extends to Nuremberg, and the Neckar takes 1,000 ton barges to Plochlingen above Stuttgart; and by the Rhine Valley itself, above Kehl, railways connect the Rhine waterway and all West Germany that taps it with Switzerland, and thence through Italy to the Mediterranean port of Genoa. The Rhine is one of the most used river waterways in the world. It enables barge-trains of 6,000 to 7,000 tons to reach Duisburg at the Ruhr confluence, of 5,000 tons to reach Mannheim, and of 1,000 to 2,000 tons to ascend to Kehl. The river itself is navigable up to Basle during about three months of high water in the summer, but the swift current makes navigation difficult, so that traffic is commonly transferred either to the railway or to the Alsatian lateral canal.

THE INDUSTRIAL AREAS OF WEST GERMANY

(I) Foremost among these is the Ruhr-Rhineland region, which has made rapid recovery from immense war-time damage, and now ranks once more as one of the world's greatest industrial concentrations in population and in volume and variety of output. Two great assets have contributed to its striking growth: abundant deposits of excellent coal of different kinds, especially coking coal; and its situation at one of the main cross-roads of Europe, whence two waterways lead to the sea, both capable of carrying traffic in heavy materials. The fuel and power resources are outstanding. In addition to the yearly output of about 130 million tons of coal, mainly from east of the Rhine, upwards of 90 million tons of lignite (equivalent in thermal value to some 20 million tons of coal) are obtained from the Ville Ridge west and south-west of Cologne; besides which some hydro-electric power is generated from falls on the rivers of the Sauerland Plateau (Fig. 67).

The whole densely populated, predominantly industrial area of the Ruhr-Rhineland, containing nearly 8 million inhabitants, comprises the core belt and three peripheral sub-regions. The core is the almost continuous urban area between Duisburg and Dortmund in the Ruhr and Emscher Valleys, in which nearly half the total population is concentrated. Just south of this lies the Sauerland, notable as the birthplace of the great metallurgical industries of the Ruhr. It consists of the northern section of the Rhine highlands, and in common with them is composed of ancient rocks and is dissected by rivers, in the valleys of which, notably of the Wupper, specialised industries have developed from earlier crafts. Here deposits of iron ore, now more or less exhausted, have given rise to local long-established metal-working industries, but the highland region as a whole is of limited use for agriculture. A second sub-region is the wedge of lowland, the Cologne bay, which extends up the Rhine Valley from Düsseldorf to Bonn, separating Sauerland and Siegerland from the eastern terraces of the Ardennes. This fertile tract, containing the one important lignite field of West Germany, shares in the commercial and industrial life of the Ruhr in the two large river cities, and has developed independent textile manufactures in several towns west of the river, which will be described later. Finally, the eastern terrace slopes of the Ardennes form a distinct sub-region, in which two small coalfields[1] at the foot of the Hohes Venn on the Belgian border have enabled the old-established textile and metallurgical industries of Aachen and neighbouring small towns to survive.

The Ruhr coal-measures underlie an elliptical area, the longer axis of which lies approximately along the Rhine-Herne Canal. It extends for over 60 miles from west of the Rhine to beyond the middle Lippe. The seams dip from the surface just south of the River Ruhr under

---

[1] In one of these production has ceased now that cheaper coals are available from Dutch Limburg and the Belgian Kempenland.

beds of chalk and sandstones north of Essen to depths of over 3,000 feet north of the Lippe; though this general northward dip is interrupted by several shallow anticlines running ENE.–WSW., with intervening synclinal basins. The uppermost of the numerous seams of the whole region are gas coals rich in volatile constituents, now worked mainly north of the Lippe. Below these are the valuable coking coals, and lowest of all semi-anthracite seams, generally too deep for mining in the central parts north of the Ruhr, except here and there on the buried anticlines. Two-thirds of the coals raised are of the coking class, mined in the central part of the coalfield, which contains

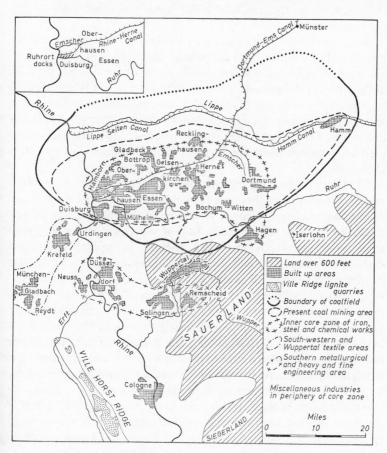

Fig. 67. The Ruhr–Rhineland industrial area. Inset map showing Ruhrort docks.

by far the largest deposits of coking coal in Europe. In the outcrops south of the River Ruhr only the geologically oldest semi-anthracite or steam coals occur, but as these seams have been much disturbed by earth movements associated with the elevation of the adjacent high-lands, and have been worked for a long time, the output from them is relatively small.

The Ruhr region itself specialises in three main forms of industry among others, namely iron-smelting and steel manufactures, heavy engineering, and the synthetic chemical group, all located in the chief mining areas where the large supplies of coal required for these industries are on the spot, and water is easily obtainable for certain chemical processes.

West Germany produces some 13 million tons of iron ore, mainly from the Harz Foreland and Siegerland, but as the ores are in general low grade, yielding only about 4 million tons of metal in all, the bulk of the iron ore consumed in the Ruhr blast furnaces is imported. A large proportion consists of high-grade mineral obtained from Sweden and other countries via Emden and Rotterdam, though increasing quantities of the minette ores from Lorraine (p. 199) are likely to be used since the establishment, in 1952, of the European Coal and Steel Community.

The heavy engineering industry has had special advantages through vertical integration in obtaining favourable terms for its requirements of iron and steel and of power resources, all produced in works controlled by the same management. In post-war years, having recovered from war damage, it has expanded remarkably in response to the world demand for machinery and equipment and to the German demand for constructional steel of all kinds e.g. for re-building and for the rapidly expanding shipbuilding industry. The manufacture of a wide range of synthetic chemicals, including dyestuffs, pharmaceutical products and artificial substitutes, is also based largely on coal and lignite and the by-products of coal derived from other branches of industry. These are treated by elaborate processes of distillation and synthesis, the outcome of practical research in which German chemists have excelled. In view of the chain use of materials as noted above, from raw coal and pig iron to finished products, in the industrial organisation of the Ruhr, it is not surprising that vertical integration developed there on a vast scale. Giant enterprises such as Krupp's and huge combines (cartels) came to control great sections of industry from the mining of coal to the marketing of a whole range of finished products.

The close-knit urban area known as the Ruhrgebiet in Germany extends from the river-port town Duisburg-Hamborn, at the confluence of the River Ruhr with the Rhine, to beyond Dortmund in the east, and from Recklinghausen in the north to Witten and Hagen on the middle Ruhr in the south. The main hub of this highly developed industrial area is Essen, between which and Duisburg-Hamborn lies Oberhausen-Mülheim, another example of the coalescence of two originally separate towns. East of Essen and on towards Dortmund there is a succession of towns the largest of which are Gelsenkirchen and Bochum. This compacted group forms the greatest industrial district in Europe. Yet the Ruhr district is by no means all that matters in the life and economic activities of the lower Rhine lands, though its influence extends throughout. Fully half the total population lives in places outside it to the south and west, where a wide variety of specialised industries including the whole important textile group has developed, in many cases from early independent beginnings. Some of the towns, Aachen, Cologne and Düsseldorf for example, are much older than the mushroom agglomerations of the Ruhr, and have long been centres of commerce and manufactures, and of administration and cultural life.

A little to the south-west, away from the smoke haze of the Ruhr, Krefeld together with Uerdingen has specialised in silk manufactures among other industries, and beyond that lies the sprawling group of München-Gladbach and Reydt, now grown together as a continuous town in which cotton manufactures are the principal industry. A few miles up the Rhine from Duisburg the old town Düsseldorf has grown to be a great commercial city, having close connections with the Ruhr, and a variety of industries, including large engineering works. East of this city in the Wupper Valley lies a cluster of three towns, namely Wuppertal (formerly Elberfeld-Barmen), where manufactures of textiles such as cottons and artificial silks are the main branch of industry, and Remscheid and Solingen, which are the leading continental centres for the production of cutlery and fine tools.

Cologne, another 20 miles up the Rhine from Düsseldorf, is in a class by itself. Its site was chosen by the Romans for a military camp, because of the situation at a comparatively easy crossing of the Rhine, on the west bank, i.e. the Roman side of the river. In early days Cologne was a centre of travel and trade on the main route from the Franco-Belgian plains into Germany, that lay between the forests and marshes to the north and the unfrequented forested highlands to the south. It has retained throughout its importance as a centre of transport and trade and of civil and religious administration, enhanced in modern times by the construction of railways converging upon it, the rise of the Ruhr, and the opening up of the rich lignite field in the Ville Ridge west of it. Prior to the last war it had large business interests and a variety of industries, mainly of the lighter forms; and though it suffered appalling damage in that war, it has risen Phoenix-like from the destruction, to be the great focus of economic activities that its geographical situation makes it.

Aachen, with its local coal supplies (p. 244) and some iron, lead and zinc ores formerly worked but now exhausted, has become a centre of brass manufactures as well as of textiles. It lies on the trans-continental railway route from Paris to Cologne, and like that city, it has historical associations from the distant part. Over a thousand years ago it was the capital of Charlemagne's empire, but with the break-up of that empire it was reduced politically to the position of a border town, while retaining some importance as an ecclesiastical centre. In the modern age it has been left in a kind of backwater of German industrial development, situated as it is in a rather confined basin. Bonn is also an old city built near the site of a Roman camp. Its situation, however, at the apex of the lowland bay, and the absence of any east-west transverse route, have prevented it from growing beyond the stature of a provincial university town — until quite recently. The reasons for the choice of Bonn as capital of the Federal Republic were partly geographical, namely its attractive residential situation on the Rhine highway and near the 'centre of gravity' of West German population, and partly political, similar to those that have led to the choice of other federal capitals such as Ottawa and Canberra, namely to avoid favouring any one large existing provincial city unduly.

(II) The Middle Rhine region, though smaller in area and in the range of its manufactures than the Westphalian region, and destitute of mineral resources, is nevertheless a highly important focus of commerce and industry. Situated immediately above the sixty-mile stretch of the Rhine Gorge, it is nearer the geographical centre of West Germany than the lower Rhine lands: its centrality being made more effective by the valley routes from the north-east by the Wetterau depression, from the east by the Main, from the south-east by the Neckar, and the south-west by the Nahe, converging there upon the Rhine highway (Fig. 63).

This region fills the triangle of lowlands at the confluence of the

Main with the Rhine, the angular points of which are marked by Mainz, Hanau (east of Frankfurt) and Mannheim-Ludwigshafen. Except for the breaks made by the valley routes just mentioned, it is surrounded by highlands, by the Hercynian Taunus on the north, the Odenwald on the south-east, and the Triassic sandstone Hardt Plateau on the west, all of which rise from the lowland region along well-marked faults, and thereby sharply define its limits. The Tertiary and Recent alluvial deposits of the Rhine Rift and lower Main Valley are generally fertile, and the shelter provided by the highlands which shield these valleys, in particular from cold northerly air streams, gives them an unusually warm and sunny climate for their latitude. Good wines for example, are produced from vineyards planted on the southern slopes of the Taunus and the eastern side of the Rift Valley. The agricultural population is dense, and this together with the urban population numbering over two millions, makes the region one of the most thickly populated in Western Europe outside the Ruhr.

In this middle Rhine nodal area, Frankfurt has long been a centre of trade and finance, and Mainz, once a Roman settlement, was the seat of an archbishopric throughout the Middle Ages, but in the present century manufactures, linked with and contributing to the trading activities, have risen to prime importance, although the raw materials and semi-manufactures used, as well as the coal or other fuel supplies required, have to be transported from a distance.

Much industry is concentrated in the twenty-mile belt along the Main from Mainz to Frankfurt, especially in the smaller towns such as Rüsselsheim, where the Opel motor-car works are situated, and others near Wiesbaden and Frankfurt where there are large chemical and specialised machine-making factories. Wiesbaden itself is a spa residential town, frequented from Roman times owing to hot salt springs in the neighbourhood. Among the outlying towns of the Mainz-Frankfurt district, the largest is Darmstadt towards the foot of the Odenwald, which previous to war-time destruction had chemical and engineering industries. Some forty odd miles up the Rhine outside the orbit of Frankfurt, lies the twin river port Mannheim-Ludwigshafen, which with a population of nearly 450,000 forms an urban group of great economic importance. Mannheim on the east bank is the leading up-river port on the Rhine as the point of transfer (to railways and small river craft) of the heavy traffic in coal, grain and petroleum for the Neckar basin and the upper Rhine regions including Switzerland.

It has a variety of elaborating industries arising out of its trade in both directions, and also shares in the chemical manufactures developed on a remarkable scale at Ludwigshafen across the river, which produce aniline dye-stuffs, synthetic nitrogen, and plastics among other materials. This town was the headquarters of the I. G. Farben Industrie, a combine which controlled the whole range of chemical manufactures, and was the largest organisation in this branch of industry in Europe prior to 1944.

(III) Another distinctively industrial area, that of Lower Saxony, lies along the northern margin of the Middle Weser and the Harz highlands from Osnabrück in the west to Helmstedt in the east at the entrance to the Berlin corridor. Though it overlaps the highlands in places, it is in the main a transitional zone between the predominantly hill and mountain country of the Mittelgebirge and the open drift-covered North German Plain. Its underlying structure is that of a syncline floored with sedimentary rocks from the Triassic to the Cretaceous tilted upwards against the older highlands. These are covered for the most part with the products of glaciation: a broad wedge of loess (the western section of the Börde) reaches as far as Minden on the Weser where it becomes quite narrow, beyond which the surface deposits are mainly sand and gravels. The rich agricultural lands of the Börde east of the Weser contributed to the early rise of a number of historic towns, the largest of which are Hanover and Brunswick; and the potash and rock salts of the underlying rocks east of Brunswick have furnished primary materials for the later growth of chemical industries in these and other towns in West Germany.

This foreland belt has been followed by the main lines of movement between Central and North-Western Europe from the earliest times. It is now traversed by the main trunk railway from Berlin to Cologne, which, after passing Brunswick and Hanover forks beyond Minden to reach the Ruhr and Cologne, either direct by the Bielefeld gap, or round the north-western tongue of the Middle Weser highlands via Osnabrück and Münster. The Mittelland Canal linking Berlin with the Dortmund-Ems also runs through this zone parallel with the main railway in the section Brunswick-Osnabrück and, at its crossings of the Aller and Weser rivers, connects with their navigable lower stretches down to tidewater at Bremen. These waterways, together with numerous other railways from north and south meeting the arterial system in the great junctions at Hanover and Osnabrück, give the zone excellent communications with the Ruhr-Rhineland and the major ports Hamburg and Bremen. The compensating advantage of good external connections by railways and waterways has been an essential condition for the development of industry in this region which, though it has some deposits of low-grade iron ore, of potash and common salts, and also of mineral oil,[1] has itself quite inadequate fuel and power resources.

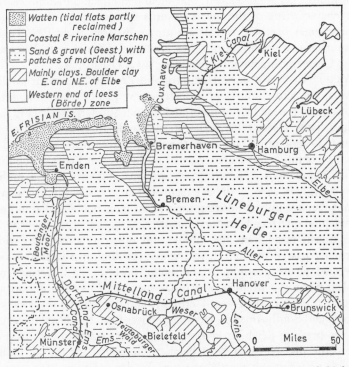

Fig. 68. North-West Germany: surface deposits, canals and sites of chief towns.

The four largest towns Hanover, Brunswick, Bielefeld and Osnabrück together contain over a million inhabitants, half of whom are in Hanover. The great majority of these people, and many more in smaller towns, depend on manufacture for their living. The metallurgical group of industries is very general and far the most important, its expansion having been encouraged by the pre-war German Government. Large iron and steel works have been erected at Salzgitter

[1] In a small field north-east of Hanover, which produces about 2½ mill. tons p.a.

south of Brunswick, using the low-grade ore of the Harz foreland, and there are some heavy engineering works at Hanover; but much more typical of the region than these somewhat artificial creations is light engineering in its various branches, especially machine making, in which almost every town of any size has a share.[1] The chemical group is also well represented, especially at Hanover where synthetic rubber and motor fuel are produced; and sugar-refining and food processing are characteristic of the towns towards the east in the Börde zone, where sugar beet and cereals are grown in large quantities. Textile manufactures, important in other industrial areas in both West and East Germany, are notably lacking except at Osnabrück.

(IV) The two great ports Hamburg and Bremen, with their satellite towns, are active centres of industry as well as of commerce, set as enclaves in a wide belt of moorland, marsh and farmlands (Fig. 68). Their lively associations with external trade from the times of the Hansa League earned for them the status of free cities, confirmed by their recognition as separate *Länder* in the present Federal Republic. With populations numbering 1·8 millions and over half a million respectively in 1959, both have recovered in large measure from enormous damage inflicted during the war on their port installations and residential quarters. Hamburg, however, has lost a large proportion of the transit trade from the middle and upper Elbe regions, which formerly passed through it, and which (in diminished form) is now diverted where possible to the Baltic ports in East German and Polish territory.[2] Bremen, which has specialised more in import and export trade for north-west Germany, and in shipping services with North and South America, has suffered less from the dismemberment of the pre-war Reich. In one way both ports stand to gain in trade from the disasters that have befallen Germany, for the 55 million people crowded now into West Germany depend more than ever for their living upon exporting manufactures in exchange for imported supplies of foodstuffs and other materials.

Hamburg is situated about sixty miles up the Elbe from the open sea, but as the tidal range is relatively small, vessels can berth at open quays, and their movements up and down the river-estuary are less restricted by low-water conditions than at London. But in order to accommodate the larger ships and to save time in their turn-round, an

---

[1] Noteworthy here are the Volkswagen car works (the largest in West Germany) at Wolfsburg near Brunswick.

[2] Rostock in East Germany and Scezecin in Poland.

outport has been constructed at Cuxhaven on the west shore of the estuary. Like other live cities, Hamburg has grown outwards from the original compact nucleus, incorporating Altona and Harburg among other formerly separate places, and now covers 150 sq. miles within its administrative boundaries.

The prime impulse for the remarkable growth of Hamburg has come from its rôle as the paramount port of the pre-war Reich, as it is now of the Federal Republic; it has, in fact, been one of the half-dozen greatest ports of the world in volume of trade. A secondary, yet powerful impulse has proceeded from the growth of industries associated with oversea trade. Foremost among these is shipbuilding, in which, in the hands of firms such as Blom and Voss, Hamburg is again becoming the greatest centre on the continent; and that notwithstanding the fact that the nearest effective source of both coal and steel is nearly 100 miles away. Further, a great variety of refining, processing and fabricating industries has developed in the city and its suburban periphery in connection with the oil, grain, textile fibres, rubber and other commodities handled in the port. In several ways Hamburg resembles London, not only in its situation at the head of a long estuary, in its extensive fully-developed hinterland and its world-wide shipping and trade connections, but also in the development of a broad range of industries which in the aggregate make it a great manufacturing as well as a commercial centre.

Bremen, some forty miles up the Weser from its outport Bremer-haven, has been rather overshadowed by Hamburg as a German North Sea port. Yet, in some specialised forms of trade and traffic, it leads. It has a large importing trade in raw cotton, wool, grain and colonial products; it is the chief cotton market of Germany (the counterpart of Liverpool in England), and it is the headquarters of the German transatlantic passenger liner services. As at Hamburg, numerous manufactures of the elaborating kind have arisen there in connection with the commodities handled e.g. milling, oil-refining and processing of foodstuffs; while among industries of the staple-transforming type are iron-smelting and woollen textiles. On the whole however, Bremen is more of a commercial and shipping port than a manufacturing city. Still more limited in its activities is the artificial port of Emden, which is little else but the seaward terminus of the Dortmund-Ems Canal, where inward consignments of iron ore and outward consignments of coal are transferred from ships to barges and vice versa.

Greater Berlin was before the war one of the chief manufacturing centres of Europe, according to the number of persons employed and the value added to the materials by factory processes. It was the head-quarters of two gigantic organisations which produced every kind of electrical apparatus and equipment; it had extensive textile, clothing and machine-tool manufactures, in addition to large printing and publishing trades and a variety of industries engaged in preparing ordinary consumer goods for nation-wide as well as local requirements. Being entirely dependent upon external sources for supplies of fuel and power and of raw materials and foodstuffs, this city of over 4 million people owed its existence to the efficient functioning of the transport system of which it was the centre.

This essential basis has been greatly impaired. The whole city is now surrounded by East German territory and has been divided within itself, especially since the erection of the barrier wall in 1961, into two almost entirely segregated sectors. Though the Western Sector has a traffic life-line connecting it with West Germany to which it is attached politically, it has been deprived of physical connections with the Leipzig-Halle and the Baltic regions, formerly important sources for it of lignite fuel and agricultural produce respectively. Till recently the Western Sector had to obtain electric current from the Eastern Sector, and it remains dependent upon the Federal Republic for food and coal supplies. Thus the revival of the electro-technical and other currency-earning industries, needful if the Western Sector is to become economically self-sufficing, is hampered by difficulties and may be a slow process.

The Eastern Sector containing less than a third of the present 3·3 million inhabitants of the whole city, has a much more viable exist-ence. Situated near the geographical centre of the Democratic Re-public, of which it remains the capital, it has retained an important share of the direct rail, road and waterway connections of Berlin in the former Reich; in particular those with the Baltic ports Rostock and Stralsund, with Magdeburg and the Thuringian towns, with Leipzig and Dresden, and with the eastern border towns of Frankfurt-an-der Oder and Görlitz. East Berlin, in contrast with the anomalous political enclave of West Berlin, has within the limits of the new order inherited the rôles of the former integrated city.

(V) Nuremberg, Munich, Stuttgart and Karlsruhe are the four lead-ing South German towns in which, as well as in others, opportunities have been found to establish industries, mainly of the engineering and textile groups, in spite of their distances from sources of coal and metals.[1] In this respect they resemble the Swiss towns such as Zürich, in which as in South Germany the development of metallurgical and textile industries specialising in high-quality products is an expression of the painstaking mechanical genius of the Alpine race. Munich only of these South German centres of industry has abundant easily-accessible supplies of water-power; the others depend on coal and oil transported by the Rhine waterway and thence by railways or canals. All of them, however, have the physical advantage of nodal situations on important overland routes, which contributed to their early rise, and has been greatly enhanced by the construction of railways.

Nuremberg together with Fürth, with which it is continuous, is one of the dozen or so urban centres in all Germany exceeding half a million in population. Like others of its size and regional connections, it has a variety of manufactures, outstanding among which is the production of fine metal goods such as instruments and tools, and of mechanical toys, for which it has been the greatest centre in the world.

Munich has grown remarkably in the last 70 or 80 years, and now with more than a million inhabitants is the third largest city of Germany. It has long been famous for the production of beer, distributed over Germany and neighbouring countries, but its later rapid growth is related to the development of engineering (electrical and general) and other power-using industries, since cheap supplies of hydro-electricity have become available. Stuttgart is a commercial and cultural centre as well as an important manufacturing town, having a variety of industries, notably of the precision engineering class.[2] Industrially also, it serves as the organising focus of a number of small satellite towns situated in the several convergent valleys round it, which specialise in making products which require skilled labour, e.g. textiles and machinery. Karlsruhe, connected with the Rhine by a short canal, is a river port handling a considerable volume of barge traffic. Access by that waterway to supplies of heavy materials have enabled it to establish railway and general engineering works, where locomotives and rolling stock among other heavy products are manufactured.

Reviewed as a whole, West German industry is seen to be dominated by the metallurgical, engineering and chemical groups. Iron-smelting, steel manufactures and heavy engineering are concentrated

[1] The Ruhr for coal, and the Ruhr, Saarland and Lorraine for crude steel.
[2] Including the large-scale manufacture of motor vehicles (Daimler-Benz).

in the Ruhr, but the numerous secondary forms of engineering are very widely distributed. In the overall spread there is some specialisation by types in particular towns: farm implements and machinery in the leading agricultural market centres such as Düsseldorf, Hanover and Augsburg; railway locomotives and rolling stock at important railway centres, e.g. Essen, Kassel and Karlsruhe; shipbuilding at the main sea and Rhine ports, e.g. Hamburg and Duisburg; electrical machinery and equipment at Berlin, Cologne and Munich; motor vehicles in places near Frankfurt and Hanover; and general and fine engineering at Nuremberg-Fürth and Munich among other towns. Chemical manufactures are highly concentrated in three regions, the Middle Rhine, the Ruhr and Hanover-Brunswick, outside which miscellaneous branches are widely scattered.

In the export trade engineering products (machinery and motor vehicles) are the largest item, accounting for a third of the total in 1959. Other large items are iron and steel goods, chemicals, electro-technical products and coal and coke. The rapid economic recovery of West Germany since 1946 has been the result partly of the inflow of refugees from the eastern lands providing a large supply of workers, partly of direct and indirect financial subventions from Western countries and disengagement from heavy military expenditure, mainly perhaps of her good fortune in having the physical resources and the industrial experience for the production of durable goods and chemical products in demand throughout the world at the present time.

Chapter 18

GERMANY AND ITS EASTERN BORDERLANDS; III INDUSTRIAL AREAS; EAST GERMANY, BOHEMIA AND POLAND

(I) MITTELDEUTSCHLAND, the Leipzig-Halle-Magdeburg region, had become previous to the last war second only to the Ruhr-Rhineland in the volume and variety of its industrial products. Its rapid development in the period 1919–40 arose from the exploitation of its large deposits of lignite by modern techniques, combined with the strategic policy of the central Government to concentrate as much essential industry as possible in the heart of the country. The relatively large area of about 10,000 square miles (equal to one-third of Scotland) embraces all the lowlands and hillsides west of the Elbe and south of Magdeburg, bordered by the Erzgebirge, Thüringer Wald and Harz Highlands: it is mostly co-terminous with the basins of the Saale, Elster and Mulde tributaries of the Elbe. Now entirely in the German Democratic Republic, it has been re-organised in the three divisions (*Länder*) of Saxony, Saxony-Anhalt and Thuringia, replacing the old rather confused pattern of provinces.

The loess and marl-loam soils of the Leipzig bay and its western extension into the Thuringian Basin are highly fertile and are intensively cultivated, the characteristic crops being wheat, barley, sugar beet,[1] potatoes and cattle-forage crops such as lucerne. Yet a much higher proportion of the working population of the region as a whole and especially of Saxony, is engaged in industry than in agriculture. Though there is no big concentration of industrial towns such as that of the Ruhr, manufacturing centres, ranging in size and importance from old-established commercial cities such as Leipzig and Halle to embryo towns born of new industrial developments on the lignite fields, are dotted at intervals throughout.

---

[1] Of outstanding importance in this area, which accounts for a large proportion of over half a million acres under sugar beet in East Germany.

The production of hard coal from two small fields, one between Karl Marx Stadt (Chemnitz) and Zwickau, and another near Dresden, amounting to a bare 3 million tons a year, is trifling in proportion to the requirements of industry and transport, and the available supplies of water-power are likewise small. The region is greatly dependent for its power and fuel, and for raw materials for some of the chemical industries, upon the supplies of lignite of which over 200 million tons

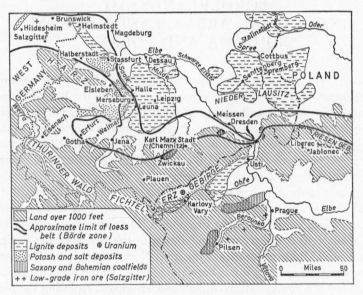

Fig. 69. Mitteldeutschland and Bohemia: relief features, loess zone and mineral deposits. (*Note*. The town formerly Chemnitz, has been renamed Karl Marx Stadt.)

are quarried per annum. The deposits occur in an area south and west of the Elbe about 40 miles wide by 50 miles N.–S. (Fig. 69), and also in another large field in Niederlausitz, east of the Elbe, where they are being worked increasingly. Much of the lignite is compressed at the quarries into briquettes[1] for industrial and other uses, or is fed into electric generating stations, some of them very large, whence the cur-

---

[1] Lignite, known as Braunkohle in Germany, being of late Tertiary origin (p. 25), occurs near the surface in seams, often 50 feet or more in thickness, and can therefore be 'mined' in open-cast pits or quarries. In its natural state it is full of moisture, and as it is very liable to crumble on drying out, it is made into briquettes by the addition of a binding substance, to make it manageable for transport and convenient as fuel.

rent is distributed to places far and near, including Berlin. Increasing
quantities are now used in large chemical factories, e.g. the Leuna
works near Merseburg west of Leipzig, for the distillation of ammonia
and motor fuels, and the manufacture of plastics and various synthetic
substitutes to meet the general shortage of ordinary metals and natural
fibres in present-day East Germany.

Potash and rock salts mined in districts east and south of the Harz,
are also exceptionally extensive. Common salt has been obtained from
the earliest times; incidentally the historic town Halle owes its name
to that mineral found in its neighbourhood. The potash salts came
into importance only after about 1860, but by 1930 this region with
its extension into West Germany was the world's leading source of
these salts and their products. The compounds of potassium, mag-
nesium and chlorine are used as basic materials for the preparation of
a variety of chemical products and for the manufacture of fertilisers.
The factories producing these derivatives from potash salts and also
those such as soda from common salt are commonly attached to the
towns in the belt from Magdeburg to Halle just east of the sources of
the minerals.

Two other forms of industry established in this region, namely the
textile and the metallurgical-precision engineering groups, are much
older than those essentially modern chemical industries. Both have
developed out of the old domestic crafts. The former, including manufactures of linens, woollens and cottons, were located in various small
towns in the Erzgebirge foreland in upper Saxony, where some water-
power was available, but with the introduction of steam power, they
became largely concentrated in factories on the Zwickau coalfield,
where Karl Marx Stadt and Plauen are the chief textile centres.
Distance from sources of supply of raw materials and the inherited
skills of the people have led to specialisation in the lighter and finer
types of the finished articles e.g. fabric gloves and stockings. The
metallurgical group is also highly specialised in the direction of high-
quality precision products. It has arisen more to the west in the
valleys of Thuringia, where it originated from domestic handicraft
industries (which are still a feature of its organisation), based on local
supplies, now largely exhausted, of tin, copper and iron from the Erz
Gebirge (Ore Mountains) and the Thüringer Wald. A remarkable
development of the precision instrument industry in pre-war years
was the huge Zeiss optical, camera and instrument works at Jena, then
of world-wide reputation.

These specialised manufactures, developed on the basis of free access to essential supplies of fuel and raw materials and to markets for their products throughout Germany and in foreign countries, suffered disruption in the post-war period. Their revival was hampered by restrictions imposed in keeping with the Soviet policy of preventing the re-integration of industries in that area, which had been one of the seats of German war potential, with those of West Germany. Some relaxation, however, has been afforded by the Soviet-East German trade agreement of 1959, whereby East Germany is free to develop up to 25 per cent of her foreign trade with external, i.e. non-Communist, countries.

An efficient system of transport by railways and roads, supplementing that on the Elbe waterway, was established under the old order. The main centres of the railway network are Leipzig and Halle, and the chief river ports are Magdeburg and Dresden, situated respectively on the north-eastern and the south-eastern borders of the region. The first three of these leading transport centres have large shares in the chemical and general engineering industries; but Dresden has been more of an elegant provincial capital than an industrial city, a characteristic that is reflected in the high-class chinaware manufactured at Meissen, a few miles away down the Elbe. A striking feature of the disposition of the towns in this Mitteldeutschland region is the four linear series of their locations — those on or near the Elbe, Magdeburg, Dessau and Dresden, those on the potash-lignite belt parallel with the Elbe, such as Halberstadt, Halle and Leipzig, the string of towns in the Thuringian basin, Gera, Jena, Weimar and Erfurt, and the upper Saxony industrial chain from Karl Marx Stadt through Zwickau to Plauen.

(II) The Upper Silesian coalfield district has been described as a young industrial landscape, the product of the diverse German and Polish ways of life, set in the midst of traditionally rural surroundings. It was developed as an integrated industrial region by the Germans during the first Reich, suffered disruption of its organisation consequent upon partition from 1918 onwards, and now under Polish control depends disproportionately upon the Baltic export markets for its main product, namely coal. The Upper Silesian developed coalfield is only part of one of the most extensive in Europe, which continues south into the Ostrava-Karviná district of Czechoslovakia; but the effective exploitation of its great resources is hampered by three physical disabilities: excessive depth of the seams except in the zones

of buried anticlines, poor coking quality of much of the coal in the
Polish-Silesian field, and continental situation on the inland borders
of the countries which have in turn controlled the area.

This area, on the margin of contact between the Hercynian and the
Alpine orogenetic systems, contains large deposits of zinc ores, which
overlap the northern section of the coalfield, and some lower grade

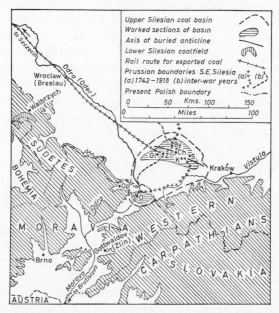

Fig. 70. Upper Silesia, the Moravian gateway and surrounding regions.
Towns on coalfields: Gl — Gliwice, Z — Zabrze, By—Bytom, Ch —
Chorzów, K — Katowice, S — Sosnowiec; in Moravia, Op — Opava,
O — Ostrava.

iron ore. The partial coincidence of metallic ores with coal-measures
(at different levels) has led to the emergence of a concentrated industrial district in a belt 25 miles long by about 12 miles wide (Fig. 70)
from Gliwice (Gleiwitz) in the west widening eastwards to include
Zabrze, Bytom (Beuthen), Chorzów (Königshütte), Katowice (renamed Stalinograd 1956) and Sosnowiec. The preponderance of the
primary forms of industry in this area of coal-pits, zinc smelters, blast
furnaces and steel works gives it a Black Country appearance. Secondary industries such as engineering and zinc-sheet manufactures have

hitherto had small chance of development. Under German control the area was used mainly as a provider of materials for finishing industries elsewhere, e.g. in Lower Silesia and Saxony, and now under Polish management the lack of skills is a serious impediment. The best prospects for its advancement seem to lie in the establishment of closer links with the more developed Ostrava-Karviná coalfield district in the Moravian Gate over the Czechoslovakian border.

In what was known as Niederschlesien (Lower Silesia), another considerably smaller coalfield lies in the folds of the Riesengebirge about 50 miles south-west of Wroclaw (Breslau). The output of this coalfield together with that of the Upper Silesian has brought the total Polish production to over 90 million tons in recent years, which leaves an appreciable margin above domestic requirements, limited by the lack of much large-scale industry. Efforts have been made to dispose of the surplus, some of it of qualities in poor demand, in export markets. To this end, rail transport facilities for handling coal have been provided from Katowice to Szczecin (Stettin) and Gdynia on the Baltic. Thus Poland has become a source of coal for deficiency countries in north-west Europe, especially Sweden and Denmark, replacing Great Britain and Germany (for the time being) in these important markets.

(III) The Czechoslovakian industrial areas in northern Bohemia and Moravia, in contrast with the Polish Silesian, are distinguished by the variety and high quality of their products, the concrete expressions of the traditional skills, creative talents and diligence of the people. While the local supplies of coal and lignite combined are considerably less than half the Polish coal production in thermal equivalent, much fuller use is made of them for industry in conjunction with the resources of timbers, glass sand, kaolin and some lower grade iron ore. Northern Bohemia is deficient in coal. The small coalfield near Pilsen is approaching exhaustion, and the 3 million tons yearly output of the Kladno-Rakovnik field near Prague, with less than half as much from that near Pilsen, would alone be quite insufficient to maintain the extensive metallurgical and other coal-using industries without large additional supplies from the Ostrava-Karviná district of Moravia,[1] which also furnishes crude steel. That district and Northern Bohemia

[1] The total production of coal in 1957 was about 24 million tons, and of lignite 49 million tons. More than three-quarters of the coal came from the Ostrava-Karviná field in northern Moravia; most of the lignite was quarried in the Ohře valley of Bohemia.

are, in fact, linked in a partnership in which each provides some of the primary materials for the finishing industries of the other.

The region of Northern Bohemia, in the basins of the upper Elbe and its tributaries the Ohře and Berounka and the lower basin of the Vltava, has been richly endowed by nature with a variety of striking scenery, with fertile lands and considerable mineral resources.[1] In the hands of its human occupants, it has become one of the most highly developed in Europe in both agriculture and industry. Outstanding in the latter group of activities are the metallurgical and engineering works of Prague (which, like those of Birmingham, produce almost anything made of steel and metal alloys from railway locomotives to electrical apparatus and fine tools), and the Skoda works of Pilsen, renowned for their engineering products, especially machine tools.

World famous also is the artistic glassware manufactured in the Ohře valley and at Jablonec in the extreme north-east, and equally graceful is the porcelain china-ware made in the Karlovy (Karlsbad) district from the local kaolin. Cotton and woollen textile manufactures are also important, the chief centres being Liberec in the north-east, Usti on the Elbe and Jachymov near Karlovy Vary; and the abundant supplies of coniferous and hardwood timbers have furnished the raw materials for manufactures, especially of furniture and paper. In addition, there is a large group of traditional processing industries based on agricultural products — brewing, e.g. of Pilsener beer, sugar refining, and manufactures of preserves and sausages in great variety.

The Moravian tectonic depression leading from the Danube to the Oder valley in Upper Silesia, though primarily a rich agricultural region, has in recent times made much headway in industry. Soft coal deposits near the nodal town Brno have helped it to become a great woollen textile centre, though it now gets coal from the Ostrava-Karviná district. The coalfields there, the southern continuation of the Polish-Silesian (Fig. 70 and p. 260), have given rise to a concentration of industry in the frontier belt Opava-Ostrava-Tesin, specialising in the heavier forms of iron and steel manufactures. Foreign iron ores are imported through Poland as well as some from Russia, and the crude steel product is in part distributed to the great engineering centres in Bohemia previously mentioned. In the Morava Valley, about fifty miles east of Brno, the small town Zlin (for some time

[1] Including besides those already mentioned, deposits of pitchblende (uranium oxide) in the Jachimov valley about 10 miles north of Karlovy Vary.

called Gottwaldov) was chosen by Bata for the site of his shoe factory, which before the war had grown to be among the largest in the world in output, the products finding ready markets in many countries.

THE NEW ORDER IN CENTRAL EUROPE IN RELATION TO GERMANY

The present territorial division of Germany into two states separated by political and economic barriers, and the re-shaping of the economies of East Germany, Czechoslovakia and Poland towards conformity with Soviet policy, cut across former alignments of trade related to geographical factors. Two obvious examples are the following: (1) The extensive exchange by land routes of diverse products between the mainly agricultural regions east of the inter-German boundary and the highly developed industrial areas west of it has been greatly reduced. (2) The Elbe River highway, formerly a great artery of traffic and export trade for Central Germany and Bohemia, has been deprived of its natural outlet and much of its usefulness by the boundary intersection above Hamburg. The balance of exports from those areas available for oversea markets has been diverted from Hamburg to the less serviceable Baltic ports.

The general effect of the post-war political changes in Central Europe has been to divide regions that are geographically continuous and economically complementary into two separate compartments, one turned west, the other east, back to back along the inter-German boundary. West and East Germany, Bohemia and the Vistula Basin of Poland all belong physically to Peninsular Europe, and to Western Europe in the culture and the normal trade relations of their peoples. The rather indefinite, non-geographical demarcation between the predominantly Germanic people west of the Oder-Neisse and Bohemia, and the predominantly Slav peoples to the east, did not, prior to the recent changes, prevent the development of considerable inter-regional trade and human intercourse, and the settlement of many Germans in the lands to the east.

Under the present order that line of demarcation between Slavs and Germans has been sharply defined. In the years 1945 to 1955 over 10 million Germans were expelled or fled from the regions east of the Oder-Neisse, some from as far away as southern Russia and Rumania —probably one of the greatest mass migrations of people in all history. These and others since have been crowded into the existing East and West German territories, especially the latter, which by 1956 had received over 10 million refugees, including those from East Germany that gained entry. Under pressure from the east originating in Russian policy, over 72 million Germans have been squeezed into 136,000 sq. miles of territory, 55 million of whom were in 1959 living within the area of 95,000 sq. miles of the Federal Republic, including West Berlin, resulting in a density of nearly 580 per sq. mile in West Germany and an overall density of 540 per sq. mile — in lands of which considerable parts are of little use for agriculture. If pre-war Germany was over-populated, as was stated in support of the claims to more *Lebensraum*, post-war Western Germany must be much more so.

Emptied of Germans, the lands to the east of the de facto Polish-German border are inhabited almost exclusively by peoples of the Slav group to which also the Russians in the main belong. All those in the present Poland and in Czechoslovakia have been gathered into the Soviet orbit, and the economies of their respective countries geared in the main towards integration in an eastern bloc. East Germany has also been swept into this group, so that the effective line of division is the boundary between the two Germanys. However, following upon some recent relaxation of the over-ruling eastward orientation of East Germany, Poland and Czechoslovakia, their trade with the outer world seems likely to increase. East Germany and Poland both have commercial ports on the Baltic through which they conduct some overseas external trade, and Czechoslovakia exports by these and other routes various specialised manufactures. The general re-deployment by means of authoritarian planning of the trade and industry of these lands, and their restricted access to Western and oversea markets, have delayed their recovery from the destruction and dislocation of war time. All of them, including even East Germany, have considerable agricultural and fuel resources, sufficient with some movements of essential products between them, e.g. of hard coal from Poland to East Germany, and additional supplies of iron ore and coke from Russia, for the establishment of balanced economies and a return to moderate prosperity.

In order to maintain themselves according to Western standards, the people of densely populated West Germany have to compete more actively than ever in the open world markets,[1] for their former large

---

[1] The proportion of urban (mainly industrial and commercial population), well over 70 per cent, is greater than that of any other European country except Great Britain.

exports of industrial products to East Central Europe and the Danubian lands have been greatly reduced. Faced with this altered situation, West Germany has become a member of the European Common Market, the European Coal and Steel Community and other West European economic organisations (p. 11). The re-unification of Germany, if ever achieved, would, by the re-establishment of an integrated German economy, probably lead to some restoration of the former extensive trade with South-Eastern Europe; it would also certainly strengthen the capacity of German industry, already effective in West Germany, to compete in West European and oversea markets.

Chapter 19

THE LOW COUNTRIES. THE
NETHERLANDS AND BELGIUM

THE inclusive title Low Countries, which gives popular expression to
an outstanding feature of the geography of the Netherlands, is commonly used for convenience to cover Belgium as well,[1] although very
little of the latter shares in that feature of unusually low elevation. In
point of fact, while about 40 per cent of the Netherlands is below sea-
level at high water, and the mean elevation of the country as a whole is
the lowest of any in the world, the larger part of Belgium is well-
drained plain, and the Ardennes section averages 1,200 feet in
elevation and exceeds 2,000 feet on the German border. Yet it is the
depressed zone within the coastal sand-dune belt of North and South
Holland, Zeeland and Belgian Flanders, rendered habitable and
productive by extraordinary protective and drainage works, that has
been the home of peoples to whom the modern Netherlands and
Belgian states owe their existence, and who have in their time made
great contributions to European civilisation in both the arts and industry.

The Romans, repelled by the damp climate and by the maze of
waterways, then more widespread and confused than now, had little
interest in the seaward parts of these lands on the fringe of their
empire; they held to the higher and drier ground along the northern
edge of the Ardennes for their line of communications between Gaul
and Cologne. Not till the early Middle Ages did this region begin to
be what it has been ever since, a centre of movement and activities in
Western Europe. With the development of sea transport and trade in
North-West Europe, the Narrow Seas became a highway for shipping
between the northern and the southern regions of the continent,

[1] Since the Netherlands, Belgium and Luxembourg agreed to establish free trade
among themselves in 1947, the collective title Benelux adopted by them has come
into general use as a geographical term. It has the merit of being a conveniently
brief title for three states that are geographically continuous and now form a single
economic unit. The name Holland for the Netherlands is not accepted in that
country, where it is used only for the provinces North and South Holland.

especially after the rise of the Hansa League. The main shipping route skirted the coast of the Low Countries between the Straits of Dover and north-west Germany, as it still does. This gave the people of those coastlands opportunities for engaging in oversea commerce, of which they have throughout made good use, specialising in transit trade. In this medium the Dutch, utilising their wealth of inland waterways, have excelled. By the sixteenth century their merchant fleet outstripped that of the previously all-powerful Hansa League, thanks in no small measure to the migration of herrings from the Baltic to the North Sea.

For the development of external contacts and commerce the people of the Low Countries have had distinctive advantages arising from their midway and singular riverine situation on the coast of North-Western Europe. The convergence of inland routes upon the sea highway is made especially effective by the fact that the Low Countries lie astride the mouths of the Rhine, Maas (Meuse) and Scheldt; all are navigable for some distance inland, and the Rhine to not far from the Alpine passes and the Rhône-Saône Valley that lead down into the Mediterranean. Moreover, just across the Narrow Seas lies Britain, which for centuries past has had active trade relations with the neighbouring parts of the continent. Thus, in the modern commercial age, the Low Countries have been a region of intersection of the frequented sea-route along their coasts with inland lines of traffic and trade, which, converging upon those lands from the continental interior, branch off from them to the British Isles and to transatlantic countries via the Channel.

In order to exploit the favourable situation for trade, the Dutch and the Flemings had to render their unpromising, partially submerged lands habitable and productive. These people have, in their age-long struggle for mastery of incursions by the sea and of flooding by rivers, shown persistence and ingenuity. The creation of the polders, begun by the Dutch about 1000 years ago with the draining of the marshes and lagoons behind the coastal sand-dune belt, has been continued at intervals ever since, and is to be crowned by the completion of the work in progress for the reclamation of large areas in the southern parts of the Zuider Zee (p. 272).

In converting to agricultural uses the redeemed land of the new polders and the sandy stretches along the shore and also inland, the Dutch and the Flemings have likewise shown persistence and ingenuity. They have literally re-made the land in many parts, removing the saline impregnation from new polder lands, canalising and re-distributing the flow of the rivers, re-conditioning the top acid peaty layers with sand and marl brought from elsewhere, and making good the deficiencies of sandy soils with catch-crops and fertilisers. Note-worthy in this connection was the early employment by the Flemings of the rotation of food-crops with fodder and root crops to eliminate the customary fallow, a practice that spread from Flanders to England and other countries of Western Europe from the eighteenth century onwards.

The people of the Netherlands and Flanders have been essentially stable and positive in their ways of life. They have displayed in an unusual measure some of the finer qualities of the blended Germanic stock to which the majority of them belong: tenacity of purpose, an instinct for orderliness, constructive talents and commercial enter-prise. The last two of these qualities were applied at an early stage to manufactures, as for example the textile industries of Flanders and the shipbuilding and the fine pottery of the Netherlands. The result of these early advances in trade and industry was a precocious development in the late Middle and early Modern Ages of urban life and a high civilisation in the small corner of Europe covering Flan-ders and the south-west Netherlands, whose inhabitants excelled in the refined arts such as painting and literature as well as in the practi-cal arts of science, invention and industry. Their commanding situa-tion in Western Europe at the onset of the seafaring age was the only really advantageous factor which, exploited to the full, led to their great achievements. The Dutch indeed, small nation as they were, held supremacy for a time at sea until in the seventeenth century they were displaced by the British, better placed and better endowed with harbours, and stronger in men and materials.

The enviable key position of the Low Countries, together with their relative weakness for self-defence, caused them to have a chequered history for several centuries previous to the general settle-ment after the Napoleonic wars in 1815. In that re-arrangement of the territorial division of Europe, a United Netherlands Kingdom was set up comprising Belgium and Holland which, however, was short-lived. A revolt in Belgium against the king's autocratic rule led to a separation in 1831, when Belgium was recognised as an independent country, its irregular boundary with the Netherlands being defined in close accord-ance with the former southern boundary of the United Netherlands when their independence was recognised by Spain in 1648.

It has evidently been for the long-term advancement of the peoples of the Netherlands and Belgium that they went their own ways. They differ at least in part in language;[1] the majority of the Dutch are Protestants, and the Belgians Catholics; and they have followed somewhat divergent paths of economic development since 1830 in keeping with their respective traditions and natural resources. Both made striking economic progress and gained rapidly in population from 1850 onwards till the 1914–18 war, when Belgium was overrun and Flanders became a cockpit. In that war the Netherlands escaped invasion and material destruction, but Belgium suffered heavy damage; while in the last war, though both countries were occupied for five years, the measure of losses inflicted on them was reversed. The Germans were careful to keep the Belgian buildings and equipment intact, intending to make use of them after the war, but left a trail of destruction behind them in the Netherlands. The rapid recovery made by Belgium after the first war, and by the Netherlands since the last war, is evidence that the peoples of both still possess the vitality which their ancestors displayed in their struggles against the forces of nature and would-be overlords.

THE NETHERLANDS

The Netherlands consist essentially of a low plain covered with deposits of recent origin, dipping gently towards, and in parts below, the level of the North Sea. The only exception to the general flatness appears in the Maastricht salient in the extreme south-east, where the land rises towards the Ardennes to 1,000 feet on the German border near Aachen. Apart from this limited area, the platform of sedimentary rocks underlying the Netherlands has apparently been subsiding at intervals with a general westward dip, and what remains above sea-level now is composed almost entirely of waste materials left by ice and by rivers in the late glacial period and since, or of sand piled in a succession of dunes along the coast. Well over half the entire country has an elevation of less than ten feet above mean sea-level. That intermittent subsidence has taken place is indicated by the alternate layers of clay, silt and peat on the floors of the polders west of the Zuider Zee.

In view of the special attention that is given to agriculture and horticulture in the Netherlands, the varied nature and constitution of

[1] Though Flemish is closely akin to Dutch, French is the language of nearly half the people of Belgium, and has a traditional status as the leading official medium.

the soils is a fundamental element of the geographical setting. These differ greatly in fertility according to the modes of their formation. The majority belong to five classes: the sands of the coastal dune belt, continued north-east into the Frisian Islands; the silts, peats and marine clays of the polder belt from the extreme north-east across the Zuider Zee into the islands in the south-west; the deltaic alluvial type

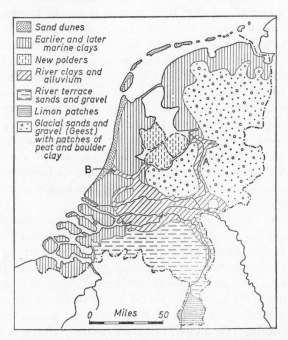

Fig. 71. The distribution of surface deposits in the Netherlands. Based on *Kleine Geologische Overzichtskaart van Nederland*, 1947. Note. The belts of river deposits at A (the present course of the Ijssel) and at B mark former post-glacial exits of the Rhine.

in the south along the courses of the rivers; the mixed glacial and fluviatile deposits with extensive sandy tracts, in the large area once covered by ice, which lies east of the Zuider Zee and north of a line from near Amsterdam to Nymegen; and the river-borne sands and gravels of the Kempenland region in North Brabant. In addition to these main classes, there is a small area of loess (limon) on the higher ground in the Maastricht salient. Thus the character of the soils in the Netherlands is closely related to the evolution of the surface geology, more clearly so than in most countries, because of the youthful development of the general topography (Fig. 71).

The Sand-dune Belt. The chain of sand dunes along the coast has been built and extended north-east from material carried by the relatively strong tidal currents sweeping through the Straits of Dover since that breach occurred 6,000 to 7,000 years ago. A wide belt of sandy shore is exposed at low tides, from which the prevailing westerly winds pick up loose particles and carry them landwards (cf. the Landes coast of France p. 175). Though the dune chain is continuous in North and South Holland Provinces except for two navigation canals, it is broken in the south by the tidal mouths of the rivers, and in the north by channels between the Frisian Islands which connect the shallow Wadden with the main North Sea. In the middle continuous section it forms a protective barrier, upwards of ten miles wide, for the polders behind lying below sea-level, and it also provides well-drained sites and wholesome water supplies for a string of towns on its margins, e.g Haarlem and The Hague. Much has been done here, as in other sandy tracts of the Netherlands, to improve the siliceous soils by the addition of balancing materials such as marl, and by the liberal use of fertilisers.

The Polders. The topography of the western inner coastlands of the Netherlands has lent itself to the creation of polders, and the general inherent fertility of the land so reclaimed has been a strong inducement for the Netherlanders to undertake such works, seeing that their country is scantily endowed with fertile naturally-drained land. The impoldering of the lagoons inside the coastal dune belt centuries ago was the first of a long series of such works. By stages, the deltaic islands of Zeeland, the alluvial belt along the triple river system in the south, and a belt inside a strip of marine and boulder clays on the coastlands in the north-eastern provinces Friesland and Groningen, have been taken in hand. In the last and greatest undertaking, that of the reclamation of the Zuider Zee, four polders, together covering about 900 sq. miles (over half a million acres), have been, or are in course of being created inside the enclosing dam, 18 miles in length, completed in 1930 (Fig. 71). These new polders will add another tenth to the area of productive land of the country, needed for the sustenance of the fast-growing population.[1] The high proportion of alluvium

---

[1] The population of the Netherlands increased from 9½ to 11 millions in the 10 years 1946 to 1956, i.e. nearly 16 per cent in this short period, and to 11·6 millions by 1959.

and clay silt in the polder soils renders them very fertile. But in spite of careful regulation and control of the drainage by means of canals, sluice-gates and power-driven pumps, the water table is commonly high on the newer as on some of the older polders, which are therefore better suited to meadow grasses and green crops than to cereals.

The Riverine Polders. The Lek, the Waal and the Maas have excavated broad shallow valleys, floored with clays and alluvium, in the coarse sediments deposited by them in early post-glacial times. The rivers themselves have been confined by massive embankments to protect the adjoining interfluves. These, as mentioned above, have been converted into polders, and together form a fertile, densely populated zone called the Betuwe, bordered on the north by the sandy glacial outwash ridges of the Veluwe, and on the south by the likewise sandy and infertile Kempenland.[1] Another narrower belt of polders lies along the course of the Ijssel branch of the Rhine from Arnhem to the Zuider Zee.

The Glacial and Fluviatile Deposits. The surface deposits of the glaciated country east and south-east of the Zuider Zee have been re-sorted in parts by rivers and streams in the considerable interval of time since they were left by an early advance of the Scandinavian ice-sheet; the original glacial topography has been modified and subdued by subsequent normal erosion. Apart from the northern coastland and polder zone in Friesland and Groningen, and the Ijssel valley, the area is covered with primary or re-sorted glacial products; among these the sand and gravel type predominates, forming the characteristic Geest landscape, especially on the surviving morainic ridges and outwash tracts, such as those of the Veluwe south-east of the Zuider Zee. As in the neighbouring north-western region of Germany, peat bogs are common in this country of low undulating relief, where waters percolating through the sand are apt to form underlying impervious hard-pan. Elsewhere the natural vegetation of the rather acid soils is mainly moorland with scanty tree growth, and as such is of little use to man. Here also, however, steps have been taken to rescue parts of the land from waste by draining bogs, removing the hard-pan, and by layer-mixing and reconstituting the soils in ways similar to those applied on the coastal sand belt.

In the absence of pronounced physical features, the Netherlands can most readily be divided into geographical regions in accordance

---

[1] This is the northern continuation of the Belgian Kempenland, described in some detail below, p. 286.

with the above classification of surface deposits in relation to their origin and land-use. The Maastricht salient in South Limburg is exceptional because, being a slice of the Cretaceous and Palaeozoic Ardennes Foreland, it differs radically in rock structure from the rest of the country. The generalised distribution of surface deposits in the Netherlands indicated in the map Fig. 71 is the leading factor which, with others arising out of the development of commerce and industry, determines the distribution of population shown in Fig. 74.

CLIMATE AND AGRICULTURE

The climate of the Netherlands is similar to that of Eastern England, though rather more extreme, especially in the regions east of the Zuider Zee, where the mean January temperature is little above 32° F. The western half of the country, comprising most of the productive land, is naturally milder, though there exposure to cold northerly and easterly winds causes frequent cold spells, and frosts and fogs are common during the six winter months. July temperatures and yearly hours of sunshine are both somewhat higher than in south-east England. Climatic conditions are thus fairly favourable for the cultivation of cereals and other temperate crops; but the more delicate horticultural species have to be grown in glasshouses of which there are many thousands of acres.

Dutch agriculture is distinguished by the relatively high proportions of the productive area used as meadowland and for horticultural purposes,[1] and also by the acreage devoted to rye and oats among the cereals, twice that to wheat and barley. The excess of meadowland over total arable is partly an expression of response to the rather misty and temperate climate, but more because of the prevalence of moist clayey soils in the reclaimed lands; rye and oats, especially rye, are the leading corn crops because these are more tolerant of sandy soils and dampness of ground and atmosphere than wheat and barley (see pp. 51–3). Potatoes are also widely grown both on the polders and the Geest. These three leading field crops, rye, oats and potatoes, together occupied nearly half the total arable acreage in the years 1958–9.

Netherlands agriculture is in the main of two distinct kinds: the intensive arable linked with dairy-farming of the polders; and the

---

[1] In the Netherlands 54 per cent of the farmland is classed as meadows, compared with 38 per cent in West Germany and only 12 per cent in Denmark. On the other hand, the proportion of the productive land used for horticulture, namely 5·6 per cent, is higher than that of any other North-West European country, if vineyards are excepted.

rye-oats-potato type of the Geest and other sandy tracts, as on similar lands in Germany. The former varies according to soil and water-table conditions. Apart from the highly specialised horticulture both in the open and in glasshouses, mixed farming is practised where-ever possible, though much of the land is best given to pastures. The rotation crops include (a) wheat, barley and potatoes, mainly for human consumption; (b) dual-purpose crops such as sugar beet and oats, providing both foodstuffs and forage; and (c) a variety of fodders for live-stock, chiefly roots and clover. Much of the farming is directed towards the maintenance of dairy cattle and pigs[1] as well as poultry, all fed on home-grown fodders and by-products, supplemented by large quantities of imported maize and of oil-cakes from oil-seeds imported for margarine manufacture. Dairy-farming with pig-raising is the leading source of agricultural income. The Netherlands have evolved the Friesian breed of dairy cattle, to yield large quantities of low-fat milk, suitable for the production of special 'lean' types of cheese, e.g. Edam and Gouda, which with other dairy products have formed the most valuable item (about a quarter) of all the country's exports.

The horticultural industry has been developed mainly for the export trade. Though the specialised production of flower bulbs in the Haarlem polder is famous, the mainstay of the industry is the cultivation of small fruits, vegetables and plants for seeds. Unlike the cultivation of primeurs in Mediterranean France, this Dutch horticultural industry is not helped much by the climate; it rests upon the high fertility of selected polder soils, the patient labour and skill of the personnel, and the extensive use of glasshouse protection. The chief market for much of the produce has been Great Britain, but the flower bulbs command world-wide sales. An interesting offshoot of the general arable farming is the utilisation of rye and potatoes as industrial raw materials as well as for human food. Gin is distilled from rye grain, cardboard products are made from rye straw, and industrial alcohol is manufactured from surplus potatoes.

On balance, the Netherlands are deficient in food supplies for the increasing population. Upwards of a million tons of wheat and other food grains are imported, in addition to large quantities of fodders such as maize for live-stock. The Netherlands have developed the

---

[1] See Table p. 56 for numbers of live-stock. Sheep are few. In the Netherlands (as also in Switzerland, Denmark and Belgium in all of which good land is relatively limited), cattle are kept wherever possible in preference to the less profitable sheep.

major forms of their agricultural industries on lines not unlike those of Britain's manufactures. They use imported raw materials, such as feeding stuffs and fertilisers in combination with their land resources and their intensive labour, to provide exports which pay in part at least for the large quantities of imported cereals and other food and fodder products. They can make the best use of their limited fertile land in special ways for which it, especially the polder land, is well adapted, leaving the large-scale production of cereals to other countries that have plenty of productive land available, and have relatively little labour to work it.

MINERALS AND MANUFACTURES

The Netherlands have very modest mineral resources (see Table p. 26) and limited supplies of home-produced raw materials, yet this small country has built up a wide range of manufactures, some on a considerable scale. The 12 million tons of coal produced annually in the Kerkrade-Heerlen district in south Limburg[1] are insufficient; imports of coal exceed exports by 4 to 5 million tons per annum. In addition, net imports of 6 million tons of crude petroleum and petroleum products[2] are needed to supplement the output of about a million tons from Schoonebeek in south-east Drenthe, which may, however, be increased following the discovery of other sources. The only other mineral of importance (excluding peat) is salt from the mines in the Hengelo-Boekelo district near Enschede (Fig. 72).

All the leading branches of industry are well represented. Foremost among them is the metallurgical and engineering group, including manufactures of electrical apparatus, and the construction and repairing of ships, which together employ about one-third of the industrial workers. Blast furnaces are in operation at Velsen near Ijmuiden at the entrance to the North Sea Canal, and iron and steel works at Utrecht, the output of crude steel amounting to a million tons per annum. For shipbuilding and the ancillary engineering industries the leading centre is the Rotterdam-Schiedam-Dordrecht area at the entrance to the Rhine waterway, followed by Amsterdam. Manufactures of electrical apparatus of all kinds ranging from motors and

---

[1] Coal-mining in the Netherlands is restricted by the uneconomic depths of the seams both in parts of south Limburg and in almost all the neighbouring Peel district where considerable deposits have been proved.

[2] The Netherlands refine great quantities of oil in transit and plan to refine still more. In 1957 they imported $13\frac{1}{2}$ million tons of crude petroleum, and exported over 7 million tons net of petroleum products.

transformers to lamp bulbs and radio sets, are very widely distributed over a number of inland towns, among which Eindhoven in Kempen-land specialises in the large-scale production of electric lamps and radio sets, and Utrecht in that of generating machinery. Another widely distributed branch of industry is the textile group producing cotton and artificial silk fabrics especially, as well as woollens and

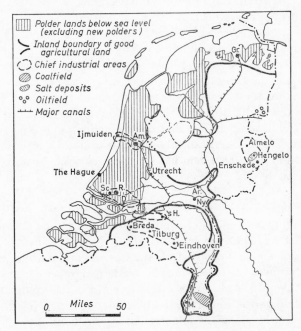

Fig. 72. The Netherlands: polders, mineral resources, industrial areas and major canals. Am. Amsterdam, Ar. Arnhem, D. Dordrecht, Gr. Groningen, M. Maastricht, Ny. Nymegen, R. Rotterdam, Sc. Schiedam, 's H. 's Herto-genbosch.

linens. This form of industry has largely developed in, or has shifted towards the poorer agricultural regions in the eastern provinces where wages are relatively low, at places such as Enschede and Hengelo in the east, which manufacture cottons, and Breda, Tilburg and Eindhoven in North Brabant.

Besides the two major branches of industry, others of considerable proportions are the processing of foodstuffs, the chemical group, oil-refining and tin-smelting, and manufactures of earthenware, glassware and footwear. The first of these deals with tropical products such as cocoa-beans, oil-seeds and cinchona bark (for quinine extract), as well as mainly imported cereals such as wheat and rice, and home-grown horticultural products (made into preserves). It is concentrated largely in the chief ports, having had long connections with the East Indies (now Indonesia). In the chemical group, both heavy products such as fertilisers and the lighter products such as pharmaceutical preparations are manufactured, the latter especially at Amsterdam. Huge oil-refineries are in operation at Rotterdam, and large tin-smelting works at Arnhem. Glazed earthenware is manufactured at Delft, which has specialised in the production of decorative tiles, and at Maastricht. Manufactures of leather goods, especially footwear, have developed in the Langstraat, a string of villages and small towns in a belt extending some twenty miles west of 's Hertogenbosch. Of all the towns in the Netherlands, Amsterdam has the greatest variety of in-dustries, for in addition to its share in shipbuilding and various lighter manufactures, it is second only in the world to Antwerp in the diamond-finishing trade, and has long been associated with printing and publishing.

COMMUNICATIONS, COMMERCE AND TRANSIT TRADE

Agriculture and industry would by themselves be unequal to supporting the Dutch people at their relatively high standard of living. Profiting by their situation astride the sea-exits of the Rhine and the Maas, at a focus of trade routes in Western Europe, they have for centuries derived wealth from extensive entrepôt and transit trades. The leading port is Rotterdam (population 740,000 in 1960), which handles large shares of the imports and exports both of the Nether-lands and of the Ruhr-Rhineland area of Germany. It is situated on the Lek close to the estuarine mouths of the Waal (the main distribu-tary of the Rhine) and of the Maas, and is connected directly with the sea by the New Waterway which takes the largest ships. It is also linked with other parts of the Netherlands by four main systems of canals supplementing the Rhine-Maas waterways: one running north inside the sand-dune belt and joining the North Sea Canal from Am-sterdam to Ijmuiden; another from Arnhem on the Lek to Groningen in the north-east; and a third, the Zuid-Willems Canal, which cuts across the great bend of the Maas, giving direct connection with that river below Maastricht; joining which, at a point north-east of Eindhoven, there is the Wilhelmina Canal from the tidewaters of the Maas delta (Fig. 73). The through waterway from Rotterdam into

Germany is along the Lek-Noord-Mervede and thence into the Waal
(Fig. 75). There is also a route through to Antwerp via the Noord and
Hollandsch Diep. Rotterdam, having recovered in full its commercial
and industrial activities after severe war damage, now ranks as one of
the greatest ports of the whole world.

Amsterdam also shares in the entrepôt and transit trades, specialising in the handling of colonial products. It arose as a port on the

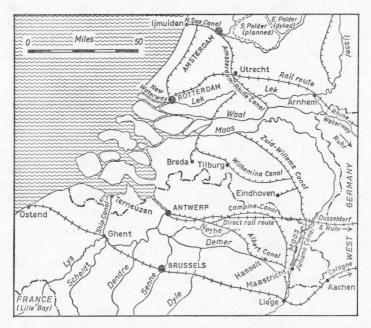

Fig. 73. The Rhine–Maas–Scheldt area of the Low Countries: through
railways and chief internal canals.

sheltered Zuider Zee (which could take the smaller ships of former
times) at a point which was near and central to the early-created
polders. Its oversea and merchant trade increased rapidly after the
Age of Discovery when Dutch navigators became active, and it
expanded further with the growth and economic development of the
Netherlands colonial empire. In order to provide access to the port for
ships of ever-increasing size and draught, the North Sea Canal was
constructed to Ijmuiden in 1876. In the recent reclamation of the
Zuider Zee a shipping channel has been provided which connects
Amsterdam with Lake Ijssel, and thence with the north-eastern

provinces. A new canal has also been constructed giving the city a direct link with the Rhine and so with the eastern Netherlands and Western Germany. Provided with all these inland and external water-way connections, and having the further advantage of centrality in the populous western section of the Netherlands, Amsterdam is in a position to compete with Rotterdam for trade. Its various activities besides extensive commerce — its functions as administrative capital and as the leading cultural centre of the country, and its diversified manufactures — have contributed to its status as the first city of the Netherlands. Its population, which was nearly 900,000 in 1956, will soon reach the million mark, if the present rate of growth is maintained.

The Hague ('s Gravenhage), a city of about 600,000 inhabitants, is the only other really large urban centre in the Netherlands. It is the legal capital and the seat of the Government, containing the Houses of Parliament and the royal residence, and also the International Court of Justice. It has been laid out spaciously as befits the official capital, on a site near the outer margin of the coastal sand-dune belt, some-what removed from the busy commercial life of the towns farther inland. Like Amsterdam and Rotterdam it has been gaining population, though chiefly of wealthy people and those retired from active life. Other towns except Utrecht (260,000) all contain less than 200,000 inhabitants. Some of them have been mentioned above as centres of industry of one or more branches. Several, such as Utrecht and Leyden, are old towns that have survived and grown by grafting new industries upon their shrunken historic functions.[1] Others have arisen by reason of special conditions, e.g. Haarlem as the commercial capital of the bulb-growing district, Alkmaar and Gouda as centres of cheese production, Groningen as the regional and administrative capital of Groningen Province, and Hook of Holland and Flushing as outports for 'ferry' shipping services with England.

The main concentration of towns, including the three large cities, is largely related to the intensively developed and densely populated western polder zone. Another group including Dordrecht, Nijmegen and Arnhem lies along the great river waterways. Away from these main urban groups are two strings of towns, all associated with industry or mining more than with agriculture, that including Breda, Tilburg and Eindhoven in the sandy borders of the Kempenland, and

---

[1] Both were great seats of learning in the 17th and 18th centuries, and still rank among the leading university towns of the Low Countries.

that including Enschede, Hengelo and Almelo in the Geest country, on the German border. Medium-sized towns, ranging in population from 50,000 to 150,000, are numerous. Urban life, noted above as a feature of the early development of the Low Countries, is equally, if not more marked in the present-day Netherlands, where the people increasing in numbers faster than in most other European countries must turn more and more to industry.

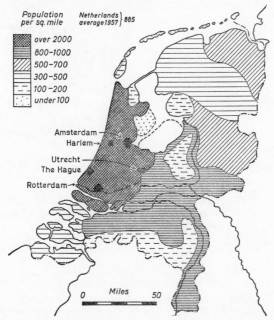

Fig. 74. The distribution of population in the Netherlands. Low densities in the southern Kempenland, the Peel marshes, the Veluve and the new polders contrast with the remarkably high density in North and South Holland, where the five large cities marked contain a quarter of the entire Netherlands population. There, as well as in the riverine country, industry and commerce no less than intensive agriculture contribute to the livelihoods of the crowded inhabitants. Sources: *Digest of the Netherlands*, The Hague, 1958 and *Physical Planning in the Netherlands*, The Hague, 1955.

THE HISTORICAL BACKGROUND

The human element looms large in the geography of the Netherlands. In no other country in the world is the land, as it now is, so much the work of men's hands. The disorderly landscapes left by melting ice, vagrant rivers and transgressing seas have been transformed into coherently serviceable forms which bear the stamp of the

personality of the people — their instinct for tidiness and their reso-
lute persistence. In the period 1900–50 more than 1¼ million acres
were won from water and waste land, resulting from the completion of
parts of various long-term reclamation projects.

Because the making of the present-day landscapes in characteristic
parts of the Netherlands has been the work of the Dutch people
through the centuries, and because their present political existence

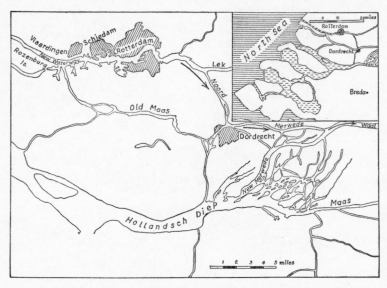

Fig. 75. The Rhine–Maas delta and Zeeland: dyked areas S. of Rotterdam
liable to flooding. In the flood disaster of 1953 over 350,000 acres were
invaded by the sea, and in order to guard against a repetition of this misfortune, the Delta Plan has been taken in hand, to be completed in about
20 years. Waterways based on Netherlands Survey 1949, scale 1:200,000
(=3·15 miles to 1 inch), and later map for changes since 1953. The inset
map shows how the completed Plan will by the construction of sea-wall
dams, convert three arms of the sea into a freshwater lake, the Delta Lake
to be. Plans have been prepared for the construction of the future Europort
to occupy Rozenburg Island.

and economic life are also in no small measure the outcome of their
resistance to foreign masters and of their commercial enterprise in the
past, historical geography stands in the forefront of the geographical
picture of their country. The Dutch people have suffered great
reverses in bygone times from which they have made sure, if sometimes slow recovery. Land lost to the sea has been regained, foreign
domination has been overthrown, loss of supremacy at sea has been

succeeded by great expansion of sea-borne trade. Our times too have brought them disasters. Their land has suffered total invasion and much material destruction, and a large colonial empire has melted away. Yet from the first of these misfortunes rapid recovery has already been made, and the loss of imperial trade and material wealth caused by the second has in part at least been made good by a thrifty use of resources to extend the area of productive land and to expand industrial output by investment in buildings and plant.

The people of the Netherlands have to rely now for the support of the increasing population almost entirely upon what they can make of the situation and the limited resources of their own small country. Works are planned which will enable both agriculture and industry to expand, and also assist the further development of commerce. Among them are the reclamation of the southern and western sections of the Zuider Zee, the building of inter-island sea-walls to form the 'delta lake', and the construction of ports on Rozenburg Island south of the New Waterway (Fig. 75), in particular Europort (designed to serve Western Europe in general) at the North Sea end of the island opposite Hook of Holland, where also vast new steel works and installations for the bulk handling of oil, coal and ore are to be erected. These and other works are being undertaken with characteristic Dutch enterprise and thoroughness.

Chapter 20

BELGIUM AND LUXEMBOURG

BELGIUM resembles the Netherlands in some respects — in the gradual fall of the lowlands towards the partly submerged delta region, in the sand-dune and polder belt along the coast and in the sandy Kempenland (Campine)[1] region on its border. But otherwise there are essential differences between them in their general physical geography, as well as in the detailed features of the elements they have in common. Neither the modified glacial topography which characterises much of the eastern Netherlands, nor the wide river flood plains that intersect the southern part of that country, are to be found in Belgium; and whereas only a fragment of the Netherlands belongs to the Ardennes, more than a third of Belgian territory lies in the region of these highlands. Nor has Belgium been subject to recent incursions of the sea on its short stretch of coast, for the sand-dune belt there, though narrower than it generally is in the Netherlands, is unbroken and strong enough to keep out the sea without the construction of sea-walls. Belgium, in short, is almost entirely part of the solid continent well above sea-level, while the Netherlands, at least in their western half, are in their natural state more like a deltaic swamp, liable to be flooded in parts at intervals with any rise of the water-level relative to that of the land.

PHYSICAL REGIONS

Belgium covers less than 12,000 sq. miles, little more than twice the size of Yorkshire, yet it contains a considerable variety of structural and topographical features (Fig. 76). Western Belgium inland to the line of the Scheldt consists of Maritime and Inner Flanders. The

---

[1] Many place names in western and central Belgium have alternative Flemish and French forms. Excepting those names that have been anglicised e.g. Brussels, Scheldt, the general rule is to use the form corresponding to the language of the area, i.e. Flemish in the West; but the boundary is indefinite, and where both forms are current, the less common one according to the language of that part is given in brackets.

former comprises three zones. Bordering the forty miles of the North
Sea coast is a cordon of sand dunes up to a mile in width. Behind this
lies a polder belt mostly above sea-level, seven to ten miles wide, which
like the Dutch polderlands is systematically drained and intensively
utilised for crops and pastures. A third zone is the gently undulating
Maritime Flanders Plain, covered in the lower parts (below about 60
feet elevation) with extensive deposits of recent alluvium. Inland lies
the belt of generally higher ground of Inner Flanders, up to several
hundred feet in the hilly parts, distinguished in the main from Central

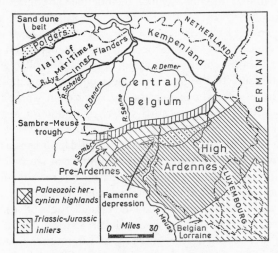

Fig. 76. The physical regions of Belgium.

Belgium by the absence of limon deposits. In the early Tertiary
period the sea covered the whole of Western Belgium as well as the
adjoining parts of the Netherlands and French Flanders, leaving in
Belgium deposits of clay in the southern parts and of sandy materials
towards the north, which dip westwards under the later accumula-
tions of alluvium and coastal sand hills in Maritime Flanders.

East of Inner Flanders the various regions are aligned more in
a direction ENE.–WSW. parallel with the Sambre-Meuse Valley.
Central Belgium (the Brussels Basin), which is the heart region of the
country in other ways besides its position, is a low plateau which
slopes northwards from an elevation of 500 to 600 feet along the
Sambre-Meuse furrow. It is approximately the area drained by the
fan of right-bank tributaries of the Scheldt e.g. the Dendre and

the Nethe-Demer-Dyle-Senne group, uniting north of Brussels. The southern half of the region is covered with fertile limon, thin in the west upon the Tertiary sands and clays, thick in the east where it rests upon the remnants of Cretaceous beds in places, and on older rocks elsewhere. North of Brussels the limon cover gives way to mixed sands and clays, which merge east of Antwerp into the mainly barren sands of the Kempenland.

The Kempenland is a plateau of low elevation which occupies the area north of the Albert Canal and extends over the border into the Netherlands. The underlying rocks, which include the Carboniferous series, slope downwards, as does the region in general, to the north-west. These are covered with layers of sands, gravels and some alluvium, averaging about 50 feet in thickness, which were deposited probably by the Meuse in the course of its wanderings when swollen with melt-water at the close of the Ice Age. These uppermost deposits being pervious, little water appears on the surface, except where the existence of underlying hard-pan causes waterlogging and the formation of lakelets, or where in some places clayey alluvium is exposed on valley floors. The leached, acid soils give rise to heathland forms as the prevailing natural vegetation with scattered growth of stunted trees. In recent times parts of the Kempenland have been reclaimed for agriculture and forestry by similar methods and with similar great expenditure as on sandy tracts in the Netherlands (pp. 268–9). On such reconstituted tracts rye is cultivated and dairy cattle are kept; market-gardening is established near Antwerp, and thousands of acres have been planted with coniferous trees. The main economic resources of the Kempenland do not, however, lie in the re-made soils, but in the coal-measures deep below the surface, which are described later.

The Sambre-Meuse depression belongs to the Palaeozoic formations that compose much of the rest of Belgium. The southern edge of the Brussels Basin, overlooking this valley between Charleroi and Liège, marks the general boundary between the relatively soft prevailing Tertiary beds with recent superficial deposits to the north and west, and the compact ancient rocks of the Ardenne region and its periphery. The Sambre-Meuse Valley itself, with the Mons district in the upper Scheldt Basin, extends for 90 miles from the French border west of Mons to the Dutch border east of Liège, with an average width of about 5 miles. The convergent valleys of the Meuse, which cuts across the western limb of the Ardennes, and of its tributary the Sambre, both valleys leading from France and continuing eastward in the main valley towards the Rhineland, have attracted traffic from early historical times. Their importance in this respect has been greatly increased during the last century or so with the exploitation of the coal-measures in the Charleroi and Liège sections of the depression, as well as in the Mons area. Here on the margin of the Ardennes in Belgium is a greater concentration of transport traffic, economic activity and population, especially in the 60 miles of valley downstream from Charleroi, than anywhere else in the long course of the Meuse from the Vosges to the North Sea (Fig. 77).

The Ardenne highland region shows definite Hercynian ENE.-WSW. trends in the alignment of the Pre-Ardenne belt bordering the Sambre-Meuse Valley, in that of the Famenne depression which separates the Pre-Ardennes from the High Plateau, and in those of the resistant residual ridges of the latter along the axes of early folding. The Pre-Ardennes, composed of Devonian limestones and sandstones, are divided into two plateau blocks by the deeply incised valley of the Meuse above Namur, namely the Condroz to the east and Entre-Sambre-et-Meuse to the west. Their average height is well under 1,000 feet, and on the lower northern slopes and in the trenched valleys the better land is taken for agriculture, while the rest is mainly covered with pine forests. The picturesque scenery of some of the wooded river gorges e.g. at Dinant and at Spa (which is also a health resort) has attracted visitors and tourists both from Belgium and abroad. The Famenne depression lies in a belt of relatively soft Devonian shales, which is followed by the Ourthe and other tributaries of the Meuse in their longitudinal courses. The deeper soils and lower elevation of the depression have resulted in more continuous agricultural settlement in it than on the highlands on either side.

The High Ardennes, generally over 1,500 feet and exceeding 2,000 feet in places on the eastern border, are composed of ancient metamorphic rocks. As such, they form a bleak moorland region, with numerous peat bogs, and some woods in the more sheltered situations. They contain no minerals of economic value, and are mostly uninhabited. The adjoining south-east corner of Belgium, defined as Belgian Lorraine, together with the greater part of Luxembourg, are quite different in structure from the High Plateau. Geologically they are the northern extension of the Jurassic and Triassic formations of French Lorraine (p. 298). As in France, these northern Jurassic beds also contain deposits of phosphoric iron ore, little of which, however, is on the Belgian side of the border with Luxembourg, which contains the main part of a wedge of these Mesozoic rocks, framed by Hercynian highlands, and drained eastwards to the Moselle by the Sure and its tributary the Alzette (Fig. 79). Geographically Luxembourg belongs to Lorraine, but in its economic relations it has been closely linked with Belgium, especially in its iron-ore export trade.

CLIMATE, AGRICULTURE AND FOOD SUPPLIES

The climate of Belgium naturally resembles that of the neighbouring parts of the Atlantic regions of Europe. Small as the country is, its extension in longitude gives rise to three sub-types of climate: (1) the Flemish, much like that of south-east England, but with greater liability to cold spells in winter when continental air breaks through; (2) the central, of which Brussels is representative, where the seasonal range exceeds 28° F. (7° F. more than in London), and the mean annual rainfall is nearly 30 inches; and (3) the modified mountain climate of the Ardennes. As may be expected, the agriculturally productive lowlands are somewhat colder in winter and appreciably warmer in summer, and their frost-free growing season is slightly shorter than that of southern England. In these parts climatic conditions are favourable for the cultivation of all ordinary temperate crops and even make it possible to grow some of warm temperate origins such as tobacco (in sheltered valleys) and table grapes (in greenhouses without artificial heating).

The population of Belgium had increased to approximately 9 millions in 1957, which gave an average density of 765 per sq. mile of the whole country; but less than 59 per cent of the area is classed as either arable or meadowland, so that in effect there are more than 1,300 inhabitants per sq. mile of agriculturally productive land — far more than can be supported on even the richest land in temperate latitudes. The typical agricultural unit is the small family farm, off which any surplus produce above the owner's or tenant farmer's requirements is sold to town markets. Two-thirds of the pre-war Belgian farms were under five hectares (twelve acres), and only one per cent over 50 hectares. For many of the small farmers and the members of their families, farm work is a part-time occupation, supplemented by employment in neighbouring towns. In those conditions the large-scale cultivation of cereals is not practicable, though in the aggregate about a quarter of the arable acreage is devoted to the bread grains wheat and rye (260,000 hectares out of 1·05 million ha. in 1955–6).

Mixed farming is the general rule, in which oats, roots and green crops, and sugar beet have important places in the customary rotations. All these provide fodders for live-stock, especially dairy cattle and pigs. The proportion of occupied land under permanent pasture in Belgium is small compared with that in Great Britain or the Netherlands, so that less hay is available for winter provender. A special feature of land-use round the larger towns, notably Brussels, is the intensive 'spade' cultivation of vegetables and small fruits, the more delicate in glass houses. Much of the cultivated land in Flanders and the northern parts of the Brussels Basin is of the predominantly sandy type, rather infertile in its natural state. In those parts much has been done to improve the quality of the soils by the skilful employment of green manuring, i.e. ploughing in catch-crops to supply humus, and by growing forage crops for cattle, mostly stall-fed, the manure from which is fed to the hungry land. These methods have formed the basis of the continuous rotation cropping which originated in Flanders.

The high density of population in Belgium necessitates large importations of foodstuffs and fodder materials to supplement domestic production. The general practice is similar to that of the Netherlands, namely to concentrate on dairy cattle and pigs in line with the rotation series, and to make good the deficiencies in cereals etc, with supplies from abroad. Considerably more than half the requirements of wheat are imported, and also large quantities of maize and oil-seeds. In spite of the weight given to live-stock in the agricultural economy, Belgium has to import additional supplies of meat and dairy produce. Its resources of productive land, whether naturally fertile or artificially improved, are clearly limited in proportion to the needs of the population, 63 per cent of whom are urban dwellers.

FORESTRY V. SHEEP FARMING

Nearly 19 per cent of the area of Belgium is covered with forests or woods, most of which have been planted and are managed by public forestry authorities. Coniferous trees are favoured for two reasons: they yield serviceable timber in much shorter time than do deciduous trees; and they succeed on the sandy tracts in the Kempenland and other northern parts, as well as at lower elevations on the Ardennes. In both these classes of country, it is considered that better use can be made of the land for growing timber than as rough grazings. Correspondingly, little land is left of the kinds that are commonly used in other countries for sheep pastures. Of all the countries in Western and

Central Europe, excepting Denmark and Sweden, Belgium has the fewest sheep, little more than 160,000 all told.

MINERAL RESOURCES AND MANUFACTURES

The modern industrial development of Belgium, dating back well over a century, has been closely associated with the Sambre-Meuse coalfield. The Carboniferous rocks in this belt hard up against the Ardennes have been subjected to much faulting, and workable seams are restricted to the Mons (Borinage), Charleroi and Liège sections. The first of these was formerly the main centre of production, which has since shifted eastward to the other sections. The output of the Sambre-Meuse zone has latterly shown a tendency to decline, partly because the coal-seams are difficult and costly to work, and partly because the great bulk of the coal now raised consists of grades unsuitable for coking. After rising to well over 20 million tons per annum, production has fallen back to round about 17 million tons (1958), less than two-thirds of the total Belgian production. The cost factor is a drawback; without subsidies the Sambre-Meuse coal would be the most expensive in Europe.

The shrinking supplies from the Sambre-Meuse fields have been offset by the rising production of the more recently developed Kempenland coalfield, which lies in a belt extending for 25 miles east of Turnhout, parallel with the Albert Canal. The reserves there are estimated to be three times as great as those of the Sambre-Meuse region, and the coals moreover are of good coking quality. Unfortunately the seams all lie at considerable depths, sinking from about 1,600 feet in the east to beyond the workable limit west of Turnhout. In spite of this disadvantage, production in the Kempenland coalfield is stimulated by its accessibility by way of the Albert Canal to both Antwerp and the Liège area. A further inducement to expand output there lies in the fact that Belgium normally imports 5 to 6 million tons of higher-grade coals, though in bulk these are largely offset by exports.[1]

Deposits of zinc in the Calamine-Moresnet district north-east of Verviers near the German border have been worked for a long time, but production there is now of small account compared with the large

[1] There are considerable inward and outward movements of coal and coke between Belgium and neighbouring countries of the European Iron and Steel Community. On the average of the years 1957–8 Belgium imported 5·4 million tons of coal and coke and exported 4·6 million tons.

quantities of unrefined zinc consumed by the smelting works round Liège and other metallurgical centres; and the small average annual output of low-grade iron ore, (equivalent to less than 50,000 tons of metallic iron) mined in Belgian Lorraine in the south-east, obviously forms an extremely small proportion of the requirements of the iron and steel works which produce some 6 million tons of crude steel per annum.

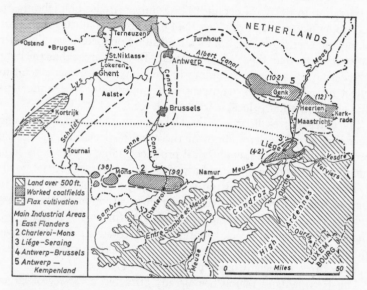

Fig. 77. Belgium and Netherlands Limburg: worked coalfields, industrial districts. The dotted line indicates the approximate division between Flemings (N) and Walloons (S). The figures in brackets against the worked sections of the coalfields give the production in millions of metric tons, average 1957–58.

Thus almost all the iron ore and non-ferrous metals required for extensive Belgian manufactures of steel and steel products and of zinc and copper products must be imported, and part of the coking coal or coke consumed in the furnaces as well. The nearest and the chief sources of iron ore are Luxembourg and French Lorraine, the latter the more important, and much of the semi-refined copper and zinc concentrates have been obtained from the ex-Belgian Congo. In view of Belgium's deficiencies in respect of iron ore, non-ferrous metals and coking coal, it is noteworthy that steel and base metals contribute nearly 30 per cent of the value of all exports. Processing in its wide sense is a basic element of the Belgian economy.

Most of the Belgian heavy metallurgical industries have from their early start been located in the productive parts of the Sambre-Meuse coalfield where, although both iron ore and coke besides almost all the metal ores have to be obtained from elsewhere, they tend to remain through geographical inertia. Some modern zinc- and copper-refining plants have, however, been established in the district east of Antwerp, using Kempenland coal, and some iron and steel works are in operation in Belgian Lorraine. The Sambre-Meuse belt labours, in fact, under several disadvantages. Not only are its coals unsuitable for coking and costly to mine, but its inland situation loads it with heavier transport costs than those of the Antwerp-Brussels area; thus the light engineering industries, expanding in Belgium as elsewhere, tend to collect round those two main centres of population, where the supplies of labour and the local markets are large.

The chief centres of large-scale steel manufactures and engineering are Liège and Charleroi. Both of these have specialised in making secondary or finished metallurgical products, some of relatively high value e.g. cutlery, firearms and a variety of non-ferrous metal goods at Liège, and electric apparatus and equipment at Charleroi. In contrast with Liège, which has an attractive situation on the Meuse and has remained fairly clean in appearance for an industrial town, Charleroi is a typical 'black country' centre. In addition to large iron and steel and engineering works, it has chemical industries and glass manufactures, especially of plate and window glass.

The Kempenland region has already attracted a variety of large-scale industries besides zinc-smelting, e.g. manufactures of chemicals such as fertilisers, and of glass, as well as many of the specialised artisan type. It is likely to develop as a major industrial area in time, but of the modern character, with works and workshops generally dispersed rather than gathered in urban clusters.

Flanders has been famous in the past for its woollen and linen manufactures. The former declined relatively with the rise of the Yorkshire industry, and the latter has lost momentum owing to the general contraction in the demand for linen goods in recent years. The cotton textile industry has outdistanced its forerunners in Flanders, though woollen manufactures remain in some strength. The cotton industry has become centred mainly in Ghent and the neighbouring smaller towns such as Lokeren, Aalst (Alost) and St. Niklass (St. Nicholas) which obtain supplies of raw cotton, imported by way of the canal connecting Ghent with Terneuzen on the Scheldt Estuary in

Netherlands territory. The linen industry has been traditionally associated with the flax-producing region of the upper Lys valley at Kortrijk (Courtrai) and smaller towns close to the French border. There the textile group remains the leading form of industry, but on a more modest scale than in the neighbouring Lille-Roubaix district of French Flanders. To these traditional groups of manufactures using natural fibres Flanders has in recent times added those of synthetic fibres which, as in various other textile districts of Western Europe, are of growing relative importance.

Though Flanders has been and is the greatest textile region of Belgium, Verviers in the Vesdre valley east of Liège has long-established woollen manufactures, associated originally with supplies of wool from sheep formerly kept in numbers on the neighbouring parts of the Ardennes. Zinc-mining there has declined to insignificance, but the woollen industry remains, now using mainly imported wool.

Besides the above somewhat specialised areas, a belt of quite varied manufactures extends across Belgium from Mons and Charleroi in the south, through Brussels to Antwerp and its satellite towns in the north. Almost every branch of manufactures is established at one place or another in this belt, the aggregate output of which is very large. Some forms of industry are peculiar to the two large cities, among them shipbuilding and diamond-processing at Antwerp (which now handles two-thirds of the world's rough diamonds), and manufactures of refined furnishings and furniture at Brussels. The majority are scattered over dozens of smaller towns, most of which are grouped in circular patterns round the large urban centres, Antwerp, Brussels, Charleroi and Mons. Each of these serves as a nerve centre for its group of subsidiary towns, controlling and integrating their economic activities by means of fully developed radial systems of transport.

TRADE AND TRANSPORT

The large volumes of foodstuffs and bulky raw materials imported, and the corresponding large quantities of finished and semi-finished goods exported, are the concrete expressions of the framework of the Belgian economy. Like Great Britain's it is based upon trade and manufactures, but, unlike Great Britain, Belgium has only a small tonnage of merchant ships, about one-tenth of that of the Netherlands. Industrial resources other than coal are few and scanty; labour and organisations are the key factors. Though much of the extensive external trade is with the three neighbour countries, the Netherlands,

France and Germany, sea-borne trade accounts for upwards of half the whole, and of that over 80 per cent passes through Antwerp. This port, moreover, shares in the transit trade of the Ruhr-Rhineland region of Germany, in which it has the advantage of being considerably nearer than Rotterdam by the direct railway route (Fig. 73), and thus has become one of the half-dozen major ports of Western Europe. Internally, it is connected with the Sambre-Meuse region by two main systems of canals, the Albert to the Meuse near Liège, and the Central via Brussels to Charleroi, and it is also linked with Ghent and western Flanders by the Scheldt waterways and canals; externally it communicates with the open seas by the Scheldt Estuary in Netherlands territory, through which (and along the Rhine waterway as well) free transit was assured under the terms of the treaty with the Netherlands in 1839.

Ghent and Bruges became important trading cities in the late Middle Ages, when they could be reached by sea-going ships. As active ports they declined with the silting of the waterways, the passing of the wool trade and the shifting from Flanders of the main currents of Western European commerce. Bruges contains reminders of its former greatness in the historic buildings which were erected by the cloth merchants; but, although its connection by canal with the sea (at Zeebrugge) has been restored, it cannot now be anything more than a minor port, owing to its restricted hinterland and the increase in the size of ships. Ghent is better able to compete for trade. It is much more central to the industrial districts of Flanders, and the Ghent-Terneuzen Canal takes vessels drawing up to 24 feet of water.[1] It is the second port, and third in population (161,000 in 1957) among the towns of Belgium, though quite overshadowed by Antwerp. Ostend, like Dunkirk (p. 204), has an artificial harbour excavated in the shelving sandy shore, but it handles little heavy merchandise. It has grown as the port for fast passenger and goods traffic with England, and as one of a number of popular resorts on this invigorating sandy coast.

Of the larger towns situated at intervals along the Sambre-Meuse Valley, Charleroi is almost purely industrial. Namur and Liège, though also industrial towns, owe much of their historical, and a large part of present-day importance to their situations as centres of communications. Liège lies at the confluence with the Meuse, of the

---

[1] This canal is to be deepened to take the largest vessels, so that Ghent may become a great inland port like Manchester.

Ourthe and the Vesdre, which bring the eastern half of the Belgian Ardennes into its orbit. On the wider national and international plane, Liège is the meeting place of three major lines of communication and commerce — by the Albert canal from Antwerp, by the Sambre-Meuse Valley from France, and by the Vesdre Valley from Cologne, from which it is only about 70 miles distant by the much-used railway through Verviers and Aachen. Commerce and industry combined have contributed to its growth as the fourth city of Belgium, containing over 157,000 inhabitants in 1957. Namur, situated at the point where the Meuse turns east and is joined by the Sambre, has long been a strategic route centre. Its modern development is related more especially to textile and miscellaneous manufactures, and to the large-scale movements into Belgium of iron ore from Luxembourg and Lorraine.

Well provided as the lowlands of Belgium are with inland waterways, they have besides a dense network of efficient railway transport, the arterial lines of which radiate from Brussels. This city has the advantage over many other capitals of being near the geographical centre of the lowland area of less than 8,000 sq. miles, into which are compacted the vigorous life and varied activities of more than 8 million people. In a limited way Brussels is an inland port, accessible for smaller vessels by canal from Antwerp. It has the further peculiar advantage of lying just north of the line of division between the Flemish and the Walloon (French-speaking) population of Belgium,[1] and is thus in a position to hold in hand and to regulate the somewhat diverse outlooks and interests of both elements. Having all the attributes of a capital city, being the hub of the network of communications and the chief cultural centre of the country, and having a great variety of processing and light industries, Brussels has grown far beyond any other Belgian town. Its population approaching a million in 1958 is nearly four times as large as that of Antwerp, the next in size.

The People and the Country

As a political unit Belgium is a comparatively new country not much more than a century old, and its people thus lack the corporate maturity that comes from centuries of experience in living together as

[1] This line begins in Belgium at the French border just south of Kortrijk (Courtrai), and runs east slightly south of Brussels to some distance north of Liège (Fig. 77). The proportion of Flemings is now about 55 per cent of the total population.

a nation. The Belgian population, like the Swiss, consists in the main of two elements, Germanic and French, of which the former is more numerous in both countries. But whereas free co-operation has been the keynote of the Swiss Federation, the relations between the two elements in the population of Belgium have lacked complete harmony, owing to the reluctance of the formerly dominant French section to concede terms of parity to the Flemish, growing faster than it in numbers.[1] Belgium is a kingdom, and having adopted a unitary

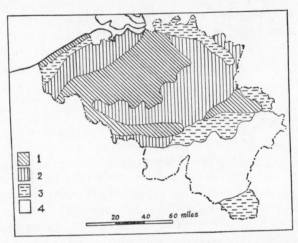

Fig. 78. The distribution of population in Belgium. Per sq. mile: (1) 500 to over 2,500, (2) 250 to 500, (3) 150 to 250, (4) under 150. Based on officially estimated figures of population 1957, and C. Mertens. *La Répartition de la Population Belge.*

form of government is not likely to change over to a federal constitution on the Swiss model. A solution of the difficulties may emerge in time with the absorption, already in progress, of Walloons from the Sambre-Meuse region into the industrially more active Flemish-speaking areas. In the meantime the French element is apt to suffer from a minority complex.

Belgium, less the unproductive parts of the Ardennes, has an average population density of well over 1,000 per sq. mile, one of the highest for a comparable area in the temperate regions, and is moreover but moderately endowed with fertile land and with mineral resources, (see above p. 288). Yet the country as a whole has been relatively prosperous. While it is true that the people like those of the

[1] It is estimated that by 1980 Flemings will outnumber Walloons by 2 to 1.

Netherlands make the most of their opportunities and resources by enterprise and hard work, Belgium has had two distinct advantages compared with the Netherlands and several other North European countries; she emerged from the last war with productive equipment more or less intact; and in addition to having relatively large coal resources, she was able to draw upon the Congo Territory for valuable supplies of minerals for industry such as copper and zinc, and of various forest and plantation products.

The Belgian economy like the British, depends for its successful functioning upon the free flow of international trade. It is highly vulnerable to disturbances caused by warfare in Europe, or to general trade depressions originating abroad. Thus Belgium, being a comparatively small country, has been desirous of entering into arrangements such as the Benelux Customs Union, which widen the range of her markets free from vexatious tariffs and restrictions. For similar reasons also, Belgium has joined the European Common Market group of countries. Yet whatever steps are taken, a population problem of an economic order remains; that of maintaining a reasonable standard of living for increasing numbers of people who desire to stay at home on a land of limited resources, who in the absence of any large sources of income from invisible exports e.g. from shipping services, must earn their livelihood mainly by industry.

LUXEMBOURG

The general features of the physical structure and the iron ore trade of Luxembourg noted incidentally above (p. 287), may now be related to the general make-up of that small country. The independent Grand Duchy of Luxembourg (granted a constitution in 1841) is a kind of pocket area in the Ardenne region, inhabited by people of mainly French speech, and enclosed by French, Belgian and German territory. It covers an area of barely 1,000 sq. miles, about one-third of which belongs to the Ardennes, and the rest is composed of Triassic and Jurassic rocks of lower elevation (Fig.79). The Lias beds of the latter on the French border contain the deposits of low-grade phosphoric iron ore, of which about 7 million tons containing upwards of 2 million tons of metal are extracted per annum.

Before the introduction in the 1880's of the Thomas-Gilchrist process for treating phosphoric ores, Luxembourg was a poor agricultural country. Exports of iron ore to Belgium and the establishment of large iron and steel works have brought some wealth, though all the coal and coke requirements have to be imported. This modern heavy industry producing $3\frac{1}{2}$ million tons yearly of crude steel is concentrated on the iron ore field at Esch-sur-Alzette and neighbouring small towns, and together with mining and quarrying employs

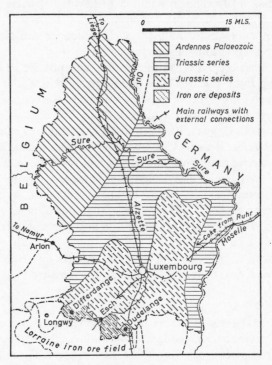

Fig. 79. Luxembourg: geological structure, iron ore field and through railway routes.

about a quarter of the working population. Of the rest the majority are engaged in agriculture for local requirements. The total population is about 320,000, of whom nearly one-third live in the two largest towns, namely Luxembourg, the capital, and Esch-sur-Alzette on the iron-ore field.

Chapter 21

THE BALTIC LANDS. THE SCANDINAVIAN COUNTRIES AND FINLAND

THE Baltic lands, Scandinavia, Denmark and Finland, constitute a distinctive region, remarkable not only in its structural features and its anomalous high-latitude climate, but also in the virile and constructive adaptation of its peoples to the exacting conditions of generally harsh environments. The area as a whole is composed of two parts, the outer Atlantic maritime and the inner northern Baltic basin, the line of division being roughly the boundary between Norway and Sweden and thence southwards through peninsular Sweden. Notwithstanding this distinction and the fact that both Norwegians and Danes have turned outwards to the high seas rather than inwards to the Baltic, Norway and Denmark form integral parts of the Baltic lands by geographical situation as well as by the contributions of their peoples in the past to the creation of a distinctive Scandinavian world.

The Fennoscandian area, comprising the Baltic Shield together with the Caledonian highland zone, was unattractive for settlement except on the coasts in early times, as much of it still is owing to high relief, the general poverty of the soils and the hard climate of the northern parts. The meagre agricultural resources of those lands except in a few favoured spots, together with the abundant supplies of timber for the construction of ships in early times, prompted the Scandinavian peoples to take to the sea for fishing, and later to seek outlets for increasing population by oversea colonisation. The impressive expeditions of the Northmen or Vikings in their dynamic period from A.D. 800 to 1,000 led to the settlement of the Faeroes, Iceland and western Greenland by Scandinavians (whose descendants form the present-day population of the Faeroes and Iceland). They also led to the earliest discovery by Europeans of North America (on the coasts between Labrador and Cape Cod). The vigorous outward drives of the Northmen from Norway and Denmark in that period led also to their well-known settlements along the eastern coasts of Britain and the Channel coast of France in Normandy (the former kingdom of the Northmen). With the consolidation of the Anglo-Norman power under the Normans, these southern avenues of oversea settlement were closed to further ventures. Thenceforward Scandinavian expansion by landings in force came to an end, except for the occupation of Finland by Sweden and for Swedish ventures in the eastern Baltic lands.

Thrown upon their own lands of limited agricultural and commercial resources, the Scandinavian peoples found themselves in a backwater until after the middle of the 19th century, when they began to benefit from the improvements in transport and the rapid progress of mechanical invention. In the meantime pressure of population at home, and the attractions of newly developed lands in North America and elsewhere for able-bodied emigrants, caused the Scandinavian countries to lose heavily by emigration. Norway, having the least productive land, suffered most in this way; the number of people of Norwegian descent now living in the United States is said to exceed the total population of Norway.

Since about 1880 the tide of general economic development has clearly turned in favour of the Scandinavian countries. Cheap sea transport has enabled them to find ready markets abroad for bulky products such as timber, wood pulp and iron ore. The development of means of generating hydro-electric power has eased the problems of the three northern countries in obtaining supplies of fuel and power for industry; it has further enabled Sweden and Norway in particular to establish wide ranges of electro-chemical industries, including the manufacture of nitrogenous and other fertilisers, e.g. by fixation of atmospheric nitrogen, which have benefited their agricultural industries by increasing the yields of meadows and field crops from the commonly leached soils. The invention of processes by which soft woods such as spruce can be converted into wood pulp, paper and rayon has made it possible for the peoples of Scandinavia and Finland to find other profitable uses of their most abundant raw material, besides producing sawn timber and fittings made of timber.

These and other technical advances, together with the intelligent efforts and organisation of peoples able to take advantage of, and even to improve upon them, have contributed to a general increase in prosperity in the 20th century, notably in Sweden. In all the Baltic countries there is now a large and growing industrial output and, in all except Finland, more people are engaged in the manufacturing group of industries than in agriculture.

Though the three northern countries have some features in common in both their physical and their human geography, differences between them in situation, structure, natural resources and political history have caused each to follow its own special path of economic development. Thus Norway, poor in agricultural resources and having no great mineral wealth, has taken advantage of its situation and fine natural harbours to specialise in maritime pursuits. Sweden, endowed with considerable resources of minerals as well as of timber and water-power, has developed important metallurgical and wood-processing manufactures as the mainstays of her economy. Finland, a country of forests, marshes and lakes leaving little good agricultural land except round the coasts, and for centuries under foreign domination, has had to rely, as she still does, upon forest products as the main source of income. Denmark, on the other hand, differing fundamentally in structure from her neighbours of Fennoscandia, and having no significant natural resources other than the fertile soils of the ground moraine, has become the most specialised dairy- and pig-farming country in the world.

General Structural and Relief Features (Fig. 80)

Much of the extensive knowledge that has been gathered concerning the complex structural development of the Baltic lands is of greater geological than geographical interest. Yet some of the basic physical features and economic distributions can be adequately explained only by reference to geological processes spread over vast periods of time from remote ages to the present day.

Three major structural elements compose the Baltic lands: the Pre-Cambrian Baltic Shield which forms the bedrock of the whole of Finland, most of Sweden and part of Norway; the metamorphic Palaeozoic series of the Caledonian zone along the western border of the Shield; and the later stratified Cretaceous rocks in Skåne and Denmark. The existing relief has resulted primarily from the effects of the Caledonian orogenesis, together with subsequent differential movements in the surface of the Shield, especially its marked upward tilting towards the Caledonian zone; though the agents of erosion, notably glaciation, have played a large part in modifying the details of the surface features.

The Scandinavian highlands and the Caledonian structures. A belt of highest relief runs NE.-SW. from northern Norway along the Swedish-Norwegian boundary, rising to an average height of 3,000 feet in the Kiolen ridge, and thence into south-west Norway, where it broadens into a series of plateaux which exceed 6,000 feet over considerable areas. North of the Oslo depression this highland belt is composed of three structures: the uptilted edge of the Baltic Shield, the Caledonian overthrust and the Caledonian root zone, in that order from east to west. In southern Norway the Caledonian fold zone, turning westward in the so-called Bergen arc, breaks through the Archaean

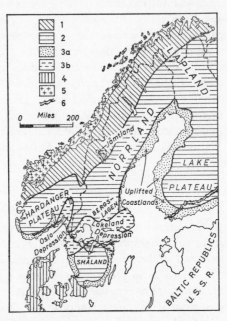

Fig. 80. The structural regions of the Baltic Lands. 1. Caledonian. 2. Baltic Shield. 3a. Uplifted coastlands. 3b. Lakeland and Oslo depressions. 4. Cretaceous platform. 5. Outer Archaean belt. 6. Salpausselkä, Central Swedish and Ra end moraines.

elements to the fiord coast, thus separating the high plateau of the Jotunheim and Dovre Fjells on its north-west flank from the Hardanger Plateau south-east of it. This plateau is continuous, but for the Oslo depression, with the Baltic Shield platform of Sweden.

West of this highland zone the land falls away steeply; abruptly into the sea on the fiord coastland of south-west Norway, but from Trondheim northwards into a longitudinal depression on the outer margin of the Caledonian root zone, beyond which an irregular belt of Archaean rocks extends along the coast. East of the highland axis in Sweden there is a comparatively gradual slope into the shallow Gulf of Bothnia, in contrast with the generally steep descent on the west.

In the Caledonian orogenesis great masses of Cambro-Silurian rocks were forced up out of a geosyncline to the west of the Baltic Shield. These were thrust eastward over the Shield in a huge nappe, now much broken by fractures, for a distance of 80 miles in places and well beyond the present Swedish boundary (Fig. 81). Though the

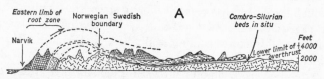

Fig. 81A. Section approximately 75 miles E.S.E. from Ofoten Fiord (Narvik) showing denuded Caledonian overthrust composed of schists and limestones lying upon original Cambro–Silurian beds. Source, *Atlas over Sverige.*

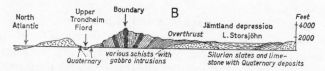

Fig. 81B. Section approximately 160 miles E.S.E. from Atlantic in lat. 64° 10′ N. showing root zone, overthrust, Jämtland depression and portions of the basal Shield rocks. After A. C. O'Dell and others.

sedimentary rocks became metamorphic and resistant under the great pressures that generated the thrust movements, they have suffered heavily from millions of years of erosion acting especially on fracture belts. Their eastern front in Sweden has been worn back to a sinuous edge called the Glint Line (Scandinavian Klint=cliff), leaving outliers here and there; and portions within the main surviving overthrust nappe have been removed by erosion, thus exposing the basic Archaean rocks in 'windows'. On the outer Atlantic margin the Archaean belt has been attacked intensely by the agents of erosion acting especially along the numerous fractures. The coastal zone has been cut into a succession of magnificent fiords, and has been frayed into one of the most intricate coasts in the world, with a long string of hundreds of islands called the Skerryguard (Skjaergård) marking the former extent of the mainland.

The Pre-Cambrian Baltic Shield. Having undergone repeated compression, elevation and peneplanation, the Shield is almost entirely composed of crystalline and metamorphic rocks, mainly gneisses and schists. Submerged for a time in the early Palaeozoic era, it was covered with Cambro-Silurian beds which, following upon general re-elevation, were for the most part stripped off by erosion. These strata have survived only in some down-faulted areas such as the Jämtland basin in north-central Sweden and the Oslo depression, and on the eastern margins in Russia, where the Pre-Cambrian platform dips underneath them.

Though the Shield has resisted folding since Pre-Cambrian times, it has sagged in the medial zone of the Gulf of Bothnia, and is seamed with faults and fractures running NW.–SE., N.–S. and E.–W., many of which separate upthrust tabular blocks and horsts from down-faulted depressions. Examples of these tectonic features are extremely numerous. The scores of horsts in southern Sweden as well as the Småland Plateau are fault-bounded uplifts; the lake basins of the central Swedish lakeland belt, and the Jämtland Basin and the Oslo depression already mentioned, are some of the zones of downward displacement; and many of the lakes in Finland are aligned NW.–SE. along bands of weakness caused by fractures. Owing to these vertical movements the surface of the Shield is far from even. This old land mass has, in fact, been much disturbed, more in the southern parts than in the northern, by earth movements associated with mountain building elsewhere, especially in the later periods of its long history.

The Cretaceous platform of Skåne and Denmark. A NW.–SE. fault in south-west Sweden marks off the Cretaceous beds of Skåne and Denmark from the Shield structures except for some horsts composed of ancient rocks in Skåne, aligned with the boundary fault. The thick chalk strata which form the bedrock of these two areas are however, masked by glacial deposits and appear only in cliffs here and there on the coasts. Though Skåne and Denmark owe their surface features, except for the horsts in Skåne, to the mantles left by the Scandinavian ice-sheets, they belong structurally to the Central European Plain.

THE EFFECTS OF GLACIATION

The ice-sheets deposited great masses of transported rock waste within the southern limits of the Baltic lands and beyond them. That of the last glaciation left two main belts of moraines, an outer one of terminal moraines which curves round from northern Germany into the Jutland Peninsula, and an inner belt deposited during a long period of rest in retreat, which includes the Salpausselkä ridge extending 300 miles across southern Finland, the Ra moraines in the Oslo depression, and others along the southern margins of Lakes Malar and Hjälmaren in Central Sweden (Fig. 80).

On the inner concave sides of these moraines a wide zone is characteristically strewn with winding eskers and drumlin mounds consisting of varied mixtures of sand, gravel and clays including boulder clay, with intervening 'tunnel' valleys[1] and hollows, often occupied by lakes or bogs; but most of eastern Denmark and of Skåne in Sweden have a cover of ground moraine in the form of fertile boulder clay. On the outer margin of the terminal moraine in Jutland a zone of outwash sands extends to the North Sea coast, but the corresponding outwash zones of the terminal moraines in Finland and Norway have been mostly covered by marine clays. The interval of time since the final disappearance of the sheet ice has in general been too short for the subaerial weathering agents to form fresh soil on the mountains and plateaux of Scandinavia and on the interior of Finland scoured by ice, or for a maturely developed drainage system to come into being on the hummocky lowlands. On the former such soil as exists is derived from morainic debris with patches of downwash and peat; on the latter the common occurrence of lakes and swampy tracts inland from the coastal belts, has led to a concentration of settlements on the naturally drained moraines and eskers, wherever the soils could support agriculture.

Though glaciation in itself has produced little fertile land except where it has left tracts of boulder clay, its subsequent indirect effects in causing changes in relative land and sea-levels have contributed much to the agricultural resources, particularly of Finland and Sweden. Extensive belts of marine clay occur along the southern coast of Finland and on the Bothnian coastlands of Finland and Sweden; similar belts extend also across both the lakeland region of Central Sweden and the Lim Fiord depression of Jutland, as well as on coastal patches in south-east Norway. Wherever the climate is not too severe, the accessibility and comparative fertility of these marine clay belts have caused them to attract a population who live by agriculture and fishing.

These deposits resulted from a sequence of post-glacial changes

---

[1] Formed by melt-water streams issuing from frontal tunnel-like caves in the retreating ice-sheet. The so-called fiords (German förden) on the Baltic coast of Schleswig-Holstein are the submerged valleys of such westward-flowing glacial streams, and thus differ in origin and form from true fiords.

which developed as follows. As the ice-sheet withdrew to Fennoscandia, an ice lake formed in the southern Baltic basin, enclosed by a land bridge connecting south Sweden with Denmark. With further melting away of the ice-mass, and the consequent rise of the general sea-level, a passage opened over the lakeland depression of Sweden, and the

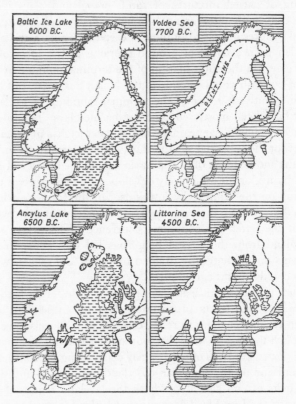

Fig. 82. Four stages in the recession of the Scandinavian ice-sheet. Source: *Atlas over Sverige.*

Yoldea Sea[1] was formed covering an extensive area (Fig. 82). At a later stage the land in the southern Baltic area, relieved of its previous load of ice, began to rise faster by isostatic adjustment than did the general sea-level through accessions of melt-water; a Dano-Swedish land bridge was re-established, converting the Yoldea Sea into the

[1] This and the names Ancylus and Littorina of post-glacial bodies of water in the Baltic region have been adopted from those of the characteristic shell fossils found in the deposits laid down in each in succession.

Ancylus Lake, which overflowed across Denmark. In a subsequent stage the continued rise of the general sea-level from the melting of ice-sheets, without a corresponding rise of the land by isostatic adjustment, caused the North Sea to break through over the region of the Danish islands; the Ancylus Lake became the Littorina Sea which, with further adjustments of relative land and sea-levels, and the development of channel connections with the North Sea along glacial melt-water valleys through the present Danish straits, was the direct fore-runner of the existing Baltic Sea.

Hence the melting away of the great ice-sheet set two counteracting processes in operation, though the isostatic rise of the unburdened land has in general lagged behind the eustatic rise of the sea-level; the land is still rising at the rate of several feet a century towards the head of the Gulf of Bothnia, long after the disappearance of the Scandinavian ice-sheet. There the total elevation of the land by over 1,500 feet has greatly exceeded the rise in the level of the seas and oceans, while in Denmark and southern Sweden the two processes have produced nearly balanced effects and, if anything, the present slow rise of the sea is causing it to encroach upon the land. This explains why post-glacial marine deposits cover comparatively wide belts on the coast-lands of Finland and of Sweden north of the River Dal, whereas in southern Sweden and Denmark they are restricted mainly to the former sea passages across Central Sweden and northern Jutland. Western Norway has shared in the isostatic rise of the neighbouring parts of Sweden, but the general steepness of the land above and below water has precluded the emergence of any extensive marine beds. It is generally thought, however, that the strandflats at several levels on the margins of some of the fiords and Skerryguard islands have resulted from marine erosion in periods when the land stood at lower levels than now, relative to the ocean.

The present Baltic (or East Sea) and its three associated gulfs of Bothnia, Finland and Riga occupy an area of 170,000 sq. miles of shallow basins, generally less than 50 fathoms deep, partly on the southern margin of the Baltic Shield, and partly (in the two large gulfs) in zones of sagging of the Shield. The Baltic has the character of an inland sea, free circulation between its waters and those of the outer seas being much impeded by the threshold form and constriction of the Danish Straits.

Thus largely insulated and apart, the Baltic 'Lake' has a very small tidal range, and as it receives at least three times as much water from rain and rivers as it loses by evaporation, its waters are brackish to fresh; and the salinity ranges from about 15 per mille near Denmark to 2 per mille at the head of the Gulf of Bothnia, compared with upwards of 34 per mille in the North Sea. The excess of water accumulating in the Baltic causes an outflow of relatively fresh water through the Sound into the Kattegat, but there is a reverse under-current of salt water, which accounts for the much higher salinity in the Danish area than at the heads of the gulfs.

The comparative freshness and the shallowness of the inner Baltic have two effects of geographical significance. The marine fauna differs from that of the outer seas, being restricted to species adapted to the peculiar conditions of temperature and salinity; and the inshore waters, especially those of the gulfs of very low salinity, are liable to be closed to shipping in winter by freezing. Solid surface freezing which puts an end to shipping during four to six months in the Gulf of Bothnia, may in very severe winters cause even the south-ern Baltic ports to be out of service for weeks.

CLIMATE, NATURAL VEGETATION AND AGRICULTURE

Scandinavia and Finland are situated in an area of climatic transi-tion from south to north as well as from west to east. The cool temperate climate of Denmark and southern Scandinavia passes into a sub-Arctic type in Lapland; and the dominant Atlantic influence on the western coastlands gives way to semi-continental conditions some-what sharply eastward of the Scandinavian highlands, but only gradually from the Jutland peninsula to southern Finland. In this region of contending climatic controlling forces the continental tend to push out from northern Russia towards Swedish Norrland, and to be encircled on the north round northern Norway and on the south across Denmark, south Sweden and the Baltic by the Atlantic in-fluence. Whereas the northern Bothnian ports are closed by ice for five months in the winter, Helsinki in south Finland, and Murmansk on the Arctic coast of Russia, can generally be kept open with the help of ice-breakers. Correspondingly, at the height of the short summer season of the Lapland region, mean temperatures there are little lower than those of places in the Baltic approaches. The Scandinavian highlands act as a distinct climatic barrier screening the interior lands from the humid and relatively equable conditions prevalent on the Norwegian coast.

Precipitation is generally sufficient for the growth of trees and crops, wherever temperature and soil conditions permit. It is excessive in western Norway, where it amounts to over 80 inches in many places. It declines to under 25 inches in Central Sweden (21·6 inches at Stockholm) and to less than 20 inches in the northern coastlands of Sweden and most of Finland, where however, the low rate of evapora-

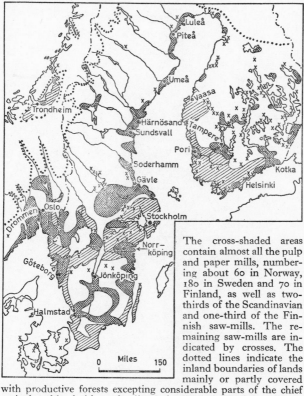

The cross-shaded areas contain almost all the pulp and paper mills, numbering about 60 in Norway, 180 in Sweden and 70 in Finland, as well as two-thirds of the Scandinavian and one-third of the Finnish saw-mills. The remaining saw-mills are indicated by crosses. The dotted lines indicate the inland boundaries of lands mainly or partly covered with productive forests excepting considerable parts of the chief agricultural lands (shown by diagonal ruling, cf. Fig. 85).

Fig. 83. Scandinavia and Finland: forest lands, saw-mills and wood pulp and paper mills.

tion and the slow melting of winter snowfall raise the effectiveness, making it sufficient for plant growth. There the setbacks are opposite in kind; the lack of active sunshine, the leached soils, and the not uncommon poor drainage inducing the formation of bogs, restrict the areas of productive forests and the extension of agriculture.

The predominant form of natural vegetation in the Baltic lands is forest. The Central European mixed type reaches into south-east Norway and thence across Sweden a little north of Stockholm, but selective clearance has removed most of the deciduous woodland in Denmark and Scandinavia, leaving indigenous or planted coniferous stands in areas unsuitable for agriculture. In the rest of Scandinavia and the greater part of Finland coniferous forests, composed mainly of

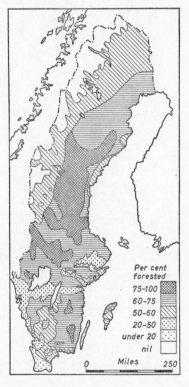

Fig. 84. The distribution of forests in Sweden. Source, *Atlas over Sverige*.

spruce and pine, have become established within the limits set by latitude, altitude and soil conditions (Fig. 83). High altitudes and exposure to strong winds greatly restrict the forested areas in Norway, confining them chiefly to the south-eastern region, and high latitude in northern Sweden and northern Finland causes coniferous forests to give way to scattered woodlands of stunted birch. Swedish Norrland and the Lake Plateau of Finland contain the largest areas of productive forests, and both are supplied with special natural facilities in waterways and water-power for their exploitation. Sweden, having more productive forested land than Finland and four to five times as much as Norway,[1] leads by far in the output of timber and forest products, the more so because of a higher average yield of wood per unit of area.

Scandinavia and Finland are situated in areas of transition in agriculture as in climate, from temperate to cold temperate types. Wheat, rye and deciduous fruits such as apples and pears cannot be ripened properly north of a line from Trondheim along the Dal River into southern Finland, and very little sugar beet is grown anywhere in Scandinavia and Finland except in south-west Sweden, although it is commonly cultivated in Denmark. North of the above line arable farming is restricted, by the shortness of the growing season, to the less exacting cereals barley and oats, with larger proportions of fodder crops and rotation grass, the latter more for hay than pasture. Even so, farming is possible only on the scattered relatively flat stretches of fertile soil, the largest of which are the Norrland coastal belt and the Jämtland and Trondheim depressions. Live-stock, mainly dairy cattle, provide the bulk of the farm products of these northern regions, which depend upon supplies of staple foodstuffs such as wheat and sugar from districts farther south or imported from abroad.

In southern Scandinavia and southern Finland wheat and potatoes are important crops together with all those grown in the northern regions. The cultivation of rye, formerly a staple crop, has declined in all three northern countries in favour of oats, and also of wheat with the introduction of fast-maturing varieties such as those adapted to Canadian conditions, the oats and the inferior wheat being used chiefly as animal fodders. In Denmark only, of all the four countries, is a larger acreage given to rye than to wheat for reasons explained later (p. 344). The following Table shows the relative importance of the four chief cereals, sugar beet and potatoes in Scandinavian agriculture.

Production average 1956–57 (1000 tons)

	Wheat	Rye	Barley	Oats	Sugar beet (root yield)	Potatoes
Norway	43	—	307	159	—	1201
Sweden	831	249	585	990	1786	1755
Finland	188	120	317	679	247	1474
Denmark	270	302	2981	819	2467	1961

[1] Estimated areas of *productive* forests (1,000 sq. miles): Sweden 88·2, Finland 66·7, Norway 19·0. See also Table p. 45.

The generally cool and cloudy climate of the northern Baltic lands is more favourable to the growth and cultivation of pasture grasses and forage crops than of bread cereals. As the cattle are housed and stall-fed six or more months in the year (up to eight months in parts of Finland), very large supplies of hay and fodders are required for their maintenance. In general, rotation grasses, clover and forage crops occupy a large proportion of the cultivated land. Hay alone accounts

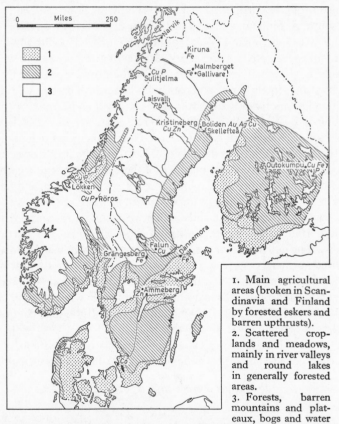

1. Main agricultural areas (broken in Scandinavia and Finland by forested eskers and barren upthrusts).
2. Scattered croplands and meadows, mainly in river valleys and round lakes in generally forested areas.
3. Forests, barren mountains and plateaux, bogs and water surfaces; scattered saeters in the south and Lapp grazings in the north. The chief exploited mineral deposits are indicated by symbols. (Fe, Cu etc); P pyrites, Co coal.

Fig. 85. The distribution of farm lands and of mineral resources in the Baltic countries.

Based on *Atlas over Sverige*; W. R. Mead, *The Scandinavian States and Finland*; and A. C. O'Dell, The *Scandinavian World*.

for two-thirds of the acreage devoted to all field crops in Norway, and for upwards of half the total in Sweden and Finland. In southern Sweden and Denmark, where the open, frost-free season is relatively long, hay is a less important crop; rotation grasses are used more as grazing pastures than preserved for hay, and a wider variety and greater quantities of crops serving primarily or partly as fodders, including oats, barley, swede turnips, sugar beet and potatoes, are grown on the farms.

In response to climatic conditions which favour green crops more than bread cereals, and also to the normal relative market prices for the various farm products, agriculture in the four Baltic countries leans heavily towards dairy-farming and the associated pig and poultry keeping. Though the production of wheat has increased in Sweden and Finland, that of the bread grains, wheat and rye combined, falls short of consumption in these two countries, and much more so in Norway and Denmark. On the other hand, even the three northern countries are able to cover their requirements in dairy produce, with a surplus for export at times, which has helped to meet the cost, as notably in the case of Denmark, of considerable imported supplies of wheat.

MINERAL RESOURCES

The known mineral resources of the Baltic lands are concentrated with few minor exceptions in four areas: Gällivare-Kiruna, Boliden, and Bergslagen-Dannemora in Sweden, and Outokumpu in Finland, all in the ancient metamorphic rocks of the Baltic Shield. The Caledonian belt of Norway contains little besides a few lean and scattered deposits of pyrites ores with some medium-grade iron ore in Finnmark, and the Cretaceous rocks of Denmark offer nothing but chalk.

The productiveness of those four leading areas makes Fennoscandia an important source of metallic minerals. The deposits of phosphoric iron ore in the Gällivare-Kiruna district in Swedish Lapland, of which some 14 million tons are annually exported, are estimated to constitute upwards of 90 per cent of the total West European reserves of high-grade iron ores. These deposits, containing 60 to 70 per cent of iron, were of little value until the Thomas-Gilchrist process for the treatment of phosphoric ores came into general use from 1880 onwards, and the large-scale development of the extensive Kiruna ores awaited the construction of the railway to Narvik in 1902.

At Boliden near the port of Skellefteå, about 150 miles south of Gällivare, a large mineralised zone was discovered in 1924 underlying thick deposits of glacial drift. The ores there yield a variety of metals, including copper, lead, zinc and gold, in addition to sulphur extracted from the sulphide metallic compounds, but contain inconvenient proportions of arsenic. In contrast with this new field, the Bergslagen district in the middle Dal basin north-west of Stockholm has for centuries past been a centre of mining and of metal-working industries, formerly using mainly charcoal fuel for smelting. It has, in fact, been the nursery of the traditional skills that have enabled Sweden to develop a wide range of distinctively specialised metallurgical industries in modern times. The minerals now mined beside iron ore include pyrites, lead, zinc and manganese. The copper deposits, long worked at Falun, now contribute little to the Swedish output, and the phosphoric iron ores in the Grängesberg district are mostly exported. Of greater importance now in the Swedish economy is the high-grade haematite iron ore of Dannemora, about 25 miles north-east of Uppsala, which is reserved for the domestic metallurgical industries.

An extensive ore body at Outokumpu in east central Finland, 250 miles by railway north-east of Helsinki, contains the largest deposits of copper in Europe, which give Finland first place among European countries in the production of that metal. The composite ores at Outokumpu contain also considerable proportions of iron and sulphur, and a smaller percentage of zinc. The rest of Finland produces but small amounts of copper and nickel, since the loss to Russia in 1940 of the Petsamo nickel-producing district on the Varanger Fiord. The scattered Norwegian deposits are mainly low-grade copper-sulphide ores worked at three centres, at Løkken south-west and Røros south-east of Trondheim, and at Sulitjelma 67° N. in Nordland. The only other minerals of any importance produced in Norway are quarried granite, sulphur from the reduction of the sulphide ores (pyrites), and iron from Sulitjelma pyrites, as well as from the Sydvaranger mines inland from Kirkenes on the Varanger Fiord, which are now being actively worked with the aid of coal from Spitzbergen.

WATER-POWER RESOURCES

Agricultural lands, forests and mineral deposits are three major natural resources of the Baltic lands; but, with the exception of Denmark, their endowment of the first is rather meagre, and the present

scales of utilisation of the second and third would be impossible
without a fourth class of resources, namely water-power. With modern
means of transmitting current these resources are of the utmost value
for industrial and general purposes to the people of those lands, which
furnish scarcely any fuels besides wood and peat.

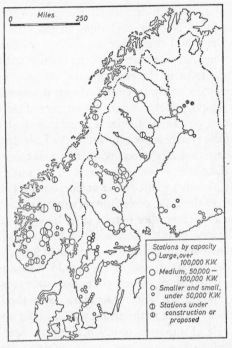

Fig. 86. Hydro-electric power stations in Scandinavia and Finland.

Norway, Switzerland and Sweden lead the world in their outputs of
hydro-electricity per head of populations.[1] They all have an unusual
combination of physical factors favourable for the development of
hydro-electric power — high relief, heavy precipitation on the highland catchment areas, a fairly open climate which enables the rivers to
keep running, large natural storage reservoirs in the forms of elevated
lakes and ice-fields, and numerous falls on the rivers from hanging
valleys and over rocky ledges and moraine-formed dams. In Finland

[1] See Table p. 26. Norway produces 6,600 kWh. of hydro-electricity per head
per annum, and Sweden over 3,000, compared with less than 1,000 kWh (nearly
all thermal) generated in Britain.

the conditions are less favourable; though storage lakes impounded by moraines exist in abundance, the generally moderate elevation of the interior plateau limits the heads of water, and the severe winters are apt to slow down the drainage system by freezing of inland waters.

With some exceptions the larger power stations in Norway and Sweden are concentrated in regional groups (Fig. 86), of which five contribute the largest outputs, namely the south-west Fiord and the Telemark groups in Norway, and those of the Lake Väner region, southern Norrland and the upper Lule River in Sweden. In both southern Norway and northern Sweden, further stations are under construction. As most of the economically available water-power in southern Sweden is already developed, the great potential resources of the Norrland region, which contains 80 per cent of the Swedish total, are being harnessed. In particular a huge power station has been constructed at the Harsprånget cataract on the Lule River, from which current is transmitted at 380,000 volts over a distance of nearly 600 miles to the distributing centre at Västerås, to serve the Lakeland industrial belt. Another giant power station on the Ume River, over 100 miles south of the Lule, came into service in 1960.

Finland has a much smaller output of hydro-electricity than either Sweden or Norway, mainly because of the less helpful physical conditions mentioned above, partly also because of a less advanced scale of industrial development, and of the loss to Russia in 1940 of the Vyborg (Viipuri) territory, which contained over 30 per cent of the hydro-electric power capacity. Denmark is naturally unable to generate electricity except at thermal stations, which are handicapped by the high price of imported coal. Considerable supplies of hydro-electricity have for some time been 'imported' from Sweden by cable across the Sound, augmented since 1953 by an additional cable, transmitting at 200,000 volts, between Hälsingborg and Elsinore.

Chapter 22

SWEDEN AND FINLAND

COVERING nearly 174,000 sq. miles, Sweden is approximately twice as large as Great Britain, but contains only one-seventh as many inhabitants (7·5 millions). Its average density of population, 43·1 per sq. mile, is lower than that of any of the other West European countries except Norway and Finland. The actual density varies greatly over the country, according mainly to the basic physical conditions of climate, relief and rock formation, the nature of the surface deposits and of the soils derived from them, and also to urban development — from an average of 166 per sq. mile in the three south-western counties to less than 8 per sq. mile in the two huge northernmost counties, which comprise more than one-third of the total area.

Sweden falls into two major geographical regions, divided roughly by the parallel of 61° N. slightly north of Gävle near the mouth of the Dal. The southern peninsular region, containing considerable agricultural and some mineral resources, is a long-settled, maturely-developed land in which the Swedish people have grown as a nation. The northern (Norrland) region, more continental in situation and climate, has till recently been a frontier area, covered largely with forests, in which the few settlements of any size were the timber ports at the mouths of the rivers. The people of the south have developed a variety of specialised manufactures, external commerce, and intensive agriculture where possible. Those of Norrland, relatively few in numbers, have depended mainly upon the extractive industries of forestry and mining as means of livelihood. A considerable proportion of them still do so, though agricultural settlement is advancing along the coastal lowland and important wood-processing and some ore-refining industries have been established at various coastal towns (see pp. 323–4).

SOUTHERN SWEDEN

In contrast with many comparatively uniform major lowland regions of Western Europe, or even with the Norrland region, southern

Sweden is a complex area of sharply differentiated land forms. It is composed of an assortment of structural elements, the cultural landscapes of which are diversified according to the human responses to their distinctive features. These may be grouped in five broad regional types, namely Skåne, the Småland (or Gotaland) Plateau, the coastlands on either side of the Plateau, Central Sweden or the Lakeland Zone, and the dissected upland country of Berslagen rising northwest to the high fjäll (Fig. 80).

(I) Skåne differs essentially in structure from the rest of Scandinavia. Its platform of thick chalk beds broken by elongated horsts of old rocks is covered in the intervening stretches with fertile boulder clay with some sandy eskers. Though it has shared in the faulting and the differential movements characteristic of southern Scandinavia, it is more akin to the neighbouring island of Zealand in Denmark in general structure and in the intensive forms of dairy-farming common to both. It covers little over 3 per cent of the area of Sweden, but its contribution to the economy of the country is proportionally much greater; over 70 per cent of the land is under cultivation, compared with about 9 per cent for the whole of Sweden.

Skåne is the chief wheat growing region of Sweden, and is the only part where sugar beet is cultivated on any large scale. It specialises like Denmark in dairy-farming and pig-keeping as basic features of the prevailing rotation systems in which fodder crops of various kinds are alternated with cereals and sugar beet. Its situation at the gateway into the Baltic has offered facilities for commerce centred at ports along the straits of the Sound, especially at Hälsingborg and Malmö at the northern and southern entrances respectively. Malmö has also developed important shipbuilding and engineering industries. Except at Malmö, now the third town in size of Sweden, and at Hälsingborg, Skåne has little manufacturing industry besides the processing of agricultural produce. It mines some 300,000 tons yearly of inferior coal; but its situation remote from the main centres of population and supplies of hydro-electric power is a disadvantage.

(II) The Småland Plateau, now standing at about 900 feet in the higher parts, is a section of the Pre-Cambrian Shield that was uplifted with block faulting in the Tertiary period, and remained an island when the surrounding parts were intermittently submerged in postglacial times. It is a barren land strewn with moraines and dotted with lakes in tectonic or in ice-formed hollows, especially on the southern margins. In this land of moors, peat bogs and forests, farming is necessarily scattered in valley pockets. The uplands have little permanent population, but numerous settlements have arisen in the marginal valleys, and even some towns as centres of communication and industry.

A striking physical feature of this roughly circular-shaped upland area is the narrow down-faulted segment of the Lake Vätter trough, the southern apex of which reaches far into the plateau. There Jönköping, the largest town within the area, has developed as an important centre of communications, of manufactures of safety matches,[1] and of metal-working industries. Other forms of industry of some importance in the Småland area are pulp and paper-making in various small towns on the eastern side, and long-established glass manufactures in the south-east noted for the artistic finish of their products.

Jönköping has direct access by Lake Vätter to the Gota Canal connecting Lakes Vätter and Väner, and continuing east from Lake Vätter by the valley of the Motala River, which carries the overflow of the lake to the Baltic Sea. Similarly the western section of the canal follows the Gota River by which Lake Väner discharges into the Kattegat at Göteborg. This through waterway across penisular Sweden, completed in 1832, is valuable as a means of internal transport linking the lakeside towns with the ports at either end, but is not much used as a short cut, alternative to the sea route through the Sound.

(III) The coastlands bordering the Småland Plateau on the east and south-east, together with the Baltic islands Öland and Gotland, are composed of Cambro-Silurian rocks including limestones, more readily weathered than the crystalline Pre-Cambrian. These eastern lowlands and the Halland coastland south of Göteborg have an irregular cover of glacial drift and are primarily agricultural areas. Karlskrona, on a fine natural harbour in the south-east corner, is the chief Swedish naval station; Visby on Gotland Island, formerly a great centre of Hansa trade, now has only local importance.

(IV) The Central Depression or Lakeland Zone, the heartland of Sweden, comprises four sub-divisions, the lowlands round Lake Väner in the west, and the Malar-Hjälmaren, the Uppsala and the Ostergötland lowlands in the east (Fig. 87). The depression widens from about seventy miles across in the Lake Väner section to twice that width in the east between Gävle and south of Norrköping. It is a

[1] Invented by J. E. Landström, and first produced on factory scale in 1845.

region of down-faulted lake basins and of low projecting horsts of ancient crystalline rocks, and is traversed by eskers trending north to south. In the flatter intervening parts there is a covering of comparatively fertile marine clays (p. 305).

These productive tracts, amounting to nearly half the total area, together with the modified maritime climate, make the Lakeland Zone

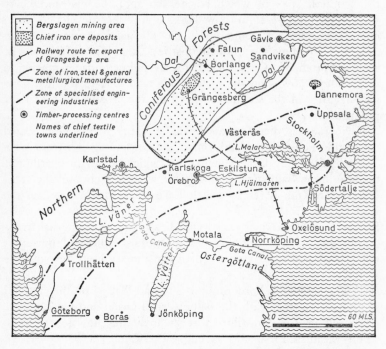

Fig. 87. The Lakeland Belt of Sweden and Bergslagen. Many of the other towns besides Gävle, Karlskoga and Karlstad have some timber-processing industries.

an important agricultural area. Cereals including wheat, are cultivated, and potatoes, used extensively as feed for pigs, are a leading crop. Here also, as in Skåne, fodder crops and temporary pastures occupy much of the cultivated land, an expression of a general tendency in all Scandinavian countries to concentrate increasingly upon live-stock, chiefly cattle and pigs.

Agriculture, however, has been quite overshadowed in modern times by the development of a wide range of specialised manufactures, a number of which command world-wide markets for their products.

The rise of Central Sweden as one of the more important manufacturing districts of Western Europe has been greatly aided by large supplies of hydro-electric power, obtained first from local sources such as the Trollhättan falls on the Gota River, but supplemented now by much more ample supplies from Norrland — from as far north as the Porjus and Harsprånget falls on the Lule River. This remarkable rise of industry in a land that has scarcely any coal and a limited range of raw materials has owed much of its impetus to a number of ingenious inventions which, applied to industry, enable finished products to be made which greatly exceed in value the cost of the raw materials used. The list is imposing; among others S.K.F. ball bearings, Primus stoves, A.G.A. lamps, Alpha-Laval cream separators, Ericsson telephones, A.S.E.A. generators and transformers, and safety matches mentioned above.

The industrial towns are in two groups: a larger one in the east, extending through the Malar-Hjälmaren zone, which is headed by Stockholm with Norrköping as an outlying centre; and a smaller one in the west centred on Göteborg, which includes not only the Gota valley towns such as Trollhättan, but others more distant, for example, Borås towards the edge of the Småland Plateau, and Karlstad on the northern shore of Lake Väner.

In both areas metallurgical and engineering industries together form the leading group, the finished products of which range from precision instruments and tools of all kinds to giant turbines and to ocean liners. In general, these industries are dispersed, but five leading towns have specialised on particular lines; Stockholm and Eskilstuna in making machinery, electrical apparatus and a variety of refined engineering products, including high-class cutlery at Eskilstuna; Västerås and Trollhättan in electrical equipment and locomotives; Göteborg in engineering products such as ball-bearings and machinery of all kinds, besides all that pertains to shipbuilding, in which it is much the greatest centre in Sweden. Another leading class of industry is the textile group, in which Göteborg and Borås have specialised in cottons and Norrköping in woollens. A third important group includes a variety of wood and timber-processing industries, producing furniture, plywood, pulp and paper. These are rather scattered in response to access to raw materials, though Karlstad on Lake Väner, which has an exceptionally large 'hinterland' of forested country, has become an outstanding centre. The only other industry in which localised specialisation has noticeably appeared is the manufacture of footwear and leather goods at Örebro at the head of Lake Hjälmaren, where also the central engineering workshops of the Swedish State Railways are situated.

Stockholm, the capital of the Kingdom of Sweden, is the leading city by far; it is the chief commercial, manufacturing and adminstrative centre of the country; its population, approaching 800,000, is more than twice that of its nearest rival Göteborg. Stockholm was originally built on an island in the exit channel of Lake Malar, a site chosen for defence for which it was admirably suited, as the approaches from the sea are safeguarded by an archipelago of islands separated by narrow channels. This situation has provided modern Stockholm with a beautiful setting in country of wooded hills threaded by waterways, on to which it has spread from the island, now the heart of the city. The only serious disadvantage of this situation is that seaborne traffic is liable to be interrupted in winter by freezing of the shallow waters of the approaches.

Stockholm has singular advantages of accessibility to the various regions of the country. It is the hub of communications serving the Uppsala and Ostergötland lowlands, both productive agricultural areas, as well as the Bergslagen mining and metallurgical region. Further afield it is linked by land and sea routes with the diverse Norrland and Götaland regions between which it lies, and also through the Lakeland Zone with Göteborg and the Lake Väner area. The only parts of the country rather outside its orbit are Skåne and the Jämtland basin; the former centres more on Malmö as a separate regional capital, the latter tends to gravitate towards Trondheim.

Göteborg is the chief port of Sweden and the headquarters of the Swedish Transatlantic shipping lines, as well as being a great shipbuilding and general-engineering centre. Its situation close to the Kattegat ensures freedom from ice in winter; it has direct connections with the Malar-Hjälmaren constellation of industrial towns, competing with Stockholm for their trade, and by the Gota Canal with places on Lakes Väner and Vätter as well as with Norrköping. Moreover, the lower Gota River, on which Göteborg stands, provides complete shelter for shipping and facilities for the construction of quays, and also of shipbuilding and ship-repairing yards.

(V) The Bergslagen area of dissected uplands is transitional between the Lakeland Zone and the plateau country of Norrland. Its forest resources and its deposits of copper, iron and other metallic ores have been the basis of a special form of communal settlement from medieval times. Each Bergslag was a kind of self-contained economic unit of peasant farmers together with miners and craftsmen, who owned a section of forests, mines and farmland, refining and working the minerals with charcoal fuel. Nowadays, with the near-exhaustion of the Falun copper and the other metallic ores, except those of phosphoric iron at Grängesberg which are mostly exported, the Bergslagen region has lost relatively to the Lakeland belt in metal working and engineering industries.

NORTHERN SWEDEN (NORRLAND)

Compared with southern Sweden, this northern region comprising nearly two-thirds of the total area of the country, is fairly simple in build. It consists of three longitudinal physical zones, the emergent coastal lowlands, the plateau zone, and the high mountain belt or fjäll. A conspicuous feature of this Norrland region is the succession of parallel consequent rivers, which, fed with heavy precipitation on the highlands, have cut broad valleys in their south-easterly courses across both the plateau and the coastlands. The large volumes of water carried by these rivers from the mountain belt into the eastern zones of relatively low precipitation, make them especially useful for the transport of logs in their middle and lower courses and for the generation of hydro-electric power (Figs. 83, 86).

(I) The coastal lowlands are a belt of land reclaimed by natural process from the shallow Gulf of Bothnia (p. 307). As elevation is still in progress, especially in the north, the shore line is creeping eastwards, rendering it necessary to construct outports for some of the older ports, now no longer serviceable. Climatic conditions which become progressively more unfavourable towards the north where the belt is widest, have retarded agricultural settlement, still in some parts in the pioneer stage.

The largest settlements are the long-established timber ports, a dozen or more of which are strung along the coast, mostly at the mouths of the rivers, among them Gävle, Sundswall, Umea, Skellefteå and Luleå. The transmission of hydro-electric power generated from up-river falls has assisted the concentration of saw-mills and pulp- and paper-mills in these ports, from which the finished products can readily be moved by sea. In any case, the transport of the raw materials as logs floated down the rivers in concentrated supplies is more economical than it would be to transport the bulky finished products from a number of small plants at scattered points inland where power is directly available. Moreover, a very large and increasing proportion o the total cut of wood is consumed in the pulp and paper factorie which need port facilities to obtain essential supplies and to expor their products to distant markets. Recent developments are the con struction of large metallurgical smelters near Skellefteå which collect

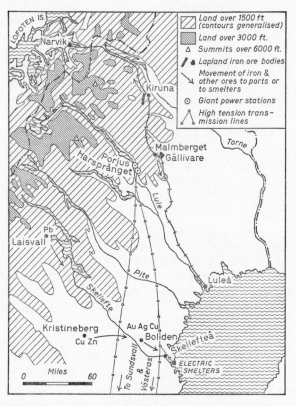

Fig. 88. Northern Sweden: relief, mineral deposits and hydro-electric power.

non-ferrous ores from Boliden and from further afield, and of iron ore smelters at Luleå, the Swedish port for the Gällivare-Kiruna iron-ore field, both plants being supplied with high-voltage current generated at the Porjus and Harsprånget falls (Fig. 88).

(II) The plateau zone is a tilted platform of ancient crystalline rocks, cut into a number of separate blocks by the incised river valleys. These residual blocks of rounded relief forms are covered with a mantle of glacial drift which, combined with gentle gradients, has contributed to the formation of numerous lakes and of patches of bog, and to a generally indecisive drainage. The acid soils and the short frost-free season of the uplands render them useless for agriculture; they have accordingly been left under forest wherever trees will grow and, except for scattered lumbermen's camps, they carry little population.

The broad valleys of the large rivers are quite different in character. They were submerged as shallow fiords in post-glacial times, while the uplands remained dry land, and sands and clays deposited in these waters now cover their floors or form terraces on their sides where not subsequently removed by the rivers, rejuvenated by the general uplift of the land. Selective agricultural settlement is advancing up these valleys, which are the natural lines of penetration, serving as links between the interior forested country and the coastlands.

III) The mountain or fjäll zone, averaging 2,000 feet in elevation, with numerous points over 3,000 feet on the Norwegian border, is formed mainly of the schists and intrusive igneous masses of the denuded Caledonian overthrusts, east of which from the Glint line the basic Archaean rocks appear at the surface except for some outliers of the Caledonian overthrusts. It is a barren area of tundra and peat bogs, intersected by valleys which are occupied by ribbon lakes and the upper courses of the rivers that issue from them. During a late stage in the dissolution of the ice-sheet an ice-wall lay along the line of the present lower ends of those lakes, forcing the drainage westward to the Atlantic. With the final disappearance of the ice-mass over Sweden, the original consequent drainage was restored, but the upper sections of the valleys were impounded as lakes by extensive moraines deposited during the halt of the ice in the last stage of its existence. In this catchment zone of alternate winter accumulation of snow and ice and of summer thaw, the lakes serve as regulators of the flow of the rivers, and thereby enhance their uses for the floatation of logs and the generation of hydro-electric power.

The Jämtland depression round Lake Storsjön forms an exception to the general desolation of the highland zone. Floored in parts with Silurian limestones and schists that yield to weathering, and covered partially with glacial drift and partly with deposits left by a formerly more extensive L. Storsjön, it is a kind of fertile oasis. It is accessible from the east by the Indals valley and from the west by the Storlien gap by which tempering Atlantic air-currents are able to penetrate; and

through it passes the only trans-Scandinavian railway between t
populous South and Lapland, that connecting Sundsvall w
Trondheim. Agriculture is the mainstay of the inhabitants who pr
tice live-stock farming with some seasonal movement of cattle to t
saeters on the upper terraces and benches. This, combined w
timber-cutting on the neighbouring uplands and some saw-milli
round the lake, has enabled the Jämtland depression to become
relatively populous enclave in the midst of almost uninhabita
wildernesses.

GENERAL ECONOMIC STRUCTURE

Half the exports of Sweden by value are composed of metallic o
and semi-manufactured forest products (timber and wood pu
while finished manufactures contribute about 40 per cent. Th
Sweden depends, to an extent exceptional in the economies of W
European countries, on exporting primary products in order to pay
imported supplies of such essentials as wheat, maize, oil-seeds, cott
and coal. The great advantage so far as Sweden is concerned, of
porting large quantities of these primary products is that, with I
ample resources of both, they make small demands for labour
proportion to value. The normal disadvantage, that such expo
involve wastage of irreplaceable natural assets, has little force
Sweden; for the forests which contribute much the largest item
continuously replenished by replanting, and the deposits of meta
ores, especially of iron, will last many years at the present rate
removal, to say nothing of still undiscovered deposits.

Manufacturing industries take about 30 per cent of the work
population, against little more than 20 per cent employed in agric
ture and forestry combined. Fully a third of all industrial workers
engaged in two classes of industry, namely the metallurgical a
engineering and the textile groups, the first of which contributes
largest of all items among exports of manufactured products.
common with a number of other countries in Europe and abro
Sweden is becoming increasingly industrialised; but she seems li
to move faster in that direction than most, in view of the great prod
tive capital investments now in progress, e.g., in the form of g
power stations and smelters, and also of her ability to produce
array of distinctively specialised manufactures based on the invent
genius of her people.

In Sweden, as in the neighbouring countries of the Baltic Shi the marked contrasts in land forms associated with the marginal temperate climatic conditions are mainly responsible for the uneven distribution of population referred to at the beginning of this chapter. Yet the physical conditions are not the sole determinants in these days of industrial development based on hydro-electric power, which as shown by an example mentioned above (p. 316) can be transmitted over great distances. Upwards of half the population of Sweden is concentrated in the central depression together with Bergslagen, and that proportion is steadily increasing, mainly because of the human choices made in the location of industry. The only other area of relatively dense population, namely Skåne, though primarily agricultural, is also becoming industrialised. Nine of the eleven largest towns in Sweden, all of which owe their growth partly or mainly to manufactures, are in or near the central depression, and the two others are in Skåne; three of these towns, Stockholm, Göteborg and Malmö, together hold nearly one-fifth of the entire population, about the same as the whole of Norrland which covers nearly two-thirds of the country.

FINLAND

Although Finland is essentially part of the Baltic Shield, and has physical affinities with northern Sweden as indicated in the preceding chapter, its intermediate situation between Sweden and the Eurasian land mass has influenced its human settlement and its political history. The Finns proper are descendants of Finno-Ugrian tribes of Asiatic origin, whose language has formed the basis of modern Finnish, but these people have not been able to hold all the coastlands against later arrivals by sea, especially from Sweden. At the present time many of the inhabitants of the west and south-west margins are of Swedish descent, while those of the southern coastlands are mixed.

Wedged between Sweden and Russia, Finland has been the scene of the contending forces of these two powers. It was under Swedish domination for over five centuries till 1809 when it fell into the hands of Russia. In 1917, as a result of the Russian collapse in the first Great War, Finland became an independent republic; but with the growing strength of the U.S.S.R. since the 1930's, it has maintained a rather precarious independence under the shadow of Russian power. Though geographical situation makes the people of Finland uncomfortably conscious of the existence and ascendency of their mighty

eastern neighbour, their trade relations are mainly with the west
countries through the Baltic.

Finland, covering an area of about 130,000 sq. miles includin
per cent water surfaces, falls broadly into three physical regions:
Lake Plateau, the coastal lowlands framing the Lake Plateau on
west and south, and the northern plateau region. The first of the
which contains the majority of the 40,000 lakes in Finland, is an a
of pine and spruce forests, with scattered agricultural settlements
some towns, e.g. Tampere, at nodal points in the lines of communi
tion threading their ways through the maze of lakes. The coa
lowlands bordering the Gulf of Bothnia and lying between the S
pausselkä and the Gulf of Finland, being covered with marine de
sits (p. 305), are the chief agricultural areas, and contain 60 per cen
the entire population of a little under 4½ millions, and nearly all
larger towns including Helsinki the capital. The northern plat
country, harsh of climate and uninviting for settlement, is a v
thinly peopled region, in which even hardy coniferous trees give
northwards to birch and sub-arctic species.

The ground moraine which covers much of the ice-polished Ar
æan rocks of the interior is composed mainly of sands and grav
especially in the numerous winding eskers and in the great Salpa
selkä end moraine. Farming there is restricted to patches of be
drained soils with some clay constituents, and since forage cr
succeed better than cereals, live-stock are the mainstay. Includ
natural meadows, less than 10 per cent of Finland has been occup
for farming, and the greater part of that, and a still greater proport
of the arable land, is on the coastal lowlands. The Table p. 52 sh
that Finland, thanks to these emergent coastlands, grows a fa
wide range of crops in spite of its high latitude, almost all of it ab
60° N.

Forests, fully three-quarters of which are productive, cover over
per cent of the land surface. These constitute the chief source
national wealth, timber and timber products such as plywood, p
and paper contributing 80 per cent of the exports. Many of the f
mers, in fact, divide their attention between the competing interests
forestry and farming, in proportions which vary from one district
another. The climate and the character of much of the land being w
they are, the forests tend to hold their own against agriculture. I
more profitable to maintain the exports of forest products than
attempt to increase the production of foodstuffs by encroaching on

forests. It would be impossible in any case to produce all the wheat and sugar now imported in large quantities.

Two-thirds of the population of Finland are classed as rural. This relatively high proportion is the result of specialisation in primary forms of production. Large-scale manufactures, except for those of timber products, of wood pulp and paper, and of textiles at Tampere, have hitherto been absent. Recently however, the people of Finland, faced with the problems of re-settling large numbers of displaced nationals and of making good the loss of agricultural output consequent upon the transfer of the Viipuri territory to Russia, are reclaiming selected parts of the forested interior for pioneer farming combined with forestry. They are also utilising their water-power resources for the further development of manufactures to assist the re-establishment of their economy. The most favoured are the metallurgical and engineering group, for which the Outokumpu deposits (p. 314) supply various metals including iron, though at present large quantities of crude steel need to be imported.

As Finland changes over from a rather unbalanced economy based largely on forest products, to a more diversified form in which industry plays a larger part, the ports are likely to grow in size and economic importance. The largest of these are Helsinki the capital, Turku in the extreme south-west, Pori on the Gulf of Bothnia, (which serves the inland industrial centre, Tampere) and Kotka east of Helsinki, the leading timber port.

Chapter 23

NORWAY AND DENMARK

NORWAY and Denmark, both in marginal maritime situations, whic differentiate them from the interior Baltic regions, have in conse quence been associated in their human activities and historical de velopment. From the times of the roving Northmen, the people Norway in particular, and those of Denmark to a smaller extent, hav been noted as seafarers and fishermen. Norway was under the domi nion of the kings of Denmark for more than six centuries from 1204 1814, when it was forcibly transferred to the king of Sweden by th victorious Powers on the defeat of Napoleon, and these close historic ties are paralleled by the affinity between the Norwegian and Dani languages. The union of Norway with Sweden, which seemed natur as forming a neat geographical entity, could not last owing not only differences in speech and traditions, but also to divergence betwee the economies of the two countries under the impact of mode developments. An agreed separation took place in 1905, and sin then Norway has gone her own way, independent of her neighbours.

Except in a common maritime situation and in its climatic ar human consequences, Norway and Denmark differ in many respec Norway is nearly eight times as large, having an area of 124,560 s miles compared with only 16,600 sq. miles of Denmark, and yet contains over a million fewer inhabitants. Its population numberi 3·5 millions gives an average density of only 28 per sq. mile, agair about 277 per sq. mile in Denmark. Norway is composed almc entirely of ancient rocks and much of it is filled with high mountai bared of soil and carved into deep valleys by moving ice; Denmark i low platform of relatively soft sedimentary beds covered with thi deposits of glacial drift material, some of which may even have be transported from Norway. Hence, while the land under crops Norway amounts to only 2·5 per cent of the whole area, that in De mark is nearly 64 per cent; if permanent pastures are included, similar disparity in the proportions of farmland appears, namely per cent and 73·2 per cent respectively.

NORWAY

The extremely mountainous build of Norway, resembling in its relief forms those of the geologically related Scottish Highlands, leaves little room for lowlands. Such as these are, they hold most of the population of that country in which productive agricultural land is scarce. The most extensive are the Oslo depression together with the Skagerrak coastland, the Trondheim depression, and the Jaeren

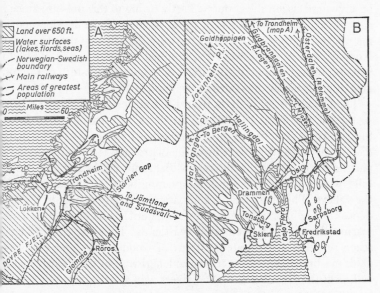

Fig. 89. The Trondheim and the Oslo regions of Norway. Note: the legend of map A applies also to map B.

coastland south of Stavanger. In addition to these three agriculturally developed areas, some deep open valleys reaching into the highlands from the Oslo region, particularly Osterdalen, Gudbransdalen and Hallingdal, support settlements at intervals along their floors and south-facing slopes; as do also the strandflats and deltaic fans of various fiords. The total purely agricultural population of the valley strips and fiord patches is small; most of the farming is only part-time, being supplemented by forestry inland and by fishing in the fiord region.

I) The Oslo depression and the adjoining south-east coastland (Fig. 89B) constitute the largest lowland area of Norway, and this area also

has the most favourable climate for varied forms of agriculture and fo
human vitality. The rainfall is less than half that on the fiord coast
and the yearly hours of sunshine are correspondingly greater, whil
the continental influence in summer and the intermittent occurrenc
of föhn winds from the west in winter, give rise to variations in temp
erature which stimulate human activity.[1] This region produces mos
of the limited crops of wheat in Norway, and larger quantities of oats
barley, animal fodders and hay, very little rye being now grown her
or anywhere else in the country. Partly owing to this pre-eminence i
agriculture, but more in recent times because of the development o
manufactures, the South-East is the most densely populated region o
Norway, and in many ways the dominating force in the life of th
whole country; though it comprises only one-twenty-fifth of the tota
area, it holds nearly one-third of the population.

The Oslo depression dates from the Caledonian revolution when
section of the Baltic Shield was let down as a trough floored wit
Silurian rocks; extensive igneous intrusions followed in the Hercynia
disturbances. In its present form the depression is a basin studded i
parts, especially towards the west, with granite ridges and lava-cappe
hills, which trend N.–S., with intervening belts of Silurian schists i
the valleys. The area owes its comparative fertility mainly to the late
deposition of morainic and alluvial materials inland and shell-ric
marine clays on the re-elevated coastlands. Thus the existing land
scape presents a variegated pattern of wooded hills and cultivate
fields in a broad depression traversed lengthwise by the slightly incise
valleys of the Glomma and other rivers, which have been rejuvenate
by the recent uplift; the whole is set in a framework of dissecte
Archaean highlands, and falls away in the south to the low peninsula
platforms of Ostfold and Westfold on either side of Oslo Fiord.

The coastlands bordering the Skagerrak are subject to much th
same climatic conditions as those of the Oslo region and similar form
of mixed farming are practised on the more fertile tracts set in a back
ground of forests. Along the coast are patches of fertile marine an
glacial deposits, behind which the land rises in picturesque hill
forested country to the highlands of Telemark. In this region, as i
the Oslo and Ostfold areas, supplies of hydro-electric power, gen

[1]	*Precipitation*	*Mean Temperatures*		*Range*
		January	July	
Oslo	25·4 ins.	24° F.	63° F.	39°
Bergen	84·4 ins.	34° F.	58° F.	24°

rated from falls on the rivers, have been a large factor contributing
to the growth of manufactures.

(I) The Trondheim depression (Trondelag) has been formed by long
erosion of relatively unresistant Silurian schists and limestones of the
Caledonian series in a belt parallel with the coast, the lowest part of
which is occupied by the inner main fiord. The fertile morainic and
alluvial deposits of this depression, especially round Trondheim,
attracted settlement at an early date. Trondheim city, founded nearly
a thousand years ago at the mouth of the River Nid, became an important regional and the chief religious centre of Norway in the Middle
Ages, and as such it has remained to the present day. The Trondelag
region, situated 63° to 65° N., is a telling example of the northward
extension of temperate climatic conditions and of general mixed
farming on the Norwegian coast; it is the most northerly area in the
world in which all the common temperate field crops, including even
some wheat, can be grown with reasonable success.

(II) The Jaeren coastland south of Stavanger has a thick cover of
glacial drift resting on a platform of ancient rocks. Its surface is
characteristically uneven with eskers and depressions, the latter once
occupied by bogs now mostly drained. The equable humid climate is
best suited to the cultivation of oats among the cereals (p. 51), which
are grown in quantity, together with sown grasses and fodders for
cattle and sheep. The dairy industry with associated pig-keeping is
general in Jaeren as in Denmark, but with the difference that sheep
are fairly numerous, kept in the open fields in winter, and removed to
upland pastures on the adjacent fjells in summer.

(IV) In the fiord region between Stavanger and Trondheim, small
farming settlements have long existed on the strandflats and alluvial
fans, especially of the 'adret' or south-facing sides. Cut off from the
inland regions by steep mountains, the people of these settlements
have had no regular means of communication except by the fiord
waterways and by sea. Many of them have been largely self-contained,
depending on farming and fishing for food and clothing, and upon
patches of forest in sheltered situations for timber and fuel. The
improvement in communications in both range and speed with the
advent of motor-driven vessels has led to changes, bringing many of
these formerly isolated settlements within the orbit of the national
economy. For example, in exchange for fish, now readily transported
to the main collecting, processing and exporting centres, the inhabitants of these settlements are able to obtain manufactured goods,

among them fertilisers for their crops and home pastures. This in turn
has brought about a general decline in the traditional saeter form of
transhumance; for the increased yield of the home pastures and fodder
crops enables the farmer-fishermen to dispense with the troublesome
movement of cattle and persons to the mountain saeters, difficult of
access. A similar tendency to abandon the saeter system has taken
place for like reasons in the inland valleys mentioned above.

All told, the agricultural resources of Norway are insufficient to
supply the needs of even the small population, so that large quantities
of wheat and of feeding stuffs for live-stock are imported. Of the total
active population only about 25 per cent are engaged in agriculture
and forestry combined, and of these many are small farmers working
on their own account. The physical conformation of the country
precludes any appreciable enlargement of the cultivated area by land
reclamation or deforestation. Except for the modern development of
manufactures utilising cheap hydro-electric power, the people of
Norway depend as much upon the sea for their livelihood as upon
their farmlands. The only class of food they produce in plenty is fish,
the large exports of which provide receipts that offset much of the cost
of imported agricultural products.

INDUSTRIAL DEVELOPMENT

Norway, as observed above (p. 315), is endowed with abundant
water-power resources, with forests covering nearly a quarter of the
whole area, and with some, though no really rich or extensive mineral
deposits. In order to develop manufactures beyond the simple forms
of saw-milling and fish-curing and canning, Norway has devised other
means of utilising the vast potential hydro-electric power resources
in manufactures, using imported raw materials to supplement those of
domestic origin. She imports, for example, large quantities of textile
fibres, bauxite and other metallic ores, crude steel, and unrefined
chemicals, which are used together with the wood, pyrites and some
metal ores of local origin (p. 314), to feed a growing range of manufactures. In all this, her maritime situation, the extraordinary number
of fine natural harbours, and her large merchant shipping fleet, are
help to minimise transport costs. The Norwegian economy, as now
being developed, is in effect based in no small measure upon assembl-
ing bulk crude materials from abroad at points where cheap and plentiful supplies of hydro-electricity are available, by means of which these
materials are converted into finished products of higher value. Now

way resembles Switzerland in general industrial structure, but Norway, owing to her situation, can afford as Switzerland cannot, to handle bulky materials which make greater demands upon hydro-electric resources than upon human skills.

The largest and most rapidly expanding forms of industry are the iron and non-ferrous metal group, which together with engineering employ one-third of the industrial workers. Outstanding among them are the electro-metallurgical industries which produce aluminium (from imported bauxite) and a variety of iron and steel alloys, e.g. ferro-silicon and ferro-chrome, all requiring great amounts of hydro-electricity for the refining and manufacturing processes, and all producing mainly for export. This kind of industry has been established in places where large heads of water are available, as in the Skien valley in the South-East, at Odda on Hardangerfiord, and at Höanger and Ardal on Sognefiord. More recently, a large electrically-powered iron and steel plant has been constructed at Mo-i-Rana in Nordland, just south of the Arctic Circle.

The electro-chemical industries, in which nitrogen-fixing plants[1] are of leading importance, are likewise established at sources, or within easy reach of large supplies of hydro-electricity, in particular at Odda on Hardangerfiord and at Ryukan and Notodden in the upper Skien valley. The major products are carbide, cyanamide, saltpetre and ammonium nitrate, besides which superphosphates and ordinary heavy chemicals are manufactured, using sulphur from the reduction of Norwegian pyrites. The output of chemical fertilisers in Norway, now far in excess of the requirements of Norwegian agriculture, provides an export surplus of considerable value.

The pulp, paper and cardboard group of manufactures, which furnishes the leading class of exports by value, also makes heavy demands for hydro-electricity. These manufactures have naturally developed especially in the south-east region which has access to the most extensive forests (Fig. 83), where hydro-electric power is plentiful, and where the longer rivers are of service for the transport of logs. The mills are situated at a number of places accessible from the sea, in an arc which extends from Sarpsborg on the lower Glomma, through Drammen (the chief centre) to Kristiansand on the south coast. From Norway, as from Sweden, much larger quantities of wood are now exported in the more valuable forms of pulp and paper than of the less valuable sawn timber; and as cutting proceeds in the forests, replanting

[1] Using nitrogen from the air.

favours the faster-maturing softwoods such as spruce rather th
timber-yielding species.

The two remaining important classes of manufactures, nam
engineering and textiles, are concentrated largely in the Oslo regi
with Oslo itself as the main centre of industry, though Bergen,
second city of Norway in population, also shares in both classes.
series of falls on the lower Glomma has been harnessed to provi
Oslo and the Ostfold towns with electricity, and Bergen lies m
way between the two great fiords where water-power is particula
plentiful.

As almost all the raw textile materials except cellulose are import
there are obvious advantages in setting these manufactures, as a
food-processing industries such as flour-milling, in or near the t
chief ports. In the engineering group, which includes manufactures
machinery, transport vehicles and electrical equipment besides so
shipbuilding and ship-repairing (p. 337), Oslo and Bergen are ag
the chief centres. In countries such as Norway and Sweden, in wh
readily transmissible hydro-electric current is the motive force
industry, manufactures in general have greater flexibility of locati
than in coal-using countries. With some notable exceptions, howev
they tend to collect in and around the larger centres of populati
where workers are most readily obtainable, and where there
greater transport and other facilities for the disposal of the products
both the home and the export markets.

FISHING, WHALING AND RELATED INDUSTRIES

Easy access to the North Atlantic and North Sea fishing wat
from the sheltered harbours of the numerous fiords, combined w
the general poverty of land resources, has caused fishing to become
chief occupation of the inhabitants of the 900 miles of coast fr
Tromsø to Stavanger. With the exceptions of Bergen, Trondhe
and Narvik, which have other than purely local connections and fu
tions, most of the ports and settlements owe their existence mainly
fishing and related industries.

Two-thirds of the Norwegian landings of fish amounting to t
million tons per annum, consist of herrings, and the greater part
the rest is cod. The former, caught chiefly in the waters south
Trondheim including the North Sea, are landed at the near
convenient ports, among which Haugosund a little north of Stavang
is a great curing and packing centre. Stavanger itself specialises

canning, especially of brisling, a kind of sprat. Of the enormous catches of herrings a large proportion is pickled for export to Russia and other Baltic countries; unsaleable fish are used to make fish meal for pigs and cattle, and the refuse is converted into fish manure.

The cod-fishing industry of the northern coast from Trondheim round the Lofoten Islands to beyond Tromsø formerly found markets abroad for the catches preserved by salting and drying, but since the introduction of quick freezing, in which Trondheim led the way, increasing quantities are sold as 'wet' fish. The whaling industry, now carried on mainly in Antarctic waters, is operated with a large fleet of catchers accompanied by tanker factory ships in which the whale oil is transported to Norway. The headquarters of the fleet are at Tonsberg and other small ports west of Oslo Fiord, and the oil-hardening factories are centred at Frederikstad at the mouth of the Glomma River.

MERCHANT SHIPPING

Norway has a mercantile shipping fleet of over 6 million tons, the third largest among the countries of the world. Owing to the subsequent replacements of heavy losses in the 1939–45 war, the majority of the vessels are modern, and in response to the world demand for oil transport, a large proportion of the new tonnage consists of tankers. The home ports of most of these ships, and the seats of the management headquarters are Oslo and Bergen (now chiefly the former), which therefore have in addition to their other activities, various ship-repairing and marine-engineering works. The earnings of this large fleet, operating mainly on foreign account, form a substantial credit item in Norway's balance of payments, estimated to amount to one-third of the total cost of the imports.

COMMUNICATIONS AND TOWNS

Norway extends some 1,200 miles by direct line from the Skagerrak to the North Cape, has a maximum breadth of 250 miles and averages only 50 miles wide in a long stretch north of Trondelag. In this disproportion between length and breadth, and in the concentration of the great bulk of the population on or near the extended coasts, Norway resembles Chile, and like Chile relies much on sea transport for communications between one part and another. Yet even by the shortest sea routes distances are great — from Oslo to Bergen over 400 miles, to Trondheim 700 miles and to Kirkenes more than 1,500

miles. Steps have been taken to overcome the drawbacks of distances
and of isolation of outlying places by establishing air services equipped with seaplanes that can operate on the quiet waters of the fiords;
but these services are liable to interruptions especially in winter owing
to storms and palls of cloud and mist.

High relief in the southern broad and more populous half of the
country hinders the construction of roads and railways. Many of the
larger fiords terminate inland in mountain walls, and though the
valleys of the larger south-eastern rivers reach far back into the massif,
stretches of difficult mountain country separate their heads from those
of the rare short valleys leading down to the fiords. Both roads and
railways are in general costly to build in Norway, but electrification of
the railways, which is the rule, helps to reduce running costs.

The main road and railway systems radiate from two centres, Oslo
and Trondheim, which are themselves connected by two trunk railways, one through Osterdalen (Glomma Valley), and the other
through Gudbransdalen (Lagen Valley). Oslo was linked with Bergen
in 1909 when the Hallingdal line was extended with feats of railway
engineering across the wild Hardanger plateau to meet the Voss line
from Bergen, thus halving the distance by sea. Two other main railway systems originate from Oslo: that which, serving the Ostfold
region and crossing the Glomma at Sarpsborg, connects with the
Swedish line to Göteborg; and another which runs south-west via
Drammen and Skien to Kristiansand, and thence to Stavanger.

Trondheim, the focus of communications by land and sea in central
Norway, is the main collecting and distributing centre for those parts,
as Oslo is for the South. In addition to the two railways to Oslo, and
that through the Storlien gap to Jämtland and Sundsvall in Sweden, a
northern line has been built following the outer Caledonian longitudinal depression to a point well beyond the Arctic circle.

The maritime orientation of Norway, noted at the outset as the
keynote of its people's history and economic development, is borne
out by the fact that all the fifteen towns of more than 12,000 inhabitants are either on or near the sea and available as ports.[1] Of these the
four largest Oslo, Bergen, Trondheim and Stavanger are major ports,
and contain between them nearly a quarter of the entire population.
As Norway advances along the path of industrialisation based on increasing supplies of hydro-electric power, the chief ports, already the
largest towns and main centres of industry, are likely to absorb a

[1] In Norway the sea unites rather than separates.

greater proportion of the population. For the natural resources and the structure of the Norwegian economy are such that manufactures must depend increasingly as they expand, upon imported or coastwise transported raw materials, and exports of the finished products.

DENMARK

About two-thirds of the area of Denmark is in the Jutland Peninsula, and the rest is composed of an archipelago of islands, of which the largest in order of size are Zealand (Sjaelland), Funen (Fyn), Lolland and Falster. Bornholm, a detached portion of the Baltic Shield, out in the Baltic Sea over 100 miles away, is a relic of the Danish rule of south-west Sweden. Of the three channels by which the Baltic Sea communicates with the Kattegat, only the Sound can be used by ocean-going ships, the others being too shallow. The Little Belt is narrow enough in its northern part to be bridged, but communication across the Great Belt, nowhere less than 12 miles wide, has to be maintained by ferry services, including train ferry.

The solid geology of Denmark is almost completely masked by recent deposits; by glacial drift over the islands and the greater part of Jutland; by late-glacial marine clays, sands and gravel in a belt across Jutland in the Lim Fiord depression; and by blown sand along the North Sea coast. The chalk and Tertiary beds, upon which these later deposits rest, are seldom exposed. Little of them is above sea-level except in northern Jutland where there are some low chalk cliffs; and were it not for the extensive deposition of drift materials, largely of Scandinavian origin, the Baltic and the North Seas would have been united by a broad passage, and the Denmark of today would scarcely have existed.

Recent slight tilting of the area as a whole by upward movement in the north-west, and sinking towards the east, has contributed to the formation of the sand-dune and lagoon belt along the North Sea coast, and to encroachment by the sea through erosion of the unconsolidated materials on the shores of the islands. Apart from these recent developments, the physiography of Denmark is the product of the Ice Age — mainly of the last glaciation and of the ensuing changes in relative land- and sea-levels (p. 307). An earlier glaciation covered the whole country, but its effects have been obliterated except for some 'hill islands' in the outwash region of western Jutland. The ice-sheet of the last glaciation halted its advance along an irregular line marked by terminal moraines (Fig. 90) and masses of outwash sands and gravels from this melting front were deposited in the remaining sector of Jutland, covering it but for the hill tops.

The youthful morainic topography, though rarely exceeding 100 metres (about 330 feet) in elevation, is very varied. The most marked features are the moraines in eastern Jutland which contain the highest points in the whole country, namely Ejer Bavnehöj (561 feet) and Yding Skovhöj (567 feet), both in a ridge north of Horsens.[1] On the inner borders of the moraines i.e. in north-east and east Jutland,

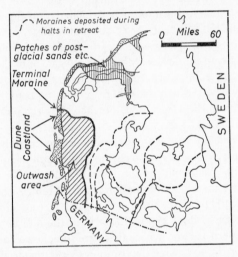

Fig. 90. Denmark: moraines and other surface deposits. The unshaded areas are covered in Denmark largely with boulder clay.

are belts of eskers, drumlins and low rounded hills interspersed with tunnel valley[2] hollows occupied by ribbon lakes and with some patches of boulder clay. The topography of the islands is less pronounced in its features. They are covered with ground moraine boulder clay, broken in Funen and Zealand by the sinuous ridges of the moraines deposited during halts in the south-easterly retreat of the ice-sheet in these parts.

The drainage system in this land of low youthful topography is naturally immature, but much has been done to rectify it where needed in order to prepare ill-drained land for agriculture. The largest rivers,

---

[1] Himmelbjerget (Hill of Heaven) 10 miles N.W. of these heights is, in spite of its name, only 482 feet high.

[2] See footnote p. 305.

little more than 50 miles in length and more like streams, are those that flow west from the higher central section of the terminal moraines north-west of Horsens. Among them is the Varde, which has breached the sand-dune belt at its mouth, so forming an inlet, on the lower part of which Esbjerg harbour has been constructed.

CLIMATE AND AGRICULTURE

Though the climate is more maritime than continental, especially in western Jutland, continental air masses are liable to break through periodically, interrupting the sequence of depressions from the Atlantic. Thus the weather varies according to which of these two forces prevail. Owing to these intermittent incursions of cold air from continental sources during six or more months in the year, the average growing period for plants is limited to between five and six months.

The precipitation is in general lower than in eastern England (21·5 ins. at Copenhagen compared with 26·5 ins. at Norwich), and the range of temperature distinctly greater (32° F. at Copenhagen compared with 22·6° F. at Norwich). The rainfall is generally reliable, with less than 10 per cent variability and sufficient for crops and pastures, but in west Jutland, where it is heavier than in the east, it has caused serious leaching of the prevailing sandy soils. Rain falls thoughout the year, and snow often in winter. Precipitation is heaviest in the summer and autumn months with a maximum in August, a distribution which is more favourable to the growth of forage and root crops than to the ripening and harvesting of cereals.

Danish agriculture has been an example of successful achievement under none too favourable conditions of climate and soils, and in face of uncertain, highly competitive markets for its products. The climate has the disabilities of more sudden changes of temperature and of shorter summers than that of New Zealand (a formidable competitor) or that of southern England. The area of naturally fertile soils is limited in any case by the small size of the country, little more than half the area of Scotland; even so, a considerable proportion of Jutland was poor heathland, which, though diligently reclaimed, is still of relatively low agricultural productivity.

The foreign markets upon which Denmark has had to rely for sales of her products have proved fickle. After the Napoleonic wars, and especially after the repeal of the English Corn Laws, Danish agriculture concentrated upon the production of wheat for export. When large supplies of cheap grain became available in Western Europe with the opening up of the American prairies in the 1870's, Denmark, unable to compete in this trade on equal terms, turned over to raising beef cattle. But this industry was short-lived, for by the 1880's refrigerated meat and live cattle were landed in Britain in large supplies, thus again undercutting the Danish trade. The Danes then, showing unusual powers of adaptation to changing conditions, began

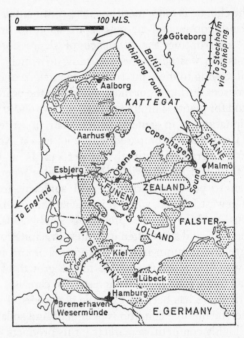

Fig. 91. Denmark and the Baltic approaches: good agricultural lands and transport routes. The areas shaded are the best agricultural lands, over 50 per cent arable (cf. Fig. 90).

systematically to develop the highly intensive form of integrated dairy-, pig- and poultry-farming, for which they are known throughout the world. The expansion of this specialised form of farming was closely associated with the Free Trade era of open markets for supplies of materials, e.g. feeding stuffs, and for sales of the products; and though that era has gone, Denmark has in large measure held her own, by very intensive use of land resources, highly efficient methods of production and marketing, and careful study of foreign, in particular the British, tastes and requirements.

In general organisation Danish agriculture has three distinctive features: a fully developed co-operative system covering the collection, processing and marketing of the products as well as the supply of farmers' requirements; small family farms, half of them less than 25 acres; and a system of specialised adult schools which provide part-time instruction in the technique of farming practice. Behind all these the State has been an active promoting agent, financing the establishment of farmers' co-operatives and the adult schools, and enacting legislation designed to adjust the size of the farms to suitable economic units.

The comprehensive co-operative organisations have been most helpful in reducing transfer costs, and in facilitating the grading and standardisation of the products, ensuring that quality is in keeping with market requirements. The development of their activities was greatly assisted by the introduction of the centrifugal cream separator (a Scandinavian invention) from 1880 onwards. This enabled the establishment of central co-operative creameries, in which milk supplies from a number of farms are pooled, the skim-milk by-product together with other by-products from the co-operative butter and cheese factories being returned to the farmer for stock-feed.

In order to maintain the output of dairy and related products, cultivation has been extended to the utmost by reclaiming sandy heaths, peat bogs and marshes, and of this arable land, now amounting to over 64 per cent of the total area, an overwhelming proportion is devoted to rotation crops used directly or indirectly as feed for livestock. Of the 2·76 million hectares of cultivated land, more than half is under rotation grasses, and the produce of fully three-quarters of the rest is consumed by farm animals.[1] Yet, though every effort is made to provide home-grown fodder, it is impossible to maintain 3¼ million cattle, over 5 million pigs and 23 million head of poultry without supplementary supplies of concentrated feedstuffs. Among them are large quantities of oil-seeds, from which oil-cakes are manufactured by extraction of the oils, these vegetable oils being used for making margarine consumed by the people in place of butter.

Having to make the most effective use of limited land resources, Danish agriculturists have given much attention to increasing the

---

[1] The average total area under the chief field crops in 1957-8 was 1·292 mill. hectares. (See Table p. 52 for selected crops.) Nearly all the barley and oats, the by-products of the wheat and the sugar beet, and the surplus potatoes were fed to farm animals, for which also fodder beet and other root crops are grown.

yields of the various crops and especially of the live-stock. Much of the land responds well to treatment with those chemical fertilisers that correct the common deficiency in lime; accordingly large quantities of phosphate rock are imported for the manufacture of superphosphates, and the local chalk is converted into agricultural lime. Great progress has also been made in raising the milk yield of dairy cattle and in increasing the conversion ratio[1] of pigs and the quality of bacon by careful breeding; and in order to get the most out of the pastures, it is a common practice to tether the cattle to movable stakes, thus saving waste of grass by trampling and securing a more even distribution of the manure.

The cultivation of cereals for bread-making or for malting is of quite secondary importance, though some of the better qualities of rye, barley and wheat are used for one or other of these purposes. The earlier practice of specialising in the cultivation of grain for export has been completely reversed. Excluding feeding stuffs for animals, Denmark now imports four times the value of cereals that she exports. However, while intensive specialisation in dairy-farming and allied forms of production has been found the most remunerative mode of utilising the limited farmland, that has its disadvantages; it is vulnerable, as the course of events has shown, both to disturbances through wars and to unfavourable movements in prices.

Gradual reclamation of the heathlands has reduced them by now to small proportions, and this incidentally has caused the number of sheep to decline to a trifling 30,000 odd in all. The leached sandy outwash and the 'hill islands' of west Jutland, formerly of little use except as rough pastures, have been brought into cultivation by removal of the hard-pan and the addition of marl and fertilisers. Meadow grasses have been sown and cattle are raised, and crops such as rye and potatoes are grown, as on similar lands in the Netherlands (p. 274). It is because rye succeeds better than other cereals on these sandy soils and those of the eskers elsewhere, that a relatively large area is given to that crop in Denmark.[2]

Steps have also been taken to check the drifting of sand inland from the dune coast north of Esbjerg, by planting marram grass and

[1] The yield of meat (and other saleable products) in proportion to fodder consumed.

[2] More land is sown to rye than to wheat, but the harvest yield of the former is smaller than that of the latter, because wheat is grown only on first-class land; this accounts for the exceptionally high average yield of 35 to 40 bushels per acre — a distorted average, in fact.

pine trees. In respect of agricultural resources and their utilisation, close parallels are apparent between the Netherlands and Denmark, in the relative scarcity of agricultural land; in the contrast between fertile tracts and infertile Geest, and in the persistent efforts that have been made to bring the latter into cultivation; and finally in the structure of agriculture which, as developed in both countries, resembles manufacturing industry by importing raw materials, e.g. feeding stuffs and fertilisers, for conversion through the medium of live-stock into finished products for export.

MANUFACTURES

Though agricultural products contribute two-thirds of the value of all Danish exports, over 67 per cent of the whole population are classed as urban dwellers, and only 23 per cent[1] of the working population are engaged in farming, of whom upwards of half are self-employed. However, a considerable number of those classified as employed in manufactures are attached to industries connected with agriculture, either in processing farm products for sale, or in producing farmers' requirements such as fertilisers and agricultural implements. Moreover, the increasing mechanisation of farming, e.g. with electrically-powered milking machines and motorised cultivators and harvesters, has contributed to a decline in the proportion of the active population working on the farms, without any shrinkage in agricultural output. Corresponding to this proportional decline in agricultural workers, there have been increases in industry and the public services.

About 28 per cent of the working population are engaged in manufactures and food-processing, compared with 40 per cent[1] in manufactures in Great Britain. The great majority of these are gathered in the Copenhagen area, and many of the rest are in the larger provincial towns, Aarhus, Odense, Aalborg and Randers. The leading branch of industry is general engineering, including manufactures of machinery, electrical apparatus and transport equipment; others of importance are shipbuilding and marine engineering, leather manufactures, textiles, the chemical group, and the pottery and cement industries. Seeing that Denmark has next to no domestic sources of fuel and power, nor any of the raw materials required for these manufactures except hides, chalk and china clay (from Bornholm), it is remarkable

---

[1] Percentage figures based on Table of economically active population, United Nations Statistical Yearbook 1955.

that she has been able to make headway in a wide range of industries, including some of the 'heavy' type.

Large supplies of bulky materials such as fuels, steel and other metals, textile fibres and primary chemical products, must be imported. The first three of these are, in fact, the leading classes of imports into Denmark by values,[1] and because Danish industry must make the fullest use of relatively cheap transport in bulk by sea, all the five chief centres of manufacture are ports. In order to save transport charges also, coal is being replaced by oil fuels for industrial purposes and by hydro-electricity imported from Sweden (p. 316). Nevertheless in 1956–8 the imports of coal still averaged over 3 million tons.

The shipbuilding and engineering industries are large consumers of steel and metal products, and for this reason, if for no other, are located in the ports. Ships are constructed mainly at Copenhagen and Odense, but the tonnage is small compared with that of Sweden. Of much greater consequence in volume of output and value in export trade are the engineering industries, among the special products of which are Diesel marine engines. Of the manufactures which use domestic raw materials those of leather and footwear are the largest. More specialised traditional forms are the glove-making industry of Randers in east Jutland and the porcelain industry of Copenhagen.

FISHING

The situation of Denmark, with extended frontages on both the North Sea and the Baltic as well as on internal territorial waters, has naturally led to the development of an important fishing industry. This provides a substantial surplus for export and for conversion into fish manure above domestic consumption for food; and because a considerable proportion of the landings consists of sea-bottom species, e.g. plaice, the value of the catches is high in relation to their weight and the number of persons employed in fishing. A special feature of the industry is the breeding of plaice in the shallow waters of Lim Fiord. Ordinary sea-fishing is carried on in the North Sea with a large trawler fleet operating from Esbjerg, the principal fishing port and centre of the export trade in fish.

CENTRES OF POPULATION AND TRADE

In order to maintain the relatively high standard of living, Denmark depends essentially upon external trade which amounts to about

[1] Followed closely, in order of net import value, by cereals, feeding stuffs and fertilisers.

£180 sterling per annum per head of the population, one of the largest in the world. Most of the extensive movements of goods passes through four leading ports, Copenhagen, Esbjerg, Odense and Aarhus, of which the first two, situated at the sea terminals of the arterial transport route across the country, are supreme — Copenhagen in general trade, and Esbjerg in exports of farm products.

Copenhagen, with nearly a million inhabitants, contains upwards of a quarter of the population of Denmark, and is the largest of the Scandinavian capitals. Its situation, now at the eastern edge of the country, was more central when Denmark ruled a large area in southern Sweden as well as Norway. But the shrinkage of the Danish dominions has not interfered with the commanding commercial position of Copenhagen on the one navigable passage into the Baltic, though that has been impaired somewhat by the construction of the Kiel Canal. As its name meaning "merchants' port" suggests, its outlook and activities have had an international maritime colouring, which appears also in the development of shipbuilding and marine engineering among its modern industries. While it owes its growth in part to geographical momentum, its remarkable modern expansion is the result of industrial accretions and the associated commerce, together with the centralised administrative and cultural functions of the capital of an advanced modern state.

Compared with Copenhagen, Esbjerg is a very youthful port, dating from about 1870, after the loss of Schleswig to Prussia in 1864. Its dramatic rise to become the second port of Denmark in both import and export trade has been the outcome mainly of the development of a large export trade in farm produce to Britain, to handle which this well-equipped port was created on the site of what had been a tiny fishing village.

THE SCANDINAVIAN NATIONS IN PERSPECTIVE

So much from so few seems a fitting summary of the contributions of the Scandinavian peoples to the advancement of civilisation in modern times. The present total population of Sweden, Norway and Denmark is under 16 millions, and a century ago it was less than half that. It is astonishing what these small nations, endowed with somewhat niggardly natural resources necessitating toil that leaves little leisure for the creative arts, have produced in science, inventions, explorations, literature and philosophy. The long list of famous names includes those of Celsius and Arrhenius in physical science, Carl von

Linné in botany, Bjerknes in meteorology, Nansen and Sven Hedin in exploration, Hans Andersen, Ibsen and Strindberg in literature, and Swedenborg in metaphysical philosophy. The Scandinavian peoples have also been in the forefront in the practical arts, as shown by the Swedish inventions mentioned above (p. 321), and by their constructive ingenuity in making the most of their limited resources. More than this, they have discovered ways of living together in socialised communities; they have translated the spirit of democracy into reality.

It appears from these Scandinavian examples, as also from those of Flanders, the Netherlands, Switzerland and Scotland, that small nations, whose peoples have had to surmount the difficult natural conditions of their environments in order to survive, develop a strong and fertile group consciousness. Their relative weakness turns their thoughts from territorial expansion to the practical and the creative arts, and there they achieve greatness out of all proportion to their numbers.

Chapter 24

ICELAND AND THE FAEROES. THE NORTH ATLANTIC AND ITS FISHERIES

ICELAND and the Faeroe Islands are situated on a broad submarine ridge which, extending from Greenland to northern Scotland and eastwards beyond the Shetland and Orkney Islands, separates the Norwegian Sea basin from that of the North Atlantic. This ridge has been the scene of volcanic activity from early Tertiary times, with extensive and repeated fissure outpouring of basaltic lavas. These compose Iceland and the Faeroes almost entirely, and appear on a smaller scale in Antrim and western Scotland. In Iceland and the Faeroes numerous sheets of basalt, totalling together with inter-bedded layers of volcanic debris many thousand feet in thickness, have been piled up by successive flows which in parts of Iceland have continued to the present day.

The general high relief, the prevailing bare and often jagged surface of the lava rock, the misty, wet and stormy climate and the isolated situations of Iceland and the Faeroes have restricted settlement on them to the less uninviting patches round the fiord inlets and in coastal valleys. Poor as these islands are in land resources, they have been and are of importance in other ways. With the Shetland Islands they served as intermediate bases, nowhere more than 300 miles from land to land, for the Vikings on their voyages from Norway to Greenland. In the present time they are centres of important fisheries in the neighbouring relatively shallow waters; and Iceland occupies a valuable strategic position between Europe and North America, which United States armed forces have been granted facilities for utilising in a base near Reykjavik.

ICELAND

Iceland, formerly linked politically with Denmark, has been an independent republic since 1944. It is 39,960 sq. miles in area, considerably larger than either Scotland or Ireland, but its population numbers only 160,000 all told. More than two-thirds of the island is utterly barren, consisting of lava plateaux between 2,000 and 3,500 feet in elevation from which great volcanic peaks rise to heights of 4,000 to over 6,500 feet. Most of these are extinct, but Hekla still erupts from time to time causing destruction of vegetation, crops and live-stock in the inhabited south-western districts, through its discharges of ash and gases. Mount Hekla is the focus of the lingering volcanic activity in the southern segment of the island, other manifestations of which are numerous hot springs, geysers and boiling mud pools.

The high elevation of the lava plateaux, the high latitude of the whole island close to the Arctic Circle, and the heavy precipitation (100 to 150 inches on the upper levels) combine to maintain ice-fields which cover one-eighth of the country. The most extensive of them and the largest in Europe, is on the Vatnajökull plateau where several points exceed 6,000 feet. The glacier tongues of this and neighbouring ice-caps feed a number of radial rivers which follow valleys incised along fractures and which commonly terminate in fiords, especially in the northern sector of the island.

The natural vegetation of the valleys and lower slopes, the only parts of the country that carry any plant life, is semi-tundra, consisting of grasses, bushes and dwarf birch and willows, with patches of bog moss and sedge. Whatever woodlands once existed have been mostly destroyed for fuel and by the nibbling of sheep, during the thousand years of human occupation. Only one-seventh of the island can be classed as productive, and most of that is indifferent meadowland and rough grazings. Not only is the proportion of land actually cultivated very small, about one half of one per cent, but the range of crops, chiefly potatoes, turnips and cabbages, is very limited. Livestock are the mainstay of the farmers, and though it is difficult to dry the hay crop, as much as possible is saved in order to carry the animals through the long winters. There are approximately four sheep per head of the population which, together with 47,000 cattle and abundant supplies of fish, provide sufficient protein foods for the people. But all cereal requirements have to be imported, as the meagre crops of oats and barley are normally cut green for animal fodders.

The proportion of the active population engaged in agriculture, now about 30 per cent, has fallen by one-half in the last eighty years, with the growth in importance in the national economy of fisheries and the recent establishment of some manufactures. More than three-quarters of the present population are classed as 'urban', i.e. living in places of over 300 inhabitants, and 40 per cent in Reykjavik, where, and also at Vestmannaeyjar (on one of the islands in a group off the south coast), curing and freezing plants are in operation. Cod form the bulk of the catches, especially at these two centres, while herrings are taken by vessels from Akureyri and other smaller north and north-west fishing ports. Formerly much of the cod was dry-cured for sale to Mediterranean, Latin American and West Indian markets, but with the introduction of the quick-freezing process, increasing quantities are exported as frozen fillets. An important associated processing industry is the extraction of cod-liver and other fish oils. Fish and fish products account for about 90 per cent of the value of all exports.

Though the Icelanders have been making attempts to broaden their economy, this must be very largely based in the future as in the past upon the fishing industry, essentially upon the landings of cod caught in off-shore waters. Because of the very slender land resources, in proportion even to the small population, the Icelanders are driven to regard their coastal fishing grounds as belonging properly to their territory. Their claim to extend their territorial waters from the three-mile to a twelve-mile limit from which foreign fishing vessels are to be more or less excluded, is not altogether unreasonable, especially in view of the growing practice of over-fishing, and the resulting depletion of the stocks of young fish.

THE FAEROES

The Faeroes, like Iceland, are inhabited by people of Norse descent, but they are still attached politically to Denmark — with a form of home-rule. Their total area is 540 sq. miles and the population in 1955 numbered 34,000. These islands are the remnants of a basaltic lava plateau which has been carved into elongated forms aligned NW.–SE., with a general downward slope in the same direction. The residual plateau stands at an average elevation of about 1,000 feet, though from it rise numerous peaks and sharp ridges to between 2,000 and 3,000 feet. Above the valleys, the same rather monotonous land forms of bare, terraced basalt sheets appear through the islands, often terminating, especially in the north-west, in precipitous cliffs on the coasts.

The climate of the Faeroes, like that of Iceland, is wet and stormy, but not so misty nor so cool, as these islands lie farther away from the Arctic Circle and also from the zone of contact between cold polar and warm Atlantic air masses. The main impediment to agriculture is the scarcity of productive land, and some even of what there is has been reclaimed from moorlands with much human effort. Such as it is, the cultivated land, which is used for growing hay, potatoes and root crops, amounts to less than 4 per cent of the total area. The supply of fuel, however, is not the problem it is in Iceland, for coal of fair quality is mined on Syderö, the southernmost of the larger islands.

The main source of livelihood for the Faeroese as for the Icelanders, is the fisheries, the quantity of fish landed averaging over 100,000 tons. The situation of the islands on the North Atlantic submarine shelf, and adjacent to its southern extensions in the Wyville-Thomson ridge and the Rockall rise, provides excellent conditions for the fishing industry, for which Thorshavn, the capital, on the largest island is the chief centre.

The North Atlantic and its Fisheries

The North Atlantic, over 1,200 miles wide between Scotland and southern Greenland, narrows to about 700 miles on the threshold of the Norwegian Sea between Norway and Iceland; and the Norwegian Sea in its turn is constricted to 450 miles between north Norway and Spitzbergen, where it joins with the Barents Sea. Into this northward narrowing area of sub-Arctic seas vast quantities of warm Atlantic water are impelled as the North Atlantic Drift through the passage between Norway and the Faeroes by the prevailing south-westerly winds. When this drift of warm water approaches northern Norway, it divides into a main branch that circulates in the Barents Sea, and a subsidiary branch towards Spitzbergen, thus contributing to an extension of the so-called Gulf of Warmth much beyond the Arctic Circle. The tendency which this inflow of warmer water has to raise the level of the Arctic seas is partly offset by a return current of relatively cold water outflowing along the east coast of Greenland in the direction of Iceland. This surface current is valuable as a carrier of plankton.[1]

The movements of the surface waters, mainly under the influence of the prevailing winds, have some influence upon the seasonal migrations of fish in search of spawning grounds; but more important in providing supplies of plankton, upon which most commercial fish

[1] Plant and animal remains (from the land as well as from the sea) sink towards the bottom, where they are attacked by bacteria forming nitrogen and phosphorus compounds. These, when carried upwards, support microscopic flora and fauna (plankton), upon which the larger organisms feed, so completing the 'nitrogen cycle', when fish are landed or die in the sea.

feed, are the upward currents in the sea-waters. These are especially marked in the Arctic region where cold surface-water sinks in winter, and is replaced by water warmer than it is, from below. Similar upward currents occur in some areas of the temperate North Atlantic seas; but, owing probably to general climatic changes, they are liable

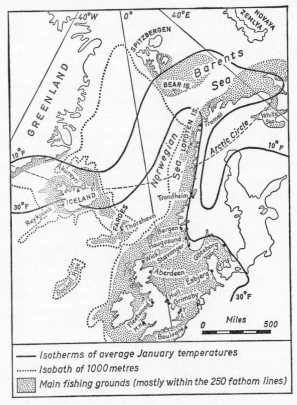

Fig. 92. The North Atlantic Fisheries and major fishing ports. M.H., Milford Haven. Y., Yarmouth. L., Lowestoft. I., Ijmuiden. Sources: *Carte générale bathymétrique des Océans. The Geography of the Northlands*— Kimble and Good 1953. *World Sea Fisheries* —R. Morgan 1956.

to shift, thus accounting for the mass migrations of certain fish e.g. of hake recently from the Channel approaches to the north-west African waters and the disappearance of Atlantic herrings from the outer Baltic.

The main feeding grounds of the two principal North Atlantic commercial fish, cod and herring, are the sub-Arctic waters rich in plankton, whence they migrate periodically in shoals to the relatively warm and shallow waters of the various banks for spawning. The banks most frequented by these fish are off the Norwegian coast, in the North Sea and on the submarine ridge between Scotland and Greenland, particularly those round the Faeroes and Iceland, all of which are accordingly major fishing grounds.

Including the Arctic seas, the North Atlantic fisheries are the greatest in the world. In the years 1955–6 the catches of fish of all kinds landed by the North Atlantic countries of Europe averaged over 6 million tons,[1] and several million more were taken by American and Canadian fishing fleets on the western side. Among the North Atlantic countries Norway has led by far with about 2 million tons, followed by the United Kingdom and West Germany with just over a million and three-quarters of a million tons respectively. These three together with France, Iceland and Denmark have accounted for $5\frac{1}{2}$ million tons out of the total 6 million. It is uncertain, however, whether these quantities can be maintained, failing the enforcement by international agreement of some restrictions upon the recent practice of taking fish regardless of size and maturity.

Though Norway and Iceland in particular export considerable quantities of their catches to countries outside Europe, much the greater proportion of all this harvest of the sea is consumed in the countries named above, mainly as human food, partly as fodder meal and fertiliser. Fish constitute an important element in the diet of North Atlantic peoples, valuable not merely for nourishment, but also because, being rich in protein and in phosphorus compounds, they contribute to physical and mental vigour.

[1] Excluding several million tons taken by Russian fishing vessels which have become very numerous and active. Russian catches exceed those of Norway and Great Britain combined.

PART II

THE WESTERN MEDITERRANEAN: THE IBERIAN PENINSULA AND ITALY

Chapter 25

GENERAL PHYSICAL STRUCTURE AND RELATED FEATURES AND RESOURCES

THE Western Mediterranean Sea, roughly triangular in shape, comprises two larger basin deeps, the Tyrrhenian and the Ligurian-Balearic, separated from each other by the Corsica-Sardinian residual massif, and a third smaller, the Alboran (named after its midway island), which occupies the elongated trough between southern Spain and North Africa and narrows westward to the Straits of Gibraltar. Except at this passage and at the straits on either side of Sicily, the Western Mediterranean is almost entirely surrounded by a girdle of highlands, the only marked breaks in which are the Rhône corridor and the Carcassonne gap between the Central Massif of France and the Maritime Alps and the Pyrenees respectively. Proximity to the most northerly extension of the African plateau areas has rendered the Western Mediterranean region especially exposed to the pincer movements of Gondwanaland in the Alpine orogenetic thrusts (and also earlier in the Hercynian) against the resistant masses of North Atlantic Europe and its former western extensions. The uplift of sedimentary beds from the floor of Tethys to form the mountain ranges of the Alpine system and the re-elevation of marginal pene-planed areas, notably the Spanish Meseta and the Catalonian Massif (see p. 403), accompanied by trough subsidence and the apparent foundering of parts now occupied by the sea, have combined to give the Western Mediterranean region as a whole its present physical form.

In contrast with the extensive coastal plains and continental shelves of North-Western Europe, the shores of the Western Mediterranean are in general marked by steepness of slope both above and below sea-level. Such coastal plains as exist are narrow and discontinuous, and submarine shelves equally so, except off the mouths of the two large rivers, the Rhône and the Ebro and from the Gulf of Valencia along the partly submerged Balearic ridge. The several sea basins exceed 6,000 feet in their deepest parts, and owing to their floor profiles just described, have average depths of well over 4,000 feet.

Because of the shallow sill at the Straits of Gibraltar (nowhere more than 1,300 feet below sea-level) the colder waters of the Atlantic are excluded, and the inflow thence to compensate for the large excess of loss by evaporation over river discharge is of relatively warm surface water. In the Western Mediterranean itself the uppermost layers have the high average temperature of 13·5° C. (56·3° F.), while below about 300 fathoms down to the lowest depths there is little variation from about 13·2° C. This sea is in fact a great reservoir of relatively warm water, more or less homogeneous in temperature. These features together with its greater average salinity than that of the Atlantic 38·5 per mille v. 36 per mille) have, as will appear later, important influences upon the climate and in this and in other ways upon human life and activities.

Almost cut off from the ocean, this Western Mediterranean 'lake' is nearly tideless. Thus the rivers, loaded with silt swept along their steep courses from the highlands subject to heavy erosion by ice in the north, e.g. the Alps, or by intermittent torrential rains towards the south, tend to form extensive deltas. These are naturally unsuitable for the establishment of ports, and in any case they have commonly been pestilential because their swampy tracts have been breeding places for malarial mosquitoes. Only in recent times have some of them been rendered wholesome and productive by means of elaborate and costly drainage works. Hence compared with North-West Europe the Western Mediterranean with its mainly unbroken shores affords comparatively few good, naturally sheltered sites for ports. Some exceptions, e.g. Gibraltar, Toulon and Taranto, are situated on basins enclosed by headlands (rock harbours), but the majority including such major ports as Naples and Barcelona, are on more or less open bays, necessitating the construction of moles for the protection of shipping.

The two main elements of the West European Mediterranean lands, the Iberian Peninsula and Italy, differ greatly in age and structure. The former is basically one of the oldest parts of Europe, the latter for the most part actually the youngest. Even the Alpine-elevated Pyrenees antedate the Alps in their origins, for they contain evidence of extensive Hercynian folding absent from the Alps but for scattered involved Hercynian massifs (p. 16); and the Meseta Plateau composed essentially of long-upstanding Palaeozoic and even Pre-Cambrian metamorphic and crystalline rocks contrasts sharply with the Italian Apennines, which comprise little besides the Jurassic

limestones of the core and the soft Tertiary beds on their flanks.
The intense pressures resulting from the northward advance in the
Alpine orogenesis have caused much buckling and faulting and vertical movements of the crustal rocks of the Western Mediterranean
area. Upthrusts, whether of folding in anticlines of fault-bounded
horsts or of general re-elevation, have been accompanied by down-
thrusts in adjacent parts resulting in synclinal troughs, block subsidence and foundering. Examples are seen in southern Spain where
the upthrust Betic Cordillera[1] is bordered by the Andalusian and the
Alboran troughs; again in the region of Peninsular Italy where the
Apennines are similarly flanked by the Adriatic and Tyrrhenian
depressions; and within the Meseta itself where the horst ranges of
the Central Cordillera and the Guadalupe-Toledo group are bordered
by the basins of Old and New Castile, partially filled with sediments
derived from the erosion of the adjacent uplifts. Here, as elsewhere in
the world, the softer Mesozoic and Tertiary strata have yielded to the
forces of compression by arching and folding, while the ancient hard
rocks have been rent by faults and fractures and have been distorted
by widespread vertical displacements.

A striking feature of the alignment pattern of the folded ranges is
their tendency to twist in sharp curves, e.g. from the Maritime to the
Ligurian Alps in north-west Italy, between Calabria and Sicily, and
most pronounced of all, at the Straits of Gibraltar; the resulting weakness at the apex points of the two latter has given rise to fractures of
rift-valley form enabling the sea to break through. The former
Mediterranean connections of the Betic-Balearic Alpine system have
been the subject of numerous suppositions by different authorities, a
selection of the more recent of which is given in Fig. 93. It is thought
that a former crustal block, of which Corsica-Sardinia and possibly
the Maures-Esterel in southern France may be remnants, foundered
in the region of the Ligurian-Balearic Sea. Its presumed existence
would help to explain the S-shaped turns of the folds from the Central
Alps through Italy into Sicily. A possible explanation also of the
north-east trend of the Balearic folds is that the collapse of that block

---

[1] This name, now in general usage following the terminology of the leading geomorphologists, has been adopted from that of the Roman province Baetica which
included the eastern and south-eastern parts of Spain. The Sierra Nevada is only
one of several ranges in the whole system. The term Cordillera (derived from
cordon = a stretched cord) is applied in Spanish-speaking countries to any extended
range or series of ranges, the mountains of which appear as seen from a distance to
be stretched in a line across the horizon.

left them free to bend northwards between the Meseta and Sardinia on the Betic alignment and link up with the Iberian Mountains, as in A and C Fig. 93. The most recent theory presumes an E.–SE. drift of the Corsardinian block, accompanied by the engulfing of a former Balearic-Alpine link and the northward thrusting of the surviving Balearic uplift as in D Fig. 93; evidence in support of this appears in the Alpine folds in north-east Corsica.

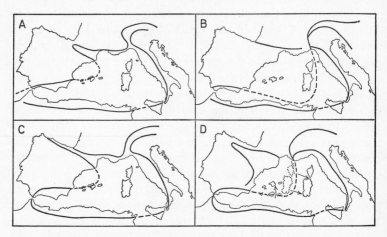

Fig. 93. Various interpretations of the Balearic in relation to the Alpine folds. A). Stille 1927. B). Staub 1927. C). Solé 1949. D). Villaplana and others 1960.

FISHERIES

The Mediterranean Sea is poor in edible fish compared with the North Atlantic coastal waters. Sardines, anchovies, tunny, mackerel and various cephalopods form the bulk of the catches. The generally scarce supplies of ordinary fish are eked out with squid, octopus and cuttle fish, which are widely consumed. Though the somewhat greater salinity of the waters may be a contributing factor, the main physical cause is the nearly uniform temperatures of the water in depth and the consequent absence of upward-welling cool currents bringing nitrates and phosphates to nourish plankton in the upper layers. The lack of good supplies of fish would not be such a serious matter, were it not that meat is also none too plentiful in the typical Mediterranean lands of summer drought and poverty of pastures. Hence the ordinance of the Catholic Church, to which the peoples of Italy and Iberia mostly belong, providing for regular meatless days. Faced with these shortages of both fish and meat, many of the poorer people have to rely largely upon beans and other pulses for supplies of protein in their diet. The people of the Atlantic shores of Spain and Portugal have naturally much more generous supplies of fish (as well as of meat in the north-west). In addition to the ordinary kinds of fish landed there for local consumption, large quantities of sardines are canned, especially in Portugal, for export.

MINERAL RESOURCES

(a) *Fuels and iron ore.* Coal and lignite, abundant in the so-called power-belt of Western and Central Europe, are scarce throughout the Mediterranean lands where the Carboniferous series scarcely exists, and the Tertiary basins, especially the inland ones in Spain, have in general been unfavourable for the formation of lignite deposits.[1] Italy produces well under a million tons of coal per annum, almost entirely in south-west Sardinia, and about a million tons of lignite mainly in Tuscany (Fig. 114), both insignificant contributions to the requirements of a populous modern industrial country.[2] Portugal, producing about half a million tons of coal (near Oporto) and very little lignite, is even worse off. Spain, however, with an output of 14 million tons of hard coal (mainly in Asturias) and a couple of million tons of lignite, makes a rather better showing, though these local supplies are insufficient for any extensive industrial development above ordinary domestic requirements in a country where wood fuel is unusually scarce.

In respect of petroleum and natural gas Italy has a distinct advantage over the two Iberian countries, in neither of which has either of these power resources been discovered in appreciable quantity. Some 2 million tons per annum of petroleum are produced (1961–2) in Italy, mainly from the Ragusa district[3] of Sicily (Fig. 114) and unusually large stores of methane have been tapped in the northern plain (Fig. 119), the output from which rose from 1 million cubic metres in 1951 to 6 million cubic metres in 1958.

Deposits of iron ore are of little account except in Spain which

[1] In this Mediterranean region of prolonged crustal disturbance during the Alpine phase of mountain building, the conditions favourable for the accumulation and preservation of plant remains as lignite, namely the gradual subsidence of extensive swampy tracts, have rarely existed.

[2] Cf. the outputs of various countries north of the Alps given in the Table p. 26.

[3] This recently-developed field has proved productive. Output has increased rapidly, and is expected to reach 5 million tons p.a. by 1965.

produces some 2½ million tons (metal content), most of it in the Basque Province and inland from Cartagena; Italy mines a little over half a million tons (in Elba and Val d'Aosta) and Portugal next to none. It is perhaps surprising that neither the widespread metamorphic rocks of Iberia nor the Jurassic formations of the Italian Appenines contain deposits of iron ore comparable with those in similar geological structures in North-Western and Central Europe (cf. Table p. 27). Moreover, in point of fact, the richer deposits of Northern Spain, formerly exported in quantity to Great Britain, are approaching exhaustion, and exports have dwindled both because of this and because increasing substantial supplies are taken by recently established local iron and steel works (p. 402).

(b) *Non-ferrous metals.* The metamorphic rocks of Iberia containing numerous granitic and associated intrusions are fairly rich in valuable minerals — especially so those of the Sierra Morena and adjoining parts on the southern margin of the Meseta, where copper pyrites occur in a belt from Huelva to Mertola (in Portugal), lead ores at Linares and Jaén and the richest deposits of mercury in the world at Almadén. Two other outstanding deposits are those of tungsten ore (wolfram) at Fundão in the upper Zezere valley in Portugal and of zinc blende at Reocin near Santander. Though most of the above sources have been worked for many years past, their outputs are still substantial.

The widespread Tertiary and Quaternary formations of Italy are naturally devoid of metal ores. Such small deposits of the non-ferrous metal group as exist in the whole country are associated with outcrops of older rocks, e.g. of tin and mercury in the 'hill islands' of Tuscany and of lead and zinc near Iglesias in south-west Sardinia. Were it not for Italy's general poverty in metallic mineral resources, most of these lean deposits might be left unworked.

(c) *Volcanic and soda-potash minerals.* Recent volcanic activity has endowed youthful Italy, in contrast with Iberia, with considerable associated deposits of sulphur and borax in a curving belt from Tuscany into Sicily. However, neither of these minerals is an asset of much value owing to their abundance in other parts of the world, notably in the United States and the Andes of South America, and in the case of sulphur because of the large supplies also available in the world market as by-products from the smelting of widespread pyrites ores.

Rock salt, which occurs abundantly in the Triassic beds at intervals from England far into Central Europe, is also found in both Iberia and Italy, which produce upwards of 2 million tons and of $1\frac{1}{2}$ million tons (NaCl content) respectively. Supplies of salt are also obtained by evaporating sea water on lagoon coasts, especially in Portugal which is devoid of salt-bearing rocks. Deposits of the rarer potash salts exist apparently in north-east Spain only, in Catalonia and near Pamplona in Navarre; about half a million tons (K_2O content) are produced, mainly in the Suria-Cardona district[1] north of Barcelona (Fig 105).

HYDRO-ELECTRIC POWER

Hydro-electric power stations in Iberia and Italy must be restricted, but for minor exceptions, to the Alps and the Apennines, the Pyrenees and the Cantabrians, and the old dissected highlands of north-western Iberia; the marked seasonal distribution of the rainfall in other parts, where also it is commonly insufficient and unreliable, make it impossible to provide continuous heads of water without costly storage reservoirs.

Italy has made great progress in developing her water-power resources, of which 70 to 80 per cent of the total potential has been harnessed. With an output of some 40 million kWh. per annum Italy holds first place among the countries of Europe, and is exceeded only by the United States and Canada in other continents. The majority of the power stations numbering upwards of 3,000 in all are naturally in the Alpine zone (Fig. 124). These contribute about three-quarters of the whole output, the Central Appennine stations about 15 per cent, and the South and the islands the balance, about 10 per cent. The decrease from north to south corresponding to the transition in relief and climatic conditions combined is noteworthy.

Spain has considerable water-power resources in the Pyrenees and westward into Galicia. Development of the more advantageous sites has been fairly rapid in recent years, especially in Catalonia, the central and western Pyrenees and Galicia, where much of the Spanish total of about 15 million kWh (1960–1) is generated and consumed both in the Barcelona region (which has no other power resources at hand) and in the Biscayan provinces of Vizcaya and Santander which

---

[1] Situated in the Ebro depression, a basin of continuous slow subsidence during the Tertiary period, in which, after its being finally cut off from the Mediterranean in the Eocene by the re-elevated Catalonian ranges, numerous sea-water salt lakes dried up leaving deposits of both common and potash salts interbedded between the marine and the overlying continental sediments together totalling several thousand metres in thickness.

hitherto have had to rely upon Oviedo or imported coal for their growing industries. In Portugal too, which has only trifling supplies of coal and no other sources or fuel and power except the depleted forests, water power is being increasingly developed, the output of current now amounting to some 3 million kWh. Most of the stations are located in the northern parts, on the Douro and its tributaries and on the Zezere River — in the regions of rugged highlands and heaviest rainfall, which adjoin the northern littoral belt of densest and most active population.

Chapter 26

CLIMATE, NATURAL VEGETATION

THOUGH the Iberian Peninsula and Italy are Mediterranean in situation, parts only of each are Mediterranean in climate. They include, in fact, at least three other varieties of climate besides the Mediterranean which is confined to southern Portugal, south and south-east Spain, the islands and Peninsular Italy from a little south of the latitude of Florence. North-western Iberia, open to tempering Atlantic influences and to depressions throughout the year, has a West European oceanic climate; the Meseta Plateau and the Ebro depression, both more or less surrounded by bordering highlands, and subject to extremes of temperature and rather scanty and uncertain amounts of precipitation, have a semi-continental sub-arid type of climate; the North Italian Plain and Alpine zone where the ranges of temperature between the summer and the winter months are considerable, and more rain plus snow falls during the six summer months than during the rest of the year, have a semi-continental humid variety of climate; the coastlands of Catalonia in north-east Spain which resemble the North Italian Plain in the absence of summer drought, but do not get its low winter temperatures, have a modified Mediterranean climate, and so also do the transitional zones to true Mediterranean in northern Portugal and north central Italy. The data on page 366 of mean precipitation (in inches) and mean temperatures (° F.) at selected stations illustrate the several varieties of climate as described above.

Peninsularity, which is such a marked feature of the geographical conformation of Mediterranean Europe, largely determines the overall climatic conditions. These are, as has been said, the gift of the Mediterranean Sea. The interlocking of land and sea, together with the disposition of mountain systems and highlands acting as climatic barriers, give rise to the various climatic sub-divisions noted.

Situated in the transitional zone between North Atlantic Europe and the Sahara, the Western Mediterranean lands are subject to air-masses of diverse origins, corresponding to changes in the distribution of atmospheric pressure over the Mediterranean Sea, the eastern

Atlantic and the neighbouring continental areas. As in other parts of Western Europe, the chief activators of air movements over the Mediterranean are passing depressions. The air-currents which reach that area have widely differing temperatures and moisture contents according to their sources. Those from the North Atlantic are normally

	Jan.	Feb.	Mar.	Apr.	May	June	July	Aug.	Sept.	Oct.	Nov.	Dec.	Mean Annual	Range
Cartagena	1·8	1·4	1·4	1·1	1·0	0·8	0·1	0·2	1·4	1·7	1·9	2·1	14·9	
(SE. Spain)	51	53	55	59	63	70	75	76	72	65	58	52		25°
Rome	3·2	2·7	2·9	2·6	2·2	1·6	0·7	1·0	2·5	5·0	4·4	3·9	32·7	
	45	47	51	57	64	71	76	76	70	62	53	46		31°
Corunna	3·2	3·1	3·2	2·5	2·2	1·4	0·9	1·2	2·2	3·5	4·2	4·4	32	
(NW. Spain)	48	49	51	53	57	61	64	64	62	58	53	51		16°
Madrid	1·3	1·3	1·6	1·7	1·7	1·3	0·4	0·6	1·5	1·8	1·9	1·4	16·5	
	41	44	48	54	61	69	77	76	68	57	48	40		36°
Zaragoza	0·6	0·8	0·9	1·1	1·6	1·1	0·7	0·6	1·1	1·4	1·2	0·8	11·9	
(Middle Ebro)	42	44	52	55	61	69	75	73	68	59	49	43		33°
Milan	2·4	2·3	2·7	3·4	4·1	3·3	2·8	3·2	3·5	4·7	4·3	3·0	39·7	
	32	38	46	55	63	70	75	73	66	56	44	36		43°
Barcelona	1·3	1·7	1·8	1·7	2·0	1·5	1·1	1·3	2·4	3·6	2·3	1·7	22·4	
	49	50	53	56	62	69	74	75	70	64	56	51		26°
Florence	1·9	2·1	2·7	2·9	3·0	2·7	1·5	1·9	3·3	4·0	3·9	2·8	32·7	
	42	43	50	63	63	72	77	76	70	61	52	43		35°
Lisbon	3·3	3·2	3·7	2·4	1·7	0·7	0·2	0·2	1·4	3·1	4·2	3·6	27·7	
	51	52	55	58	62	67	71	72	69	68	57	52		21°

moist and comparatively cool; those drawn in from the continental regions to the north, known as Mistral (p. 188), Maestrale, Tramontana or Bora in different parts, are naturally dry and cold or very cold in winter and spring, especially if they originate in the Arctic; those from a southerly point, often of Saharan origin, are abnormally dry on reaching the Mediterranean and extremely hot and dusty in the summer season, e.g. the Sirocco of Sicily and the Leveche of south-east Spain, though their ill effects are seldom felt on the northern shores of the Sea.

It appears accordingly that apart from the rainfall derived from water vapour absorbed from the Mediterranean Sea itself and deposited on the land by local depressions, the Western Mediterranean countries depend for their precipitation upon the moisture brought by air-currents from the Atlantic. Fortunately the predominant winds are westerly, especially during the winter months when they blow directly from the Ocean (Fig. 94), and the unwelcome bitterly cold northerlies and the scorching southerlies are mostly local and on the whole not very frequent visitations.

In summer the Azores high pressure system becomes enlarged and intensified owing to the heating of the land and the collection of denser cool air over the ocean. It then extends north-east to affect the Western Mediterranean, while at the same time pressure is low over the Sahara, and exceptionally so to the east over South-West Asia (Fig. 95). Following the pressure gradient the winds are mainly north-westerly, but are north-easterly over the Alboran area; and because they are anticyclonic in origin, they are generally dry. It is hardly correct to account for the summer drought of the Mediterranean region

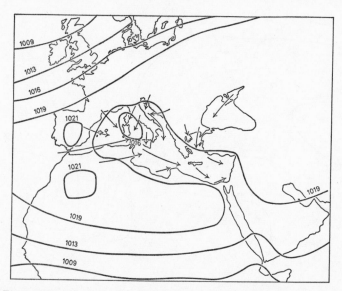

Fig. 94. The distribution of air pressure (isobars in millibars) and the prevailing winds over the Mediterranean in January.

as the result of a northward swing of the North-East Trade winds. The extended Azores high pressure system is in fact the primary controlling agent, barring the passage of Atlantic depressions and forcing them to follow more northerly eastward tracks.

In the winter season the general distribution of air pressure is the reverse of that in summer; high pressure systems tend to build up over the land, then colder than the ocean, where vigorous depressions formed on the North Atlantic Front travel eastwards, following various tracks (see pp. 31–2) including the Mediterranean Sea now open to them north and south of the Meseta high pressure area. This relatively warm body of water (p. 358) induces the passage of primary depressions and also of secondaries of those to the north, and is large enough to enable fronts to form within it between relatively high pressure air over the land and lower pressure air over the sea, resulting in shallow depressions. Thus the winds in winter are variable in both place and time, but tend to follow particular directions in different parts, e.g. north-west over the Balearic basin, north-east over the northern Adriatic and north central Italy, westerly over the Alboran basin and the southern Mediterranean generally.

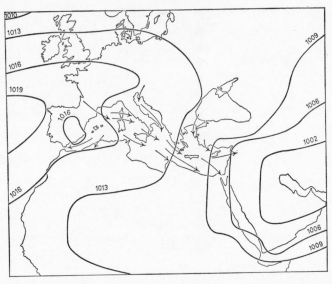

Fig. 95. The distribution of air pressure (isobars in millibars) and the prevailing winds over the Mediterranean in July.

The winter temperatures on the coastlands, especially those sheltered from the cold northerly winds, are unusually high owing to the tempering influence of the warm sea-waters and abundant sunshine; but these abnormal temperatures do not as a rule extend far inland because of intervening highlands. A climatic feature common to all the Mediterranean lands except the high mountains is the prevalence of sunshine, greatest farther south where the rainfall becomes more distinctly seasonal and the rainy days are fewer. Rome for example gets an average of 2,360 hours per annum and Catania in Sicily over 2,500, compared with only 1,466 hours at Kew in one of the sunnier parts of the British Isles. The air over the Mediterranean is normally drier than that north of the 45th parallel, where moist air-currents from the Atlantic predominate; mists and fogs are rare in the former except on high mountains, and the rains, if heavy, as they not uncommonly are, of shorter duration.

The rainfall varies greatly in average yearly amount from place to place, and is apt to be irregular and spasmodic in those parts where it is near or below the critical limits for the cultivation of field crops. It is naturally greatest on the northern mountains — the Alps, the Pyrenees, and the Galician highlands — where it falls throughout the year and (including snowfall) exceeds 60 ins. in many parts; and is least on the south-east coastlands and inland basins screened by highlands from the westerly winds, e.g. Almería 9·7 ins., Zaragoza 11·5 ins., Cagliari 16·7 ins., Taranto 17·5 ins. In these potentially productive areas where months may pass without appreciable rainfall, water supplies, where available from highland sources, are being increasingly used for irrigation, and in many other parts terrace cultivation is practised, partly because of the scarcity of productive land, but also to catch the greater rainfall on upland slopes, and to utilise the water brought by streams from still higher up.

VEGETATION

In view of the prolonged periods of intense summer sunshine it is evident that the rate of evaporation is high in those parts where the Mediterranean climate prevails, thus reducing the effectiveness of any given amount of rainfall; and though the characteristic autumn to spring maxima of precipitation coincide with the seasons of minimum evaporation, the summer drought is commonly severe enough to cause plants to slacken, if not cease their growth, and to ripen off. In northern Italy and north-west Spain on the other hand, the fairly heavy summer rainfall, less what is lost by evaporation, is generally sufficient for plants to continue growth from spring into autumn; there the check to vegetative activity comes with the relatively low winter temperatures.

The broad differences in the climatic conditions between the north and the rest in the two peninsulas give rise to corresponding differences in the seasonal rhythm of plant life and hence in its forms. The characteristic trees in the former, such as oak, beech, ash and poplar, are deciduous and grow together as forests if left undisturbed; the native trees and shrubs of the latter are evergreen, e.g. evergreen oak, wild olive and the laurel family, and are more often scattered singly or

N

in patches or in open woodlands than clustered in continuous stands. Both these types give way to coniferous species (pines and cedars) at higher elevations. In addition, three humbler types of vegetation adapted to special harsh physical conditions, namely maquis, garigue and steppe, each cover considerable areas in the drier parts.

Little of the true high forest remains except in some mountainous parts, mainly in the extra-Mediterranean north, where conifers have survived. During thousands of years of human occupation deforestation has proceeded far and wide for fuel, shipbuilding, timber and clearance for upland pastures. Once destroyed, the Mediterranean forest has difficulty in re-establishing itself, especially against the depredations of goats which nibble off young shoots. The results have been unfortunate. Widespread soil-wash on the steeper slopes subject to intermittent downpours of rain has left stretches of bare rock or 'bad lands' broken by mazes of gullies; and where plants can find some roothold, maquis and garigue, degenerate forms of vegetation composed of stunted and useless bushes, have replaced the original tree cover.

Where a fairly continuous if thin soil cover remains, a tangle of bushy or stunted evergreen plants known as maquis (macchia in Italy, matorral in Spain) has developed, common members of which among others are myrtle, dwarf holm oak and lavender, often compacted together with briars and creepers. Where the soil has been reduced to thin patches or is almost non-existent as on the rocky limestone tracts common in the Mediterranean lands, a scattered form of vegetation has appeared, composed of the more xerophytic species of the maquis and others that manage to find roothold and some moisture in patches of soil and in crevices, e.g. rosemary, broom, gorse, sage, together with prickly pear and agave (aloe) introduced from the New World. Neither the maquis nor still less the garigue is of use to man or beast, and the parts covered by them must be accounted waste lands.

The Mediterranean climate is unfavourable for members of the grass family. The common cereals do none too well even on selected lowland areas, and meadow grasses wither off in the summer drought unless supplied with water artificially. The characteristic indigenous grasses of the Mediterranean are coarse and tufty, especially those of the sub-arid southern Meseta and the Ebro depression in Spain, which can normally support little else in the way of plant life and therefore approach the dry steppe in general appearance.

The indigenous Mediterranean vegetation of generally open woodlands and steppe country was favourable to the development of early civilisations. The hardwood trees of the former were useful for constructional purposes, especially for the building of ships; and the readily cleared forest lands as well as the steppe country were serviceable for the cultivation of cereals and the pasturing of live-stock.

Chapter 27

AGRICULTURE: FIELD CROPS, ARBORICULTURE

For distribution of leading crops etc. see Figs. 102, 103 (Spain); 109, 110 (Portugal); 121, 122 (Italy)

WITH the exception of the Po Basin and some scattered smaller areas, well-watered plains suitable for the large-scale cultivation of cereals are lacking in all three countries. The generally marked if not mountainous relief, and the marginal if not insufficient rainfall over much of Spain and southern Italy, restrict the areas of fully utilised crop land for the most part to the numerous valleys and valley pockets and terraced hillsides. Typical Mediterranean agriculture partakes of both gardening and arboriculture, the former on the deeper more fertile soils (including those man-made on terraced hillsides), the latter in the forms of vineyards and olive and chestnut groves wherever space can be found for them. Though there are some notable examples of regional specialisation on a commercial basis in the production for export, e.g. of citrus fruits in Sicily, of oranges in south-east Spain, of branded wines in various districts, these are the exception. The average holding is small and the produce is mainly for local consumption; there is a general absence of draught animals or of powered agricultural machines; and the pressure of population is such that the peasants, though making the fullest use of their land by continuous labour, are often very poor.

Two main problems beset the cultivator in Mediterranean Spain and Italy: how to maintain the fertility of the soil, and how to meet the general shortage of water and of moisture in the ground during the prolonged summer drought. In the Mediterranean climate the soil is not re-conditioned by mechanical weathering owing to the absence of frost, and its humus content is liable to become depleted by oxidation. Animal manure would be a valuable corrective, supplying the much-needed humus to make the soil retentive of moisture and to keep it, in the farmer's phrase, 'in good heart'. But live-stock, other than goats and sheep maintained largely on upland grazings, are scarce in these Mediterranean lands where, apart from the difficulties of carrying the animals through the summer, food crops have the first claim. Though crop yields have been improved in recent times by supplies of chemical fertilisers, e.g. nitrogen and potash compounds and superphosphates, manufactured in the countries themselves or imported, they do not add directly to the humus content of the soil.

The scarcity of water for crops and even for drinking enforces special measures in those parts where the rainfall is negligible during six months or more, and the streams dry up. If underground waters exist, the obvious course is to tap these from springs or by sinking wells; incidentally, the availability of such supplies has determined the sites of many villages and towns. But as underground waters are not often sufficient for field irrigation, agricultural techniques have in general been adapted to meet the seasonal scarcity of water. Autumn-sown crops of grain, pulses etc. are grown on suitable plots to take advantage of the winter rains, and grape-vines and olive trees, both able to reach underground stores of moisture with their long roots, are commonly planted on hillsides or on terraces where space can be found for them.[1] In recent times large-scale irrigation works have been taken in hand by public authorities, notably in the Ebro depression and in south-east Italy (Figs. 105, 117). Long-distance canals and aqueducts have been constructed, tunnelled through hills and led over valleys, far more extensive in scope than anything left by the Romans in Italy or by the Moors in Spain.

Water supplies do not of course present the same problems in the regions of considerable summer rainfall in northern Italy and north-west Iberia; though irrigation is in fact used extensively in the upper Po Plain, especially on the rice fields and the water meadows. On the riverine lowlands of northern Italy the main problem is the reverse, i.e. how to dispose of unwanted water — to prevent rivers in flood transgressing their channels, and to drain off surplus water from the naturally waterlogged deltaic lands bordering the Adriatic. In north-west Spain and the extreme north of Portugal neither irrigation nor artificial drainage are much needed, but the oceanic climate limits the range of staple crops; wheat and barley do not succeed well there, and

[1] Wine from grapes helps to make good the summer scarcity of wholesome drinking water, thus indirectly collecting the stores of moisture in the subsoil, and making them available for human consumption. Likewise olive oil is a main source of fats in lieu of butter in the diet of the people in many parts of the Mediterranean lands where conditions are unsuitable for dairy cattle.

are largely replaced as food grains by the less esteemed rye and maize.

Agriculture, including bush and tree cultivation and market-gardening, is of greater relative importance in each of the three countries Italy, Spain and Portugal than it is in most other West European countries; larger proportions of the active population live by that industry; Spain and Portugal export far more agricultural products by values than they import, and Italy, in spite of her large and increasing population, is on balance almost self-sufficient. In all three countries there has been and is an urge to extend agricultural and pastoral utilisation to the outer economic limits — in the past by depleting the native forests of which comparatively little remains, in the present by reclaiming marshes and by increasing the areas of irrigated land.

Mediterranean agricultural products can be classified in four main groups, (I) cereals, (II) wines and olive oil, (III) fruits and nuts, (IV) market-garden produce. The first includes the warm temperate to the sub-tropical genera maize and rice, as well as the ordinary temperate wheat, barley, oats and rye. All three countries grow by preference either soft or hard wheat as the staple food grain wherever conditions are reasonably favourable, and barley, used also as a bread grain. Failing these, the less exacting rye and oats (see pp. 51–3) are cultivated extensively in the cool oceanic northern and north-western regions of Spain and Portugal, and oats also in Italy which grows very little rye. In all three countries maize also is grown and consumed both as food by the poorer people and as fodder for live-stock, especially in Italy and Portugal which have in their northern parts the climatic conditions suited to this crop. Similar, but not quite so favourable conditions for the cultivation of maize are found in scattered parts of northern Spain and central Italy. The cultivation of rice, which has expanded considerably in recent years in both Spain and Italy, is naturally confined to readily irrigable tracts, chiefly those of the Po Valley, the Ebro delta and the Valencia huertas.

The deep-rooted grape-vine and olive are at home in the Mediterranean lands of hot and more or less rainless summers; neither, in fact, is tolerant of moist atmospheric and soil conditions in the fruiting period. Both are grown on countless odd patches (and olives also singly or spaced) for local supplies of wine and olive oil, as well as on a commercial scale in various districts[1] which specialise in producing

[1] Notably Lucca in Tuscany and Apulia for olive oil; the Douro Valley above Oporto, Jerez (the sherry district) near Cádiz, Tarragona, the Monti Chianti in

superior grades of olive oil, wines or table grapes for the export markets.

Fruits and nuts of various kinds in addition to dessert grapes are produced in different parts according to the climatic requirements of the crops. Some, such as figs, apricots, pomegranates, almonds, Barcelona nuts and sweet chestnuts, are indigenous or thoroughly acclimatised in the truly Mediterranean areas where they are widely cultivated; others such as apples and pears are of temperate origin and are consequently restricted to regions having fairly cool winters and some summer rains, e.g. the Alpine valleys of northern Italy, which specialise in these fruits; a third group comprises members of the citrus family, oranges, lemons and mandarines, which originated in the sub-tropical monsoon region of southern China, and though long cultivated in the warmer parts of the Western Mediterranean, are not really suited, even when irrigated, to the prevailing dry summer atmospheric conditions there. All these fruits and nuts are grown in part at least for export, but the bulk of the chestnut crop is consumed locally like maize as a substitute for bread grains, or as fodder for pigs.

For market-garden crops southern Italy (including Sicily in particular) and south and south-east Spain have the distinct advantage of being first in the field among European countries, owing to their exceptionally mild winters and early springs, which give them a lead over their French rival in Languedoc and Provence (p. 189). Exports of products of this class from Italy and Spain have increased in recent years with the improved facilities for the transport of perishables by air, especially from Italy, which has the additional advantage over Spain of fast through railway services to West Germany and other Common Market countries. The total area devoted to market-garden crops in Italy exceeds a quarter of a million hectares (620,000 acres), of which upwards of 45 per cent is under tomatoes, mainly for export either fresh or canned. The several varieties of this plant, originally introduced by the Spaniards from South America, have found congenial conditions as an open-air crop throughout the Mediterranean regions wherever sufficient water is available.

In respect of meat and dairy products, there is a marked contrast between the summer drought areas where meat and especially butter are scarce, and the summer-humid parts of northern Italy and the Galician-Cantabrian region of Spain which are able to provide some

Tuscany and Marsala in Sicily among others for wines; and Almería in south-east Spain for dessert grapes.

surplus of animal products for the rest of their countries. Even in Portugal, which has a smaller extension in latitude than either Spain or Italy, the great majority of the dairy cattle are to be found north of the Central Cordillera. The only item in the meat and dairy-produce group exported from any of these countries is fancy cheeses (Gorgonzola, Parmesan) from Italy, and those only in relatively small quantities; but cheeses made from cows' or goats' milk are a staple article of diet in that country.

Sheep and goats, both fairly numerous in each of the three countries, are together with pigs the main sources of meat supplies in the regions of Mediterranean climate where such cattle as there are, are draught animals rather than beef cattle. Goats, which can manage to scrape a living where other animals would starve, are the popular live-stock of the peasantry; sheep, which require more grass fodder, are commonly of strains adapted to mountainous terrain and sub-arid climatic conditions, but to carry them through the summer they are often moved in transhumant flocks to highland pasturages. Outstanding among these Mediterranean breeds of sheep is the merino, evolved to withstand the hard physical conditions of the Spanish Meseta; noted more for its fleece than its flesh, this breed is now far more numerous in each of the three southern continents than in the country of its origin.

Wines and olive oil head the list of agricultural exports from all three countries, followed by fruits and nuts. These with other items, chiefly rice and market-garden produce from Italy and Spain, account for nearly one-third by value of the total Spanish exports, a quarter of the Italian and about one-fifth of those from Portugal.

Chapter 28

HISTORICAL SURVEY

THE warm temperate to sub-tropical belt of the Eastern Hemisphere, extending from northern India to the Atlantic Ocean beyond the Straits of Gibraltar, has proved exceptionally favourable in its geographical conformation for the material and cultural development of its inhabitants. In historical times advanced civilisations have succeeded one another in a generally westward progression from Western Asia into the Near East and the Mediterranean lands of Europe; to these Mediterranean civilisations the rest of Europe, and through it the modern world in general, owes the foundations of much of its culture and material advancement.

Among the distinctive physical characteristics of this medial belt of the Old World that have favoured the early advancement of various groups of its human occupants are (1) the regular seasonal rhythm of the climates of its different parts, and a general absence of extremes of temperature; (2) the wealth of inland seas, interconnected in the Mediterranean area, in the relatively quiet waters of which the arts of navigation could be practised and developed in ships constructed with timbers from the originally forested adjacent highlands; and (3) the existence of a number of fertile river valleys and plains, protected landwards by the natural defensive barriers of mountains or deserts, in some of which the inhabitants were left undisturbed or could ward off attacks for long enough periods of time to enable them to develop their resources and their opportunities for external trade, and thus provide a surplus above primary needs — the essential material basis for advancement in civilisation.

The Mediterranean peninsulas and coastlands have from the earliest times again and again attracted movements of peoples from the peripheral lands of Europe, the Levant and the Near East wherever they could establish a foothold. Common characteristics of these immigrant groups have been the vigour they displayed in establishing themselves, their quickness to seize opportunities for the pursuit of their ends, and their aptness to attain high levels of civilisation and culture. It may well be that in the past the prevailing climatic and physical conditions, especially in the Eastern Mediterranean, have been strong stimuli to bodily and mental activity, resulting in the precocious development of civilisations there, the substance of which was transmitted mainly through the Romans to the Western Mediterranean.

Thus except during the centuries of peace imposed by Roman rule the Western Mediterranean lands have had a chequered history. The numerous incursions by peoples from far and near were often followed by conquests and temporary or lasting alien settlements and territorial changes. Though this source of instability came to an end in the Iberian Peninsula by the end of the thirteenth century with the emergence of Spain and Portugal as independent States as the result of their successful drives against the Moors, it was not till well on in the nineteenth century that the patchwork of territories which composed what is now Italy was welded into a single sovereign State.

The earliest inhabitants of these countries of whom there is definite knowledge were Neolithic Mediterranean people who arrived probably from North Africa by way of Sicily and the Gibraltar Strait, when the climate became warmer at the close of the Ice Age. These were followed, and in the course of time submerged but for a few isolated remnants, by Bronze Age Indo-Europeans who made their ways from Danubia and the steppe lands beyond through the gaps behind Trieste, and thence branched southward into Peninsular Italy, and westward along the Ligurian coast. These and later influxes of more advanced Indo-European groups of Mediterranean stock formed the basic population of the Italian peninsula and of much of Iberia when Rome began to emerge — as their descendants still do in spite of all that has happened since.

The western side of Italy between the Apennines and the sea was occupied by two related groups, the Etruscans in Tuscany and the Latins in Latium. The former developed an advanced civilisation, and extended their authority over the Apennines into the Po Basin in the north and beyond the Tiber into Campania in the south; but shortly before 500 B.C. the people of Latium shook off Etruscan domination, and thenceforward their city on the Tiber pursued its extraordinary career of expansion which gave it control first of the whole peninsula, and by about 200 B.C. of much of the Mediterranean world. Though Rome had evident advantages of situation as the natural centre of land routes in Italy, its rise must be ascribed in no small part to the organising genius of the Latin people.

The first known invaders of the Iberian Peninsula after the Neolithic age entered by the south from North Africa before 2,000 B.C., and thence spread through the coastlands and inland. The Greeks, attracted thither as elsewhere on the Mediterranean shores by opportunities for trade, established early settlements which, however, they were unable to hold against the Carthaginians who from about 540 B.C. monopolised the trade of southern and eastern Spain for some three centuries till they in turn were ousted by the Romans.[1] These during the centuries of their rule left a permanent imprint on the land and its Iberian people, evidence of which is seen in the Romance languages, Spanish, Catalan and Portuguese, which have survived with little dilution the later periods of Visigoth and Moslem domination. However, the north-western Atlantic regions of broken highlands, never attractive to invaders from the Mediterranean, were occupied by Celtic peoples who came by land (from Gaul) or by sea. The inhabitants of these parts, so different geographically from the rest of the Peninsula, have retained much of their distinct individuality, in spite of political absorption into Mediterranean Spain and Portugal. This is especially true of the Basques living mainly in the region known as Vascongadas in Spain (Sp. Vascon = Basque), a peculiar enclave group whose origin is uncertain, probably pre-Celtic.

Neither in Italy nor still less in the Western Mediterranean area was Roman expansion achieved without costly struggles. Though the Romans, unlike the Greeks and the Phoenicians, were primarily a land power, and were more interested in farming pursuits than in seaborne trade, they were compelled to become a sea-power in their efforts to overthrow the Carthaginians. Here also they showed their early characteristic energy and determination. In the result, by about 100 B.C. both the Eastern and the Western Mediterranean basins had become Roman lakes. During upwards of five centuries of established Roman authority over land and sea, peace was assured for trade to

---

[1] Place names often remain to commemorate former occupants. Among those of Carthaginian origin are Mahon (in Minorca) named after Hannibal's brother Mago, Cartagena (New Carthage) and Cádiz (Gades); of Roman origin, Mérida (Augusta Emerita), Zaragoza (Caesaraugustus) and Oporto (Portus Cale); and of Moorish origin, Almería (the watch tower) and the prefix Guad- (from Wadi) in the names of a number of southern Spanish rivers, as in Guadalquivir (from Wadi el Kebir, the great river). As may be expected, names of Roman origin are very numerous in all the West Mediterranean countries.

grow between diverse parts within the Empire, Rome herself having to import by sea large supplies of grain and metals; and a common culture was imposed on the lands round the Sea and beyond to the north in Western Europe, facilitated by networks of roads (mainly for military control) in the construction of which the Romans were the world's first great masters (Fig. 96).

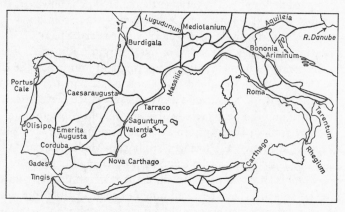

Fig. 96. The principal Roman roads in the Western Mediterranean and peripheral lands.

With the frequent border wars on the open frontiers of the fully-grown Empire in Germany and Danubia we are not here concerned, except to note that the repeated threats from these quarters ended in widespread invasions of the outer Empire. Of the causes that contributed to the general breakdown of Roman continental power two are of geographical order: the Empire had perforce spread itself too far into Central Europe (where there was no good natural line of defence) for the distant frontier to be held firm; and the Roman garrison troops constitutionally adapted to the genial Mediterranean milieu found conditions of life unbearably hard, especially in winter.

The Break-up of the Empire. Barbarian[1] and Moslem Invasions

The decline of Roman power was marked by the division of the Roman territories in the year 395 into the Eastern (the Byzantine)

[1] The Latin term *Barbarus* taken over from Greek, was commonly used to denote a foreigner, a stranger, one who was unfamiliar with Roman ways and culture, and who in that sense was considered inferior. It was applied generally to those who belonged to parts into which Graeco-Roman civilisation had not penetrated.

Empire, east of a line through the Adriatic with its capital at Constantinople, and a Western Empire centred at Rome. The former, bypassed by the Barbarian invasions of Italy and Spain and by the later Moslem drives through North Africa into Iberia, survived as a sea-state with an extensive territorial base in Asia Minor for six centuries. Until it was finally overthrown by the Turks this Eastern Empire continued a largely self-contained economic and political existence. Whereas the Eastern Empire had a marked Hellenistic bias in its culture, the Western Empire considered itself the direct heir of the Roman tradition. Hence the division in Mediterranean Christianity between Greek Orthodox and Roman Catholic, which has persisted there with adherents to both in other parts of Europe; and hence also the essentially Latin cultural background of Western Europe bounded eastward in the Mediterranean by the Adriatic Sea.

The Barbarian invaders of Italy and Spain came in scattered movements from several quarters — from the regions between the Rhine and the Vistula and from the steppe land of East Central and South-East Europe. Neither the Alps nor still less the Pyrenees have at any time proved effective barriers against migrations from the north. Prominent among the invaders were the Visigoths (West Goths) who established control of much of Spain, and the Ostrogoths (East Goths) who overran Italy. These and other invaders were relatively few in numbers compared with the indigenous Mediterranean populations, and inherited rather than displaced Roman civilisation; though the Germanic Lombards who penetrated later into southern Italy left a persistent fair Nordic element in the population, especially in the North. The Ostrogoth domination of Italy was destroyed by the Byzantine conquests in the sixth century and the Visigoth Kingdom in Spain fell to the Moslems in the eighth century.

Except for the rise of the trading cities described below, the troubled history of Italy, following the short-lived Byzantine control of the country and onwards through the Middle Ages, is of little concern to the student of geography. The most notable events were the invasions of the Lombards, who set up a temporary Kingdom, the extension of Charlemagne's dominions (later the Holy Roman Empire) to include much of the peninsula, and the establishment of the Normans in Sicily and on the mainland to beyond Naples.

The period of Barbarian invasions was succeeded by another troubled time, roughly from A.D. 700 to 1000, in which the Moslem Arabs were the chief source of conflicts by land and by sea in the Western

Mediterranean. These, hailing from Arabia and inspired at the outset by a fiery religious zeal, conquered Syria and Palestine, and thence sweeping through North Africa, crossed into Spain in 711. They soon overran the greater part of the Peninsula; but they really never established themselves beyond the northern limit of the olive (Fig. 103), which made it possible for the Christians to muster forces in northern Iberia for the reconquest several centuries later. The Moslem immigrants into Spain were composed mainly of somewhat barbarous Moors, and partly of civilised Arabs (of Near East origins), who became the leaders and developed a culture expressed concretely in fine cities, irrigation works and the cultivation of exotic plants in the south-eastern part of the country which was congenial to them.

In the meanwhile Moslems from a base in Tunis took to piracy, and by the year 900 had become strong enough at sea to capture Sicily, Sardinia and the Balearic Islands, thus gaining control of almost the whole Western Mediterranean Sea. Throughout this second period the mainland of Italy escaped Moslem attacks; the southern section of the peninsula was held by the Eastern Empire which was strong enough to retain control of the Eastern Mediterranean and the south Italian approaches, and the central and northern parts belonged to the Carolingian (Holy Roman) Empire.

The Development of Commerce.
The Italian Trading Cities

A third period of post-Roman Mediterranean history, from 1000 to 1500, saw the decline and fall of the Eastern Empire, the expulsion of the Moslems from Spain and Portugal, the establishment of Norman control over Sicily and southern Italy and the rise of the Italian medieval trading cities. It was a time of active change in the relative strength of the several contending powers. Pressure by the Turks upon the Eastern Empire resulted in the loss of the interior of Asia Minor and the weakening elsewhere of the authority of Constantinople, which finally fell in 1453. In the Iberian peninsula the Christians had by the year 1100 driven the Moslems to a line south of the Tagus and by 1257, after a decisive victory near Linares, confined them to their mainly mountainous Kingdom of Granada. The advent of the Normans in the Central Mediterranean marked a further break in the Moslem power to harass shipping either in the Tyrrhenian Sea or between Italy and the Levant.

Thus the ways became gradually opened for a revival of commerce between West and East. The initiative was taken quite early by Venetian merchants who had no scruples with whom they dealt. Out of the profits derived from trade with Constantinople and the Levant and from furnishing the Crusaders with supplies and transport they built a substantial fleet which gave them control of the Adriatic. From obscure beginnings as a place of refuge on islands in the lagoon, the Venetian Republic (established later on the Rialto group) became a centre of artistic manufactures, e.g. of glass and silks, and an emporium of traffic in luxury goods from the East supplied to Central and North-Western Europe via the Brenner Pass and Milan.

The rise of Genoa as a rival of Venice became possible when the Genoese themselves drove the Saracens (as the Moslems came to be called) out of Corsica and Sardinia and the Balearic Islands, thus freeing the Western Mediterranean from their attacks. Like the Venetians, the Genoese were interested in trade with the East, to further which they established depôts at various places in the Aegean and the Levant, and like the Venetians they profited from the Crusades. Genoa, however, was less favourably situated than Venice for overland trade with Transalpine Europe except through France, nor had it such a good natural defensive site, but it was better placed for sea trade. Utilising this advantage, the Genoese were the first to form connections with Bruges and London by way of the Straits of Gibraltar, thus circumventing the Alps and the Champagne fairs.

Three other towns of the Western Mediterranean took part in trade with the Levant, Barcelona in the thirteenth and fourteenth centuries (after the expulsion of the Moors from the Balearic Sea coasts) and Pisa and Florence in the sixteenth century. For some time Barcelona was a leading maritime city of the Mediterranean, as shown by the general adoption of the Catalan sea laws and charts of that sea. As for Pisa, it was in a vulnerable position between its rivals Genoa and Florence, which ended in its vassalage to the latter, and its eclipse when Florence acquired the port of Leghorn and built a large mercantile marine for active competition with Genoa in similar trade.

The Age of Discovery heralded the decline of these rival trading cities. Vasco da Gama's voyage to India, 1497–9, opened a way between Western Europe and South-East Asia which, by circumventing the traditional trade routes through the Mediterranean Sea and the Near East, had the effect of converting that sea until the construction of the Suez Canal into a kind of cul-de-sac. The balance of geographical advantage shifted from the Central Mediterranean to the Atlantic margins of Europe, where the maritime nations used their fleets to acquire tropical 'possessions', which they exploited as sources of products formerly obtained indirectly through Mediterranean merchants.

THE EVOLUTION OF THE MODERN STATES

The creation of the two independent States in the Iberian Peninsula dates from the Reconquest (well-nigh completed by the year 1300) which began with the liberation of the weakly-held north-western and north-central sector (Fig. 97). The emergence of Portugal[1] as a separate country was the result of southward drives against the Moors by the Lusitanians of Minho and Douro, confined on the east as far south as the Tagus by the belt of difficult terrain, a sort of no-man's land, along the present boundary between Spain and Portugal. Having cleared the littoral strip and the broken country north of the Central Cordillera, the Lusitanian Christian forces paused for consolidation and, when they resumed their attacks later, were not long in recovering the Centre and the South except for the Algarve coastland. It is mainly the impress of the Reconquest and the continued vigour of the people of the North that have given Portugal both its independent existence and its distinctive language, which is related to that of Galicia beyond the northern border.

The integration of the diverse parts that constitute modern Spain was achieved as in Portugal as a direct result of the gradual reconquest from the north, first of Old Castile and then of New Castile. Thus the Meseta region became the nucleus of the new-born Spain. Its centrality in the strategy of the liberation contributed to an initial political predominance over the diverse peripheral regions which it has retained, in spite of its relative poverty of resources; and all the more so since in modern times Madrid has become the artificially created centre of land and air communications in the Peninsula. Yet the thinly populated Meseta cannot have the naturally firm hold over the marginal regions that the Paris Basin has over the rest of France. Though Castilian is the recognised language of Spain, local forms of speech have survived in several parts, notably in Catalonia, the people of which cling to Catalan, and would moreover be politically independent if they could.

---

[1] Separated early from Galicia, the Terra Portucalis (Territorio Portugal) expanded to include the region between the Minho and the Mondego, and later, known simply as Portugal, gave its name to all the lands that came under its control.

North Spain and Portugal were fortunate in being established as independent states early enough to become maritime powers before the Age of Discovery, in which they played signal parts under the leadership of great navigators. Both succeeded in acquiring vast oversea territories, especially in the New World, where they have left permanent marks of their occupation in the composition of the populations and in the languages in current usage from the Rio Grande del

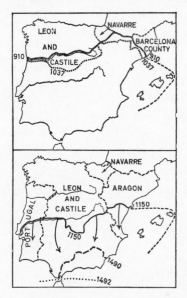

Fig. 97. The stages in the reconquest of Iberia.

Norte to Tierra del Fuego. Both, however, were too limited in manpower and material resources to hold great oversea empires; and the net result has been a continuous draining off from both Spain and Portugal of some of the most vigorous elements of their populations.

Italy did not achieve independent unity till long after the two Iberian countries. During the centuries following the break-up of the Holy Roman Empire, what is now Italy was a changing pattern of kingdoms, dukedoms, republics and papal states. Even at the close of the Napoleonic wars in 1815 it was still a patchwork of territories, two of the richest of which, Lombardy and Venetia, were held by Austria. Not till 1860 was most of the country gathered into a Kingdom, nor till 1870 was the last remaining 'unredeemed' part, the Papal State of

Latium, incorporated. These disabilities, combined with a persisting pressure of population on limited resources, have led to large-scale emigration to foreign lands. It is noteworthy that Italian has not become the language of any considerable oversea territory, as English, Spanish, Portuguese and French all have. Whether the recent expansion of industry with the help of considerable, though already largely developed water-power resources, will prove an effective palliative of Italy's population problem remains to be seen.

Chapter 29

THE IBERIAN PENINSULA: I
GENERAL FEATURES

THE roughly rectangular Iberian block, more African than European
in type, is the product of three main structural elements: a basic
Pre-Carboniferous Shield, Hercynian folds, and Alpine uplifts and
downthrows. The first of these, averaging some 3,000 feet in elevation, covers or underlies the whole Meseta region, which extends
westward well into Portugal and north-westward into the dissected
highlands of Galicia and northern Portugal (Fig. 98); the second,
superimposed on the Meseta formations and composing also the axial

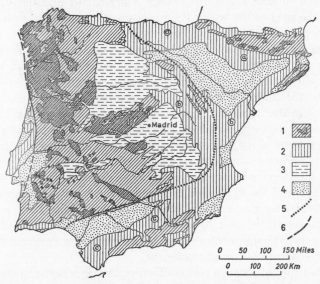

Fig. 98. The structural elements of the Iberian Peninsula. 1. Palaeozoic
elements with granitic intrusions. 2. Alpine borders of Meseta with
Hercynian cores. 3. Tertiary basins of Meseta. 4. Marginal depressions.
5. Edge of Meseta. 6. Western boundary fault.

Note. Alpine borders of Meseta mainly Mesozoic: (a) Sedimentaries of
Cantabrians and Pyrenees; (b) Cordillera Ibérica with metamorphic
Palaeozoic upthrusts; (c) Sub-Betic zone. After Solé Sibaris and
Lautensach.

zones of the Pyrenean and the Betic cordilleras, have been reduced by prolonged erosion to remnant ridges of granitic and metamorphic rocks both in the Meseta and in the later elevated border highlands; the third includes not only the Cantabrian-Pyrenean and the Betic ranges together with the depressions between them and the Meseta, but also the arc of the Iberian Mountains (Cordillera Ibérica), as well as the Central Cordilleran and other sierras of the Meseta.

Though the tableland has been a persistent structural element of the Peninsula from early geological times, it is the vigorous Alpine thrusts and resulting uplifts and downthrows that have given rise in Iberia as elsewhere in the Mediterranean region to the more pronounced land forms. These Alpine displacements have unfortunately produced physical features which are distinctly adverse to the human occupation of the area; the uplifts on the margins of the Meseta not only cause difficulty of access by reason of the steep ascents from the periphery but also contribute to its sub-arid climate; and widespread marginal faulting has deprived Spain of any extensive coastal plains — only one river of the whole Peninsula, the Guadalquivir, provides a serviceable valley passage well into the interior.

The Alpine storm, which has been mainly responsible for the E.–W. alignment of the highland ribs, has raised the arc of the Iberian Mountains which sweeps round from near Burgos in the north to the head of the Guadalquivir depression in the south. This series of uplifts, highest in the north-east, has accentuated the downward tilt of the Meseta to the west, which has been further increased by the greater erosive power of the major rivers in their lower courses where they are fed by heavier precipitation. These Iberian Mountains form in fact the main watershed of the Peninsula. From them short streams flow to the Ebro and the Mediterranean; and in them are the headstreams of the three long rivers of the Meseta (the Duero,[1] the Tagus and the Guadiana) which, after collecting the drainage of the wide interior basins, cut through defiles[2] in their descent to the Portuguese lowlands — a truly African characteristic.

While the old resistant rocks of Hercynian Iberia have responded to pressures by faulting and vertical movements, the softer Mesozoic beds flanking the border ranges have commonly been subject to fold-

---

[1] Known as the Douro in Portugal. Likewise the Miño in Spain is called the Minho in Portugal.

[2] In this connection it is noteworthy that *Tajo*, the Spanish name for the Tagus, is also a common noun meaning slit or gash. The similar Portuguese name is Tejo.

ing. In both the Pyrenees-Cantabrian and the Betic mountain systems two separate uplifts, Hercynian and Alpine, can be distinguished. The former appears in the metamorphic and crystalline axial zones where folding was followed by peneplanation; the latter in general re-elevation accompanied by folding of the mainly Mesozoic rocks on their inner margins, i.e. in the Sub-Pyrenean and Sub-Betic zones (see Fig. 98).

In general in Iberia pressures have resulted in vertical dislocations instead of folding. The most striking are those of the Ebro and the

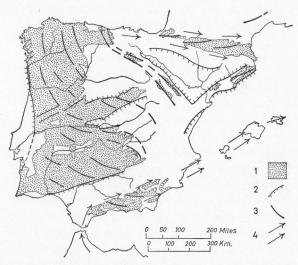

Fig. 99. The Hercynian folds and other main structural features of Iberia. 1. Hercynian cores. 2. Major faults. 3. Hercynian fold lines. 4. Alpine fold lines. After Matchatschek and Villaplana.

Guadalquivir depressions and the uplifts of the Central Cordilleran and the Iberian Mountains. The first of these was occupied until the early Tertiary by the so-called Ebro Massif of which the Catalan uplands are apparently remnants. This area, which remained dry land while successive strata were laid down in the surrounding Cretaceous seas, sank by at least 5,000 feet, with the subsequent deposition in the depression (soon cut off from the Mediterranean by uplift of the coastal belt) of great thicknesses of continental sediments. The Guadalquivir depression, formed originally as a trough between the rectilinear Sierra Morena fault and the pre-Alpine Betic Cordillera, has been filled with Mesozoic and Tertiary sediments, the former of which now rise southwards in the folds of the Sub-Betic zone (Fig. 107).

The Sierras Gata, Gredos and Guadarrama of the Central Cordillera in Spain together with the Serra da Estrêla in Portugal are typical horsts bounded by more or less vertical faults. Evidences of intense pressures are apparent in their lengthwise and lateral compression whereby they overlap partly in echelon formation, and also in the upward squeezing of the magma and of the associated metamorphic rocks to form the crystalline cores of the higher ranges. The S. Pedro and Guadalupe Sierras and the Montes de Toledo south of the Tagus constitute a subsidiary series of similar form and origin. Though lower in general elevation and shorter than the Central Cordillera, this group is equally a barrier to settlement and communications.

The Iberian Mountains in their northern and highest parts, including the Demanda, Moncayo and Cuenca Sierras, have been forced up by pressures from the south-west against the formerly existing Ebro Massif, the erosion of which supplied the waste materials that compose their older underlying sedimentary rocks. Complex faulting and north-eastward overthrusting have produced a series of ridges in which different formations including basal metamorphic rocks appear in parts at the surface. These mountains are separated from the Cantabrians by the narrow Burgos gap, but link up north-east with the Catalan ranges and south-east, as noted above, with the Sub-Betic zone. A notable feature is the break formed by the Jalon-Jiloca-Guadalaviar River Valleys (guided largely by the Catalayud-Teruel Tertiary trough) which affords a continuous routeway between Zaragoza and Valencia.

The truncation of the Meseta block by a major N.-S. fault north of the Tagus in Portugal, and its gradual sinking under later sedimentary beds south of the river, give that country a considerably larger proportion of lowland than Spain. Yet the general relief is far from level. The Central Cordillera (the Serra da Estrêla and its south-west prolongation) divides Portugal into two major regions. The northern half is occupied in the main by the severely fractured and much dissected western margin of the Meseta, and the plains south of the Tagus are interrupted by the Alto Alemtejo Plateau, a western extension of the Toledo sierras mentioned above, and by the Algarve Highlands which are a continuation beyond the Guadiana Valley of the Sierra Morena uplift. Portugal is in fact essentially a more or less subdued marginal zone of the Iberian massif — none of its four main rivers, not even the Tagus, is navigable for any distance inland from its mouth.

CLIMATE AND VEGETATION

Though Iberia is surrounded almost entirely by seas, and its general slope away to the west apparently favours the penetration of Atlantic influences, it suffers from deficiency and uncertainty of rainfall over the whole interior and the Mediterranean coastlands. Less than a quarter of the entire area, and that mostly mountainous, receives a precipitation of 30 to 40 inches, the minimum adequate amount in view of the generally high rate of evaporation.

Several factors combine to cause this fundamental disability. The first is the situation of Iberia (a) south, except in winter, of the main tracks of Atlantic depressions affecting Western Europe and (b) in proximity to the Azores high pressure system which extends northeast over it in summer (p. 367). The second is the compact form of the Peninsula bordered by highlands on all sides except the south-west, making it a continent in miniature upon which a local high pressure system commonly develops in winter. A third related factor is the diversion of the tracks of winter depressions (the main source of rainfall in Mediterranean lands) either north of the Pyrenees or through the Straits of Gibraltar.

The continentality of the interior of Iberia together with some diversity of the conditions affecting the various peripheral parts, give rise to a number of climatic regions (distinguishable as in Fig. 100), with corresponding differences in their characteristic forms of vegetation. It will be observed that these sub-divisions fall into four main

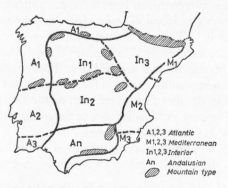

Fig. 100. The climatic regions of Iberia.

groups: Atlantic coastal, Mediterranean coastal, Interior and Andalusian. The first of these as far south as Lisbon is sufficiently well watered, the rest but for scarcely inhabited higher mountains is marginal to arid.

The Atlantic coastal group includes the oceanic north and northwest, passing south of the Serra da Estrêla into the modified Mediterranean of central Portugal, and thence into the true Mediterranean of Algarve where the summer drought lasts six months or more. In the oceanic region the vegetation is West European comprising deciduous trees and shrubs, e.g. oak, elm, chestnut, with pines at higher elevations and heath plants and meadow grasses in parts. Here as elsewhere in Iberia, many of the original stands of trees have been cleared for timber or for pastures and cultivation, though in this broken highland area there has been considerable re-planting mainly of conifers and eucalyptus. In central Portugal typical Mediterranean species such as cork oak, evergreen oak and olive become the dominant trees, while steppe plants and coarse herbage displace meadow grasses more and more towards the extreme south.

Of the three climatic sub-divisions of the Mediterranean coastlands — Catalonian, Valencian and Southern — the first is exceptional for a Mediterranean area in having comparatively dry winters following the autumn maximum rainfall.[1] Here and also on the other sections of these coastlands little of the native forest vegetation remains except for patches of deciduous and evergreen woodland on the uplands. Most of the unused land is covered with garigue (p. 370) or is bare. The Valencian section has a considerably smaller rainfall, seldom more than 16 inches, and the Southern section still less (under 10 inches at Almería). These two coastland belts are apt to suffer from the parching *leveche* in spring, drawn in from Africa by depressions following the Guadalquivir Valley: and, though south-east winds blowing into the interior low pressure prevail in summer, these collect little moisture over the Mediterranean and are still dry. These coastlands are the region of the huertas, and were it not for the supplies of water brought from the highlands inland by rivers such as the Guadalaviar, Jucar and Segura-Sagonera and smaller ones in the south, cultivation of any kind would be very scanty and scattered.

The interior regions all suffer from partial aridity and extremes of temperature; the nearly rainless summers are hot and dusty, the

---

[1] Barcelona gets 8·3 inches in the autumn months September to November and 4·7 inches in the three winter months out of a total of 22·4 inches.

winters bitterly cold, especially on the Meseta. Except on the mountains where the prevailing bare rock landscape is relieved here and there by patches of mixed deciduous, Mediterranean and coniferous woodland, any forest cover that may have existed (as seems probable in Old Castile) has long since been removed and its place taken by steppe or by degenerate forms of vegetation, i.e. matorral (maquis), or garigue scrub. Most of the open country of New Castile and also of

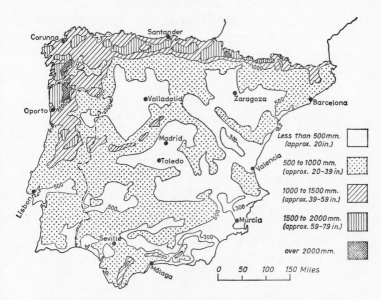

Fig. 101. The mean annual rainfall of Iberia. After Gonzalez Quijano.

the Ebro depression has apparently been steppe from time immemorial, a poor form of which appears in La Mancha and south-east New Castile in general, where the existing vegetation consists of the wiry esparto and other fibrous grasses. The enclosed Ebro basin has little to recommend in respect of climate. In spite of its apparently sheltered situation it can be bitterly cold in winter when chilled air drains down and stagnates in the depression; in summer it becomes hot and stifling, and it is dry at all seasons with less than 12 inches mean annual rainfall.

The Guadalquivir depression and adjoining mountain slopes (Andalusia) receive only about 20 inches of mainly winter rainfall in spite of the area being wide open to the Atlantic. The effectiveness of this modest rainfall is diminished by the intense evaporation during the extremely hot summers (July-August average temperature 83° at Seville and Córdoba). Thus the lowland climate is unfavourable for trees, and the predominant vegetation is of the steppe type. The uplands carry mixed Mediterranean forest in parts,[1] which becomes distinctly xerophytic eastwards away from the sea.

AGRICULTURE

It is evident from the above survey that except in the oceanic north-west and central Portugal (A1 and 2, Fig. 100) climatic conditions are generally unhelpful to varied agriculture; most of Spain is unsuitable, partly because of mountainous relief, but mainly because

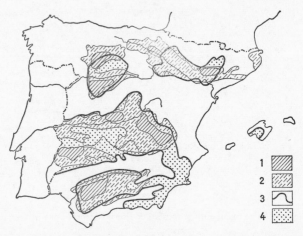

Fig. 102. The distribution of wheat and barley cultivation in Spain.
1. Areas of greatest production of wheat. 2. Areas of scattered production of wheat. 3. Limits of chief barley areas. 4. Areas in which barley is grown, but very little wheat.
Note. The correspondence of negative areas with highland regions is obvious, but there are exceptions.

the high rate of evaporation caused by strong sun heat and drying winds takes a heavy toll of the scanty precipitation. Much of Spain and southern Portugal, being natural or man-made steppe land, produces little succulent herbage for the support of dairy cattle or

---

[1] Of the Sierra Morena for example. The epithet morena (=dark) was applied to these mountains, seemingly because of their original clothing of evergreen forests (wild olive etc.).

mutton sheep. Nor is it generally possible except on irrigated lands to grow fodder or root crops in lieu of pastures. Though considerable numbers of cattle are kept in regions of low rainfall, these are mainly of breeds used as draught animals or for the bull rings. Thus the chief sources of dairy products are in the north-western sector of the Peninsula, where the humid climate promotes the growth of pasture grasses and enables maize (often fed green) and other fodder crops to be grown for the animals.

As in other sub-arid parts of the Mediterranean lands the unfastidious goat is commonly kept for milk and meat supplies. Two other classes of live-stock, namely merino sheep and pigs, are of special importance in Iberia, the former more for their wool than their flesh (which is inferior), the latter as the major source of meat supplies in many parts of the Peninsula, especially where acorns are plentiful; pork and beans form a mainstay of the Spanish diet.

All the leading cereals are cultivated in Spain and Portugal, the temperate group wheat, barley and rye extensively as bread grains. If these crops are grown without irrigation, as they generally are, they are classed as *de secano* (Sp. seco = dry), if irrigated, they are described as *de regadio*. The whole of the rice crop is necessarily in the latter class.

Wheat is the chief cereal crop in both countries, followed in Spain by barley and in Portugal by maize. Rye and oats are also grown in quantity, the former extensively in the upland country of northern Portugal, and rice too, especially in Spain which has a surplus for export. While all these six grains are used as food crops, oats and maize are fed in part to live-stock and some of the barley goes into the manufacture of beer, a popular drink in northern Spain. As maize needs fairly generous supplies of moisture, the main areas of cultivation are in the north-western region of well-distributed rainfall amounting to 40 inches or more (Fig. 101). Wheat and barley are widely grown throughout sub-arid Iberia; however, although these cereals are fairly tolerant, if autumn sown, of the Mediterranean climate, that of much of Spain is really too dry, and the yields of grain averaging less than 10 bushels per acre for secano crops (which cover over 90 per cent of the sowings), and hence also the overall Spanish averages, are very low compared with those of all other Western European countries.

This relegation of wheat and barley mostly to unirrigated lands is because more profitable use can be made of the limited irrigated tracts in both Spain and Portugal.[1] This means that in Spain at least these cereals are grown chiefly on open near-steppe· country where conditions are generally unfavourable to cultivated grasses; and as wheat and barley belong to the grass family of plants it is little wonder that the average harvest yields are poor. The wheat lands of Portugal (Fig. 109), being open to the· Atlantic and less arid than most of the Spanish, produce slightly higher yields averaging about 11 bushels per acre.

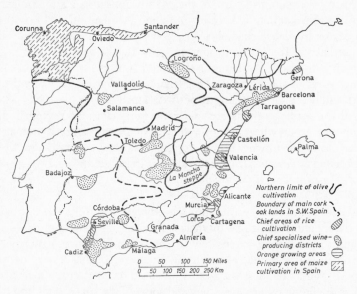

Fig. 103. The limit of olives in Spain, and the chief areas of various special forms of cultivation.

In these Mediterranean countries olives and grape vines are extensively cultivated as a matter of course, within the limits set by climate and relief. Spain is the largest producer of olive oil in the world and Portugal is the largest exporter; and both countries are leading net exporters of wines. Neither olives nor grape vines normally need irrigation, which in Spain is reserved for rice, oranges, vegetables of all kinds including potatoes, alfalfa pastures, and as much as can be spared for wheat. These irrigated tracts (huertas) are situated at

[1] There may however be some increase in the *regadio* cultivation of cereals, especially of wheat, with the completion of extensive irrigation projects in the Ebro basin (p. 404).

intervals along the east and south-east coasts at and above the mouths of the rivers (p. 406), in the Ebro depression and in some inland valley basins such as that of Granada. In Portugal the only important irrigated areas are those of the lower Tagus, Sado and Mondego valleys where rice is the chief crop (Fig. 109).

Chapter 30

THE IBERIAN PENINSULA: II
SPAIN: GEOGRAPHICAL REGIONS

ON the basis of structural components Spain is naturally divisible into five distinctive geographical regions, namely the Meseta, which extends partly into Portugal, and the wholly peripheral regions of the North-West (Galicia-Biscaya), the North-East (Catalonia-Ebro Basin), the Eastern Coastlands, and the South (mainly Andalusia). Spain is unique among the countries of Western Europe in having been built up both geologically and as a political unit round its dominant Hercynian Massif, which is more truly the central element of its structure and its human geography than the so-called Massif Central is of France.

THE MESETA

The Spanish Meseta, in its existing form after the deformations caused by the Alpine orogeny and subsequent modelling by the agents of erosion, is a tilted plateau rising from under 1,000 feet in the south-west in the valleys of the Tagus and the Guadiana to an average of some 3,000 feet in the broad central arc extending from the Cantabrians to the Sierra Morena, and to over 7,000 feet in the higher points of the Central and Iberian Cordilleras. The various overlapping series of the Central Cordillera form a kind of wall with a steep southern face, which extends from beyond the Portuguese border in the west almost as far east as the Sierra Moncayo of the Iberian up-thrusts, thus dividing the whole plateau in Spain into the two basin-like areas of Old and New Castile. Communications between these two compartments are not easy; roads and railways have to follow devious routes, making use here and there of the longitudinal passages between the several ranges.

The Leon-Old Castile Basin, smaller and more compact than the sprawling region of New Castile and Estremadura, is almost enclosed by the Galician, Cantabrian, Iberian and Central highlands, which leave only two structural gaps, that leading into the Ebro depression in the north-east and the narrow one of the Alagon River Valley between the Gata and the Gredos Sierras in the south-west. The basin coincides in fact with that of the Spanish section of the Duero, which, with its feeders, collects the drainage of the structural basin and the inward-facing slopes of the border highlands. Most of the basin is floored with continental Tertiary deposits composed of gravels, sands and clays derived from the wastage of the surrounding highlands; though towards the west the land rises on to the Palaeozoic and crystalline basic formations (Fig. 98).

Neither the soils nor the climatic conditions are particularly favourable to agriculture; except in the central and south-west parts the ground is often stony, and the rainfall averaging less than 20 inches per annum is scanty for most field crops. However, Old Castile is the main granary of Spain, producing wheat, especially in the Tierra de Campos north of Valladolid, and also barley and rye, the latter in the bleaker northern districts, but not much maize, as the climate is too dry and the growing season too short. These cereals are grown in rotation with fodder crops, mainly for merino sheep which are raised in considerable numbers. Grape-vines are cultivated on a large scale in the Tierra del Vino in Zamora Province bordering the Duero, an inland counterpart of the much more famous port-wine district lower down the same river in Portugal. Otherwise Old Castile is now for the most part open, treeless country of traditionally large estates, extensive cultivation and scattered clusters of farm labourers' dwellings.

As there are no minerals worth mentioning and little industrial activity as yet except of miscellaneous manufactures in the larger centres for local agricultural and domestic requirements, towns are relatively few and none of them really large. The most important is Valladolid, centrally situated on the Pisuerga just above its confluence with the Duero, a focus of railways which link it with Madrid, Lisbon, the chief Biscayan industrial towns and with France via Vitoria and S. Sebastian; yet its population numbers less than 150,000. Three other towns, all of which have historical associations, are Salamanca, Leon and Burgos, the first as formerly a great centre of learning, the second as capital of the medieval Kingdom of Leon which played a prominent part in expelling the Moors from northern Spain, and Burgos as a great ecclesiastical centre noted for its wonderful cathedral.

New Castile together with Estremadura is much more diverse than the northern basin. It is traversed lengthwise by the Tagus and Guadiana which have cut deeply into the plateau in the west, while between these incised valleys is the Toledo-Guadalupe upthrust. Only in the eastern parts of New Castile, in the upper Guadiana Basin, is the open, monotonous landscape of wide horizons characteristic of Old Castile to be found. This is in fact semi-arid steppe country[1] where the normally feeble streams, and even the Guadiana itself, are liable to dry up into strings of pools in summer, and where most of the land is of little use except for rough pasturage.

Northwards from this rather desolate country the landscape becomes more varied and less uninviting. In the upper Tagus Basin, where the rivers have cut down in broad valleys through the Tertiaries, both wheat and vines are cultivated; and to the west where the master rivers have excavated wide valleys in the crystalline rocks with occasional more fertile stretches, notably in the Badajoz Tertiary Basin, there is intensive cultivation of cereals and vines in the valley bottoms, and extensive cultivation of barley and merino sheep-farming on the broad interfluves — in large estates as in Old Castile. Southwards this kind of country rises almost imperceptibly to the Sierra Morena, through the steeply upwarped southern face of which the Despeñaperros defile leads down into the upper Guadalquivir Valley. Various intrusive mineral deposits occur in this upthrust Sierra Morena zone, e.g. copper at Rio Tinto and Tharsis, mercury at Almadén and lead at Linares — and coal at Belmez and Puertellano (Fig. 106).

In choosing the site of Madrid as capital of Spain, Philip II was guided more by the political motive of creating a unifying force to counteract the centrifugal tendencies of the diverse peripheral parts than by the attractiveness of climate and surroundings. However, like other West European capitals, Madrid has shared in the ever-increasing central functions of modern governments, and, with the development of some industries and of a radiating system of transport, has grown to the stature of a great city of some 2 million inhabitants. Other towns in this overall thinly populated Southern Meseta are small. Some such as Toledo and Alcantara at crossings of the Tagus, and Merida, once a great Roman military centre, have lost their strategic importance; others like Badajoz have remained the modest centres of limited, comparatively fertile districts.

---

[1] Especially in La Mancha immortalised by Cervantes in *Don Quixote*.

The North-West: Galicia, Asturias, Vascongadas

In the west of this predominantly highland region peneplaned Hercynian folds trend N.–S., while eastwards, beyond Oviedo in Asturias, both they and the Alpine upthrusts run nearly E.–W. into the Pyrenees. The Galician area, which has undergone several cycles of erosion with re-elevation at intervals, has been rent by a rectangular network of faults and has been further dissected by rivers following lines of weakness. These empty into the ria continuations of their structural valleys, the intervening headlands having been truncated

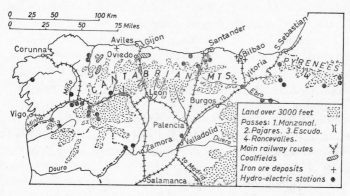

Fig. 104. North-West Spain: Galicia and Biscaya (Asturias, Vascongadas).

by the offshore continuation of the major fault northwards from Portugal (Fig. 98). On the eastern borders of Galicia the ancient platform abuts against the Alpine-folded Cantabrians. Except for the Mesozoic Oviedo Basin, they are composed of much disturbed and dislocated early Palaeozoic rocks. Near to Santander they disappear under the Mesozoic beds which continue thence into the Sub-Pyrenean zone. A marked feature of the physical landscape in this well-watered sector of the Peninsula is the number of river valleys separated by ribs of highland, both along the Biscayan coastland of short rivers and in the Galician area where some of the rivers, e.g. the Miño-Sil, the Ulla and the Tambro, are fairly large.

This north-western region has a better balanced economy than any other in Spain. Farming, fishing and manufacturing industries are all practised on considerable scales, thanks to the equable, humid climate, the numerous sheltered harbours and the resources of coal, of iron ores and non-ferrous metals, and of hydro-electric power; even

O

the characteristic mixed farming is more varied and better balanced than elsewhere in the country, with its live-stock including dairy cattle and pigs as well as cereals and fodder crops. Moreover, the Celtic and Basque elements in the population have contributed with their energy to the vigour displayed in turning to account the available resources and opportunities.

The mixed farming, in which maize, potatoes, rye and grape vines (in warm sheltered spots) are the principal crops, is intensively developed to the limits of the usable land in the valleys, on the mountain sides and on the coastal platforms in generally small farms in this densely populated region.[1] For the fishing industry of these coastlands, which provides the largest share of the Spanish landings, the chief centres are Vigo and Corunna, though these have lost some of their primacy owing to southward migration of the sardine shoals; on the Biscayan coast the Basque ports specialise in long-distance fishing, especially for cod which now heads the list of Spanish catches.

The fuel and power resources (Fig. 104) have made the Oviedo-Santander-Vascongadas belt the leading area in Spain for metallurgical manufactures, as the Barcelona district (p. 405) is for textiles. The Oviedo and smaller coalfields in Asturias produce more than three-quarters of the total Spanish output of 14 to 15 million tons of solid fuels, and Asturias and Vascongadas contribute fully two-thirds of the total $2\frac{1}{2}$ million tons (metal content) of iron ores; and these provinces contain almost all the as yet existing iron and steel and heavy engineering works (located chiefly at Oviedo, Alvilés and Bilbao) and an important share of the heavy chemical industries. Unfortunately the best Bilbao hematite ores are nearing exhaustion, so that the iron and steel works there and in the Oviedo district have to rely increasingly upon imported scrap and the inferior ores near Avilés. The former lively exchange of Bilbao hematite ores for Welsh coal has naturally declined, and the Biscayan smelters now make good with American coking coal, the local supplies being generally unsuitable for blast furnaces. Almost all the considerable towns in this Biscayan belt mentioned as centres of the fishing and the metallurgical industries are on or near the sea; so also are Gijon, the outlet of the Oviedo district, and S. Sebastian, a leading tourist resort on a fine harbour near the French border and on the most used railway between Spain

---

[1] Notably in Galicia, where the peasant farmers wring the utmost out of their land by continuous effort. The term Gallego (a Galician, typically a peasant) implies a note of disrespect in Castilian Spain for these earthbound people.

and France. The inland town Vitoria, likewise on the main international rail route, manufactures agricultural machinery and fertilisers for the Basque region in which it lies.

The North-East: the Ebro Basin and Catalonia

According to the morphological features previously described (p. 389), this area comprises three distinct structural elements: (a) the uplifted Catalonian Massif with its longitudinal valley; (b) the sunken Ebro depression filled with continental sediments; and (c) the Mesozoic borderlands of the depression, namely the sub-Pyrenees on the north, rising to the crystalline (Hercynian) Pyrenees, the Foreland zone of the Iberian Mountains on the south-west, and on the south-east a fringe, wider towards the north, along the inner edge of the Catalonian Massif. The Catalonian Massif has a complex structure (resulting from piecemeal elevation, foundering and re-elevation during its long geological history), only the general present features of which need concern us here.

The Ebro, the largest river in volume in Iberia, being antecedent to the Catalonian uplift, has cut a gorge in its tortuous passage through it, and ends in an extensive delta built up on the relatively shallow Valencian shelf. It is fed mainly by its numerous Pyrenean tributaries, the largest of which are those of the Segre-Cinca system, the Gallego and the Aragon; and on the right bank by the Jalon-Jiloca and smaller rivers. The Ebro itself is of little use as a waterway into the interior, not only because of obstacles to navigation in the gorge section, but also because it is liable to fluctuate in volume and to be obstructed by sandbanks. The Llobregat in Catalonia, like the Ebro, draws its main waters from the Pyrenees and like it has cut through the rising Catalonian Massif and has built up a delta. The smaller river Ter, in northern Catalonia, also rises in the Pyrenees, cuts through the coastal uplands and has formed a delta.

Agriculture in the North-East is handicapped by the scanty rainfall inland from the coast, notably in the Ebro depression. Except on the upper Pyrenees, precipitation nowhere exceeds 40 inches per annum, and over most of the lowland and also in the Aragon syncline (between an outer range of the Sub-Pyrenees and the High Pyrenees) it is well under 20 inches — quite inadequate in this region of unusually hot summers. Parts of the central basin are in fact near desert in their natural state. Where feasible, the meagre rainfall is supplemented by irrigation — on the river deltas and along the courses of the Ebro and its tributaries and on the northern interfluves where extensive projects have been completed or are in hand (Fig. 105). In spite of none too favourable conditions of climate and soils, the energetic Catalonians have made good use of their agricultural resources, specialising in rice cultivation on the deltas, viticulture on the hillsides and in the tectonic valley belt, and the *secano* cultivation of maize and wheat in the country north of Barcelona from Lérida to the coast. In the

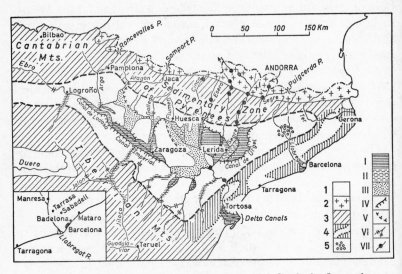

Fig. 105. North-East Spain: the Ebro basin and Catalonia. Inset, the Catalonian industrial towns. 1. Infilled depression. 2. Mainly crystalline rocks. 3. Mesozoic rocks. 4. Catalonian massif and longitudinal depression. 5. Potash deposits. I. Already irrigated. II. Irrigation works under construction. III. Irrigable, but not yet irrigated. IV. Canals constructed. V. Canals under construction. VI. Dams and barrages. VII. Hydro-electric power stations. Irrigation works and features based on *Boletín de la Real Sociedad de Madrid*, XCVI, 1960.

Ebro depression itself wheat, sugar beet and fodder crops are grown in increasing quantities with irrigation, and grape-vines without irrigation in the Logroño district higher up the valley where Atlantic influences begin to be felt. Throughout this North-East region olive plantations are a common feature, particularly in Catalonia where they extend to the French border.

Though Catalonia produces only trifling amounts of lignite and no coal nor other minerals except potash and sodium salts (p. 363), it has developed manufactures of textiles,[1] engineering products, motor vehicles and chemicals on scales which make it the prime industrial region of Spain, the heart area of which is Barcelona with its cluster of smaller manufacturing towns (Fig. 105, Inset). Yet almost all the raw and semi-manufactured materials it uses except salt and some wool have to be imported, and also until recently almost all its fuel requirements. However, with the development of hydro-electric power on the Segre river system and on the lower Ebro, the Barcelona industrial group has become less and less dependent upon foreign sources of fuels.

Of the towns inland in the Ebro depression Zaragoza has been an important route centre from Roman times (Fig. 96), situated as it is at the junction of the Trans-Meseta route from Valencia and the Trans-Pyrenean route via the Somport Pass with that along the Ebro. Midway between Zaragoza and Barcelona lies Lérida, a provincial capital in Catalonia and centre of the most extensive irrigated lands in the whole Ebro Basin. Huesca, another provincial capital, is situated on the Flumen, the westernmost river of the Segre system, near the boundary between the Ebro Tertiaries and the elevated Sub-Pyrenean zone, for which, as well as for the partly irrigated riverine plains below, it serves as the regional focus. Higher up the Ebro basin, Logroño on the main river and Pamplona on the Arga are both old towns of some importance today, the former as centre of the La Rioja wine-producing area, and the latter as capital of Navarre with access to the Basque region and to France through the Roncevalles Pass.

Barcelona, with a long tradition behind it as a great commercial city (see p. 383), is by far the leading port of the whole North-East region, and as the greatest manufacturing centre of Spain has grown to exceed one and a half million in population. Tarragona, the Roman Tarraco, has survived mainly as the outlet for the hill and valley country behind it, noted for the production of the port-type wine named after it; this is, in fact, the most important wine-producing area of Spain in terms of value of output. Tortosa, twenty miles inland on the Ebro where it emerges from its gorge tract, has grown with the transformation of the delta by irrigation canals from cattle pasturage to productive cropland; and Gerona, on the River Ter at the northern end of the tectonic valley, is both the commercial centre of an area

---

[1] The Barcelona-Gerona districts produce 86 per cent of the total Spanish cotton textiles and 60 per cent of the woollen textiles.

which includes the Ampurdán basin north of the Ter, and an important cotton and woollen textile town.

THE EASTERN COASTLANDS AND VALLEYS: THE HUERTA BELT

The eastern coastlands extending from the Ebro delta to Cartagena are backed by the southern extension of the Iberian Mountains which leave a strip of varying width along the Mediterranean, narrow in the north, widening out at Castellón de la Plana, and still more behind Valencia, but then narrowing again as far as Alicante at the northern corner of the extensive Segura-Sagonera river plain and valley huertas in the Betic region of Murcia. Thus there are two major huerta tracts, that of Castellón-Valencia and that of Alicante-Murcia-Lorca.

The essential feature of these huertas is their dependence upon irrigation waters derived from rivers such as the Guadalaviar, Jucar and Segura-Sagonera, and also from shorter ones, for the intensive cultivation of mainly exotic crops suited to the hot, sunny climate; the more important are rice, citrus fruits (oranges and tangerines), dessert grapes, vegetables especially onions, and tomatoes; though cotton and even dates, bananas and sugar-cane are also grown in places. Water supplies are a problem; the available sources are already fully used, so there is little chance of extending the irrigated lands. However, cultivation is not confined to these; the inland slopes and valley sides have long been utilised selectively for plantations of the typical Mediterranean perennials, olives, almonds and grapes for wine.

Valencia, the only town in Spain besides Madrid and Barcelona of more than half a million inhabitants, has a large export trade (through its outport El Grao) in oranges and other products of its extensive huerta hinterland, and has also a variety of manufactures, e.g. paper, silk, fertilisers and machinery, and some processing industries as well. The Murcia coastal depression, in reality the easternmost of the Sub-Betic series (Fig. 106), is large enough to hold three considerable towns, Alicante which serves as a port for the northern parts, Murcia at the confluence of the Sagonera with the Segura, which is the focal and largest town of the region, and Lorca some distance up the Sagonera Valley. Some of the produce of this area is exported more conveniently through Cartagena, separated from the Murcia depression by a highland ridge. This whole East Coastland region between the Ebro delta and Cartagena is predominantly horticultural and agricultural; except at Valencia there is little secondary industry, though iron and steel works have recently been constructed at Sagunto some twenty miles north of Valencia, using iron ore from Teruel on the main railway to Zaragoza.

The accretionary processes that have contributed to the formation of the succession of huertas along the Mediterranean Spanish coast deprive it of good natural harbours; even Barcelona has had to construct an artificial one. Except here and there where hard rocks extend to the sea, e.g. on the Costa Brava north of Barcelona, the loads of sediment discharged by the rivers into the nearly tideless Mediterranean have given rise to long stretches of sand bars enclosing lagoons in places (as on the French continuation of this type of coast in Languedoc), the largest of which is the Mar Menor in Murcia. Though inconvenient for shipping traffic, this coast provides incidentally in its lagoons natural evaporation pans for the collection of sea salt.

THE SOUTHERN PERIPHERY: ANDALUSIA

This area comprises a number of longitudinal structural sub-divisions running roughly parallel with the south coast: the axial Betic Cordillera along or close to that coast; the discontinuous Sub-Betic zone which extends to the east coast at Cape de la Nao and beyond into the Balearic Islands; the Guadalquivir depression; and the worn Sierra Morena escarpment face (Fig. 106). The large parts of this

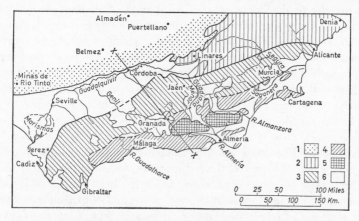

Fig. 106. South-East Spain: Andalusia and adjoining parts. 1. Southern edge of Meseta (Sa Morena). 2. S.E. continuation of Cordillera Ibérica. 3. Sub-Betic zone. 4. Mainly metamorphic elements of Betic Cordillera. 5. Crystalline 'windows' of Sa Nevada. 6. Tertiary basins of Guadalquivir and of Sub-Betic and coastal depressions. X——X Line of Section Fig. 107 After Solé Sibaris. *Geográfia de España y Portugal.* Vol. 1.

whole region that consist of more or less unproductive highlands are of little economic value except for mineral deposits here and there, though they embody some interesting morphological features.

The Betic mountain system, which with its high-level basins fills upwards of half the whole area, contains a great variety of structural and relief forms. The Sub-Betic-section is composed mainly of moderately folded Mesozoic strata, chiefly limestone (Fig. 107), in which river gorges, ravines and karstic features are common. The axial Betic uplift to the south consists of older crystalline and metamorphic rocks (granites, schists, etc.) which have been severely compressed and dislocated. In the zone of contact between these two upthrust elements, crustal weakness has resulted in partial subsidence at intervals,

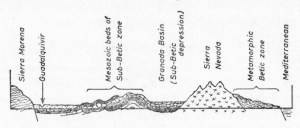

Fig. 107. Geological section N.W.–S.E. through Córdoba and Granada.
For line of section see fig. 106.

giving rise to the intermontane basins of the Sub-Betic depression. Thus the Betic 'Cordillera' is far from being a single or even a double mountain chain; it consists in fact of a series of longer or shorter ranges, known under various names, of which the highest, the Sierra Nevada, is a 'window' of the uplifted crystalline (Hercynian) core, and others in the main Betic system are for the most part simply upthrust blocks of resistant Palaeozoic rocks hardened by metamorphism.

In the Guadalquivir depression the upper filling consists of Tertiary sands, clays and loams of moderate average fertility but for occasional saline stretches. On its higher southern margin it abuts against a belt of Flysch of the Betic system, widest in the west behind Jerez; while along the main river, which has been pushed as it were against the Sierra Morena by its more powerful Betic tributaries, there are stretches of fertile alluvial and mixed soils from Linares to below Seville. As the floor of the depression is generally flat, the Guadalquivir meanders freely on much of its course, and hence is of little use for navigation above Seville, which has been made accessible for seagoing vessels only by rectification and dredging of the main channel.

As on the East Coast, evaporation here generally exceeds the rainfall which is none too plentiful on the lowlands, especially towards the east. Hence irrigation is necessary for crops introduced from lands of heavier rainfall, such as rice, oranges, cotton and maize,[1] and even for wheat in parts of the upper Guadalquivir Valley. Fortunately the Betic highlands on which the precipitation is upwards of 60 inches per annum, conserved partly as snow, give rise to perennial streams, e.g. the Genil and the Guadiana Menor, which, with the main river, provide reliable supplies of water for irrigation in the middle and lower sections of the depression. During their long occupation of the region the Moors developed systems of irrigation which have survived and have recently been extended.

Whereas the general need is to supplement water supplies, the opposite appears in the dismal Marismas swamps (occupied by a lake in Roman times) through which the Guadalquivir wanders in braided channels. These swamps have defied full-scale reclamation owing to the difficulties of systematic drainage; only in recent times have limited sections of the eastern side been drained sufficiently for field cultivation, chiefly of rice. In addition to the crops already mentioned, the typically Mediterranean olive and grape-vine are commonly grown without irrigation, especially on hill and even mountain sides, which are often terraced for vines. The three provinces Jaén, Córdoba and Seville account for 40 per cent of all the land in Spain under olives; noted wines are produced in the Jerez (sherry) district and round Málaga; and Almería is the largest exporter of table grapes.

Most forms of cultivation including viticulture and arboriculture are necessarily restricted to the lowland trough, the intermontane basins and depressions and the lower mountain slopes. Natural pasture lands of the kinds suitable for maintaining cattle and sheep are uncommon; the higher mountains are mostly bare rock, and elsewhere the prevailing vegetation at best is cork and evergreen oaks, or more commonly poor steppe, matorral or garigue. Thus except on some of the irrigated lands, mixed farming with a live-stock complement is rare, and the general rural landscape is one of continuous scattered cultivation (according to conditions of relief, soils and water supplies) with clusters of dwellings at intervals.

---

[1] All these introduced crops are grown extensively in the Guadalquivir Valley; rice on the lower left bank of the river as well as on the reclaimed margin of the Marismas, oranges round Seville, cotton in Seville and Córdoba Provinces (which produce half the Spanish total), and maize mainly in Seville Province.

Mineral deposits are or have been abundant in this region in which two, those of copper pyrites in the Rio Tinto district and lead ores at Linares, are extensive. Other smaller deposits include iron ores in the hinterlands of Málaga, Almería and Cartagena, and lead and copper ores inland from the two latter. Some of these were worked by the Carthaginians and the Romans, but not much is done with them nowadays in face of the competition of richer deposits elsewhere. For the rest, mining operations are largely in the hands of foreign undertakings, and the ores exported owing to the lack of local supplies of smelting fuel. Thus the mineral resources of the region have not hitherto given rise to any substantial metallurgical industry within it, though a start has been made by the construction of blast furnaces and steel works near Cartagena.

Towns are numerous in this region of oasis-like areas of cultivation set in the midst of poor steppe or wild mountain country. The largest by far is Seville, the fourth city of Spain, with well over 400,000 inhabitants. As a major port serving not only Andalusia but also the south-central Meseta as far as Madrid (via Linares and the Despeñaperros defile), its only rival is Cádiz, situated on a promontory which shelters a spacious harbour; but Seville has the superior advantages of a more central position and of room for expansion and for the development of manufactures, and has thus become the regional capital. Córdoba, situated eighty miles up the river, which in Moorish times was a great administrative and cultural centre, has declined relatively to the status of a local market centre with some growing manufactures, but has found some compensation for the passing of its glories in its lively tourist business; so also has Granada in its confined intermontane basin, formerly sought by the Moorish court as a place of summer residence, now by tourists to see the Alhambra palace. Most of the other leading towns in this southern region are ports with more or less specialised functions: Huelva as the outlet for the Rio Tinto copper field, Cartagena as a naval base besides serving the Murcia depression, Málaga and Almería as ports and commercial centres of their limited huertas, but also having trans-Betic railway and trade connections, the former with Córdoba, and the latter with Linares.

THE BALEARIC ISLANDS

Structurally the Balearic Islands are the surviving remnants of folds aligned E.–NE. in continuation of the Sub-Betic uplifts on the mainland. The folded series, composed of Triassic and Jurassic rocks, are best displayed in Majorca in the Cordillera Norte and the Cordillera Levante, between which there is a broad syncline filled with Miocene beds and later deposits. In each of the three larger islands the master element of the structure and relief is a folded range along the northern coast, from which the strata incline more or less steeply into the sea, and sink gradually southwards under the Tertiary and Quaternary plains. The structural features of Minorca are apparently detached continuations of those of eastern Majorca, and of Iviza those of south-west Majorca.

The climate of the islands is typically Mediterranean, and the generally scanty rainfall has to be supplemented where possible by water from mountain springs, as on terraced slopes, or from wells, most numerous along the inner foot of the northern range in Majorca. Cultivation is very varied within the limits set by the climate and the common occurrence of semi-arid garigue-covered limestone formations. Characteristic Mediterranean fruits, apricots and figs, together with almonds, are the chief tree crops; and some rice is grown on the reclaimed land on the shores of the bay in north-east Majorca. The great bulk of the wheat, barley and other field crops is consumed on a subsistence basis by the inhabitants, or is used as supplies for the increasing tourist trade.

These islands, formerly of strategic value for control of the Western Mediterranean, have had a long succession of masters — Greeks, Carthaginians, Romans, Moors and Catalans among others — until they were finally absorbed into the domain of Castilian Spain. The five centuries of Moorish occupation have left distinctive marks on the elaborate terracing of the hillsides, and the shorter period of Catalan ascendancy in the character of the people, the Catalan dialect current in Majorca, and the persisting close commercial ties with Barcelona. In modern times the islands have ceased to be of strategic or commercial importance, and have relapsed into semi-stagnation although the tourist industry is of growing importance to Spanish economy.

Even for Mediterranean lands where urban life has been exceptionally developed from the earliest times, the two larger Balearic Islands have an abnormal concentration of population each in its major town. Over one-third (130,000) of all the people in Majorca live in Palma, the capital, and about the same proportion of the inhabitants of Minorca in Mahon. This is all the more remarkable because neither commerce nor manufactures are of any importance; the only significant source of external income is the tourist traffic.

THE SPANISH ECONOMY

In spite of some recent noteworthy progress in the development of hydro-electric power and manufacturing industry in Biscaya and Catalonia, Spain is still a relatively poor country. Having very modest coal resources, no petroleum or natural gas fields and scanty supplies of timber, its main domestic source of industrial power is hydro-electricity, but even of this its output is less than half of that of France, which mines four times as much coal, to say nothing of natural gas. Some measure of Spain's industrial backwardness is its meagre production of steel, only some 2 million tons for a population of 30 millions.

Spain remains a predominantly agricultural and pastoral country, but much of it that is not useless wastes is by reason of climate and soils of low productivity, fit only for extensive herding. The proportion of the total area that can be used for intensive cultivation, whether of field crops or fruit trees or as vineyards, is small, probably not more than 10 per cent. Except in the mountainous northern parts, Spain suffers from an overall scanty rainfall and shortage of water which restricts also the areas eligible for irrigation.

Some four centuries of control of a vast colonial empire in the Americas did not help the Spanish people to fit into the modern world in which material progress is based upon a diligent quest for technical developments. On the contrary, it tended to accentuate the authoritarian qualities of the Castilian Caballero — one whose function was to command the underlings that laboured and served. This attitude of the ruling class and the deliberate, even ruthless policy of exploitation contributed to the loss of the great continental colonial empire early in the nineteenth century, just as other West European nations were building their colonial empires on more solid foundations.

Spain has been unkindly treated by Nature not only in the general scantiness of its rainfall, but also in that the Meseta, the predestined seat of any nation-wide controlling authority, is by way of being an economic vacuum — traditionally a region of latifundia and extensive pastoralism, which has little ferment of its own and little positive to give to the forcefully incorporated peripheral regions.

Hence the instability which besets the political organism, culminating not long since in a destructive civil war from which recovery has been inevitably slow, the more so because it has led to isolationism in an age of rapid change. The best hope for Spain is that it will achieve internal unity and harmony in spite of its difficult environment, thus enabling it to make fuller use both of its human material and, with external help, of what natural resources it has.

Chapter 31

THE IBERIAN PENINSULA: III
PORTUGAL

SOME of the basic features of the physical geography of Portugal have been outlined incidentally in the survey of Iberia as a whole in Chapter 25; it remains now to note the essential details of the regional geography and to add some general observations on the country and its economy.

Continental Portugal is a small country of some 34,000 sq. miles, little more than a fifth of the area of Spain, and holds a population numbering 9½ millions (1960), with an average density of about 280 per sq. mile, more than twice that of Spain. This greater density in Portugal is a reflection of its relatively favourable conditions of relief and climate and its maritime situation: barren mountains occupy only a small proportion of the whole area; moderating humid Atlantic influences prevail over two-thirds of the land, owing to the narrow E.–W. dimensions of the country and its general westward slope; and the open Atlantic has invited navigational enterprise and has led to establishment of oversea colonial and trading connections, besides providing opportunities for fishing. In contrast with Spain, Portugal is more maritime than continental in climate and outlook, and has little of the semi-arid steppe characteristic of its neighbour.

Though comparatively small in area, Portugal contains considerable diversity in its intertwining structural and relief forms (Fig. 108), and extends far enough in the latitude of transition from North-West European to Mediterranean climates to comprise several climatic regions. Related in some measure to the regional differentiation, there is also some diversity in the racial composition of the population; the basic Mediterranean stock is transfused with Celt-Iberian and even Germanic elements in the north, which with Spanish Galicia is an outpost of the so-called Celtic fringe of North Atlantic Europe, and it contains Moorish and African admixtures in the south, where the landscape is reminiscent of North Africa. This inter-blending of diverse racial stocks may be the reason why the Portuguese, unlike other West European powers, have never felt the urge to practise an apartheid policy in their social relations with the native peoples in their oversea territories.

The complex assortment of divers structural elements in Portugal

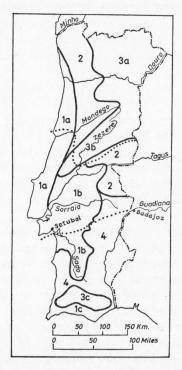

Fig. 108. The physical regions of Portugal. Lowlands: 1a Littoral belt; 1b Ribatejo–Alemtejo Tertiary basin; 1c Algarve coastland. Transitional dissected plateau 2, 2. Highlands and uplands: 3a Trasmontana Region; 3b Central Cordillera (Serra da Estrêla etc); 3c Algarve serras and uplands. 4 Alemtejo peneplain. ...... Dividing lines between northern, central and southern Portugal.

comprises three main types: (*a*) the fractured and frayed re-elevated highland extensions of the Pre-Cambrian and Palaeozoic Meseta formations; (*b*) the transitional dissected plateaux and the Alemtejo peneplain; and (*c*) the litoral and interior lowlands. A more profitable regional analysis of the country, however, takes account of the criteria of climatic conditions, vegetation and land use, as well as of structural forms, according to which it can be divided simply into three major regions, the North, the Centre and the South. The most marked geographical boundary in Portugal is that formed by the Central Cordillera (Serra da Estrêla), the southern edge of which marks off the physically and climatically distinct northern region from the rest. South of this lies the essentially transitional central region of the Estremadura coastland and the lower Tagus-Sorraia basins (Ribatejo). This central area merges into the Mediterranean South roughly along a line from Setubal to Badajoz, an ill-defined boundary owing to the northward articulation of Mediterranean influences in the river valleys.

NORTHERN PORTUGAL

This diversified region comprises four physical sub-divisions: the crystalline plateaux of Tras-os-Montes and Beira Trasmontana; the granitic batholith of the Serra da Estrêla and its outliers; the deeply dissected transitional highland belt of numerous valleys and residual spurs from the Minho to beyond the Mondego; and the triangular litoral area bounded inland by a continental fault and terminating seaward in a rectilinear sand-dune coast.

Large areas in the first two of these sub-divisions rise to over 3,000 feet, and the highest parts to between 4,500 and 6,000 feet. Precipitation is heavy on the Atlantic slope and the western heights where it exceeds 60 inches north of Oporto, but it declines inland, notably in the Douro Valley, down to 40 and even to 20 inches. Snowfalls are common in winter when the upper parts are often shrouded in mists. These mountainous areas naturally support a very sparse population above the network of valleys in which the cultivation of hardy crops extends to nearly 2,000 feet; above this they are used in parts as summer pastures for sheep and cattle, and considerable areas are under forests; this is the most wooded region of Portugal.

The transitional highland belt is a fine example of a maturely dissected region in which the agents of erosion have carved out a succession of valleys along the lines of weakness initiated by fractures. Though it receives a generous rainfall (Fig. 101), this is supplemented in the summer months by irrigation for intensive cultivation on the terraced hillsides and the valley floors. This belt carries a fairly dense population averaging over 150 per sq. mile — exceptionally high considering that prongs of highland occupy fully one-third of the whole area. Here, as also in the mountainous interior, there is a popular distinction between the Terra Quente (hot land) of the valleys and the Terra Fria above 1,500 to 2,000 feet where rye is the only food crop that can be grown.

In this hill and valley land of generally small holdings little mechanised machinery is used; oxen are preferred as draught animals and many operations are performed by manual labour. The chief crops are maize, which since its introduction in the sixteenth century has become the staple food and fodder crop, grapes from which the rather acid but locally popular *vino verde* is made, potatoes, and rotation grasses for the support of the numerous dairy cattle and oxen. The two New World plants, maize and potatoes, both of which yield more carbohydrate food per unit of cultivated area than the staple Old World crops, have contributed to the growth of population now at or above the limits of increase under existing agricultural techniques.

The famous port wine district of the Douro Valley begins well inland where the rainfall is down to 30 inches or less, and the climate is Mediterranean in character. It now extends almost to the Spanish border up the valley, deeply trenched through the Trasmontana. The vines are planted on south-facing slopes on terraces where the soil has been laboriously made up by grinding the rock and mixing it with manure, e.g. dried seaweed, and where the sun shining on the glistening schistose basic rocks raises the temperature and the alcohol content of the wine (Fig. 110).

The coastland or litoral triangle has, but for some outcrops of hard rocks from the Douro northwards, a cover of later deposits including alluvium, with a belt of wind-blown sand along the coast. As in the valleys which open on to it, cultivation is highly intensive and the land use and the density population are similar, except that fewer sheep and more cattle are kept. Along the shelving shore large quantities of seaweed are collected for use as manure, some of which is dried and sent to the valleys inland.

The undisputed centre of commerce and life in the North as far south as the Mondego River is Oporto (population 300,000), the only large town in Portugal after the capital. It dominates the specialised wine trade, and has various manufactures including textiles, which are produced also in its satellite and outlying towns, notably in Guimarães. Unfortunately the Douro has a bar at its mouth and is not accessible for larger vessels, to accommodate which, an entirely artificial harbour has been constructed at Leixoes. Outside Oporto and its surrounding urban districts, which contain over half a million people, there are few provincial towns in this coastal and valley area of mainly rural population. Two, however, are noteworthy for widely different reasons; Braga, some thirty miles north-east of Oporto, as a great ecclesiastical centre and the reputed birthplace of the Portuguese nation; and Aveiro on the Aveiro Lagoon for its salt works, its ship-yards and its paper mills supplied with wood from the extensive pine forests planted on the sandy coastal belt.

The vigorous and fertile stock of these northern parts played a leading part in the Reconquest (p. 384), and has made its Galician dialect the language of the country. Since then it has been the source of much of the human material that enabled Portugal to acquire a large colonial empire and to bequeath its language and ways of life to the people of the largest and most populous country of South America; and in the present age it has supplied streams of active migrants to the central region and many emigrants to lands of their kindred overseas.

CENTRAL PORTUGAL

The distinctive geographical features of this region are its generally moderate or low elevation, its modified Mediterranean climate and corresponding mixed vegetation, and its overall transitional character. It comprises three sub-regions: the Estremadura coastland zone which, including southern Beira Litoral, extends from the Mondego River in the north across the Tagus Estuary into the Setubal Peninsula in the south; the Ribatejo Basin merging south into the Sado River Basin; and a section of the Alemtejo peneplain including the southern part of Lower Beira which belongs to it structurally.

In Estremadura the ancient rocks of the Meseta sink along the major N.–S. fault under the Triassic and Jurassic folded strata, which in turn are covered in parts by Tertiary and Quaternary deposits, but outcrop at intervals in the much-faulted mainly calcareous upthrusts running south-west into the Lisbon peninsula, where they terminate in the granitic batholith of Sintra. These coastlands continue south into the Setubal Peninsula, the southern border of which is marked by the Serra da Arrábida running WSW.–ENE. in the Alpine alignment of the Meseta sierras.

The Mondego River may be taken as the boundary between North-West European and Mediterranean types of climate. South of it the rainfall declines sharply to less than 25 inches on the coast, and the summer dry season lengthens to three months. Thus there is a northwards extension of the transitional Mediterranean patterns of climate and vegetation on the coastland which does reach on to the interior highlands where the rainfall is heavier.

The rest of Central Portugal consists of the Alemtejo Plateau and the Ribatejo Basin. The former is simply a westward extension of the Meseta structures (p. 390) which sinks gradually into the Ribatejo

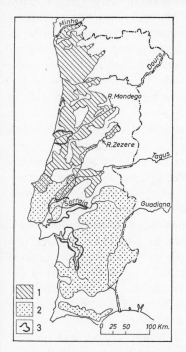 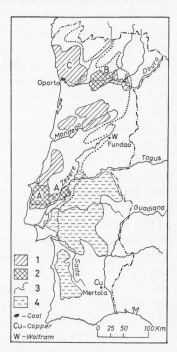

Fig. 109. The distribution of the chief cereal crops in Portugal.
1. Maize. 2. Wheat. 3. Rice.

Fig. 110. The distribution of vineyards and cork oak forests in Portugal; mineral deposits. 1. Chief wine-producing areas. 2. Areas of most intensive cultivation. 3. Inland boundary of vine cultivation. (A. Area of greatest production. B. Specialised port wine district.) 4. Chief cork-producing areas. Adapted from Orlando Ribeiro, *Portugal*, 1955.

depression where they are covered by Tertiary and later deposits, the latter including river-borne sands and gravels with tracts of alluvium in the valleys. In this central region there is some change in the composition of the vegetation from north to south, which is an expression of the essentially transitional nature of the climate; whereas north of the Tagus North-West European species are more numerous than

Mediterranean, the reverse begins to appear south of the Sorraia.

The transitional climatic conditions here are also reflected in the forms of land use (Figs. 109, 110). It will be observed that maize and wheat overlap partly in central Estremadura and in the Tagus Valley towards the north of this region, while wheat, which can tolerate summer drought, is grown to the exclusion of maize farther south. Similarly the cork oak, a thoroughly Mediterranean tree, reaches its northern limit in this area, and the large-scale production of wine its southern limit;[1] scarcely any in fact is produced south of the Sorraia River, except in the maritime Setubal Peninsula. The typically Mediterranean olive is likewise grown extensively in this central region, especially in the Tagus-Zezere Valleys north and east of Santarem.

Yet another expression of the transitional character of Central Portugal is the change within it in the prevailing types of farm holdings; the small, intensively worked mixed farms so characteristic of the North become replaced towards Alemtejo by large properties used for extensive wheat cultivation and sheep-grazing, with a conspicuous scarcity of dairy cattle. But there is one special localised crop of this region, namely rice, which demands highly intensive methods of cultivation. Its requirements of fairly high temperatures during a long growing season, fertile alluvial soils and abundant water to flood the plots in the early stages, are found in the riverine tracts of the lower Tagus, Sorraia and Sado Valleys, and also in a small area near the mouth of the Mondego, which together produce almost the whole of the Portuguese crop of upwards of 2 million tons.

The commerce and industry of the central region, and for that matter of most of Portugal south of the Mondego, are concentrated in Lisbon, the cultural as well as administrative capital of the country. Its industries include ship construction and repairs, manufactures of iron and steel, chemicals and textiles, as well as food-processing. Situated on an excellent harbour with a natural deep-water channel alongside, it has direct connections with the Portuguese oversea territories and with Brazil and is a port of call for liners plying the direct route between North-West European and River Plate ports. The population of the city is officially given at 800,000, but with the

[1] Contrary to the general impression, the grape-vine is not indigenous nor typically Mediterranean. Some of the best wines are produced outside the Mediterranean lands in regions of distributed rainfall, e.g. in North Central France and Western Germany.

twenty-four satellite towns must well exceed a million. Other towns in Central Portugal are dwarfed by the Lisbon Giant, though two of them, Coimbra and Setubal, have some individuality. The former, set among beautiful wooded hills overlooking the Mondego where it breaks out of its highland course, was once the capital of the nascent Portuguese nation and is noted for its university founded in the thirteenth century. Setubal is a great centre of the sardine fishing and preserving industries.

Fishing, not only for sardines and other offshore fish, but also for cod in more distant waters, is carried on from a score of places besides Setubal on the Portuguese coasts, e.g., from Matozinhos in the North and Portimão in Algarve in particular for sardines, and from Lisbon, Aveiro and Oporto, in that order of importance, for cod. The fishing industry employs some 8,000 vessels, mostly small, besides upwards of 9,000 workers in the preserving factories. The Portuguese are a fish-eating people, their consumption per head being exceeded only by that of the Norwegians and the Japanese.

SOUTHERN PORTUGAL

Except for the Algarve coastland this region is basically the western continuation of the southern Meseta. The ancient rocks which appear at the surface in eastern Alemtejo dip underneath the Tertiary beds of the Sado depression to reappear in western Alemtejo. There they reach the sea-coast south of Cape Sines where they cover the whole country as far as the faulted southern edge of the Algarve highlands, which are simply bulges of upthrust crystalline rocks rising from the otherwise generally peneplaned surface. According to these relief forms Southern Portugal is divisible into four sub-regions: (I) the Alemtejo Plateau, (II) central and western Alemtejo, (III) the Algarve highlands, and (IV) the Algarve coastland, each of which has characteristic features which mark it with individuality.

(I) The Alemtejo Plateau is a classical example of a peneplain reduced to a monotonously level surface but for occasional ridges and protrusions of particularly hard rocks.[1] The prevailing soil cover is the none too fertile weathered upper stratum of the basic crystalline rocks, though in some parts, notably in parts of the Guadiana embayment, there is a generally thin mantle of Tertiary deposits which may once have been more widespread. The mainly winter rainfall, averaging little more than 20 inches over the greater part, and less than that in the

---

[1] Resembling the inselberge of the African plateaux.

south-east, is apt to be unreliable, and is in any case meagre in view of the high rate of evaporation.

In these conditions of climate and soil formation the prevailing types of land use are necessarily extensive and the crop yields low, though there are some exceptions to be noted later. Alemtejo is traditionally a land of large estates into which the lands were parcelled as vast domains after the Reconquest, and, though attempts have been made to sub-divide some of the more productive parts of these for more intensive use, the natural conditions have not been helpful, and the semi-feudal economy for the most part remains.

Two forms of exploitation and of corresponding landscape appear in one part after another of Alemtejo, one of woods of evergreen and cork oaks with some intercropping, the other of extensive bare expanses given to the cultivation of cereals at intervals. The first, known as *montado*, is a primitive form of land use: the undergrowth is cut away to promote the growth of the trees, patches are cleared for growing cereals with long fallows on which some sheep may be run, and pigs are fattened on the acorns dropped from the oaks. The second is the commonest form of land use; huge tracts are devoted to the monoculture of cereals, mostly wheat, with fallows up to five years used for the pasturage of sheep. Whatever scattered trees subsist here have gnarled trunks, few branches and withered leaves. Thus in the typical Alemtejo, when during the almost rainless summers relentless sunshine pours down on the shadeless ground, the stifling heat becomes almost unbearable.[1] In this region the population is grouped in nodes round the owner's or his overseer's residence, each as a miniature self-contained unit comprising buildings for the machinery, live-stock and food-processing equipment, and simple dwellings for the permanent and seasonal labourers. Formerly languishing, Alemtejo has revived since duties were imposed on imported corn at the turn of the century; as a result mainly of the expansion of cereal cultivation there, Portugal now produces nearly twice as much wheat as maize, which used to be the chief grain.

A third form of land use is confined to the more fertile calcareous soils of Tertiary lake basins or derived from lime-rich primary rocks. These are used primarily for olive plantations, though as in the montado intercropping with cereals is practised, and as on the open campos

---

[1] Hence the saying — 'Alemtejo não tem sombra
Senão a que vem do ceu'
Alemtejo has no shade but what comes from the sky.

sheep are pastured on the shorter fallows. On some of the most fertile
tracts fruit trees, e.g. figs and almonds, are grown, and field crops such
as beans are rotated with the cereals. On such lands as these the two
more important towns, Evora and Beja, both comparatively small,
have developed as transport and market centres.

(II) Central and western Alemtejo are considerably more diversified
in surface deposits and soil types than the eastern plateau. On the
Tertiary sands and clays of the Sado depression there is a similar form
of extensive cereal cultivation with sheep-pasturing on the fallows, as
on the plateau, but with more rotation crops; rice fields are common
on the flood plain of the Sado River. West of that river large plantations of cork oaks have replaced the former poor mixed forest vegetation on the hilly country, and cereal cultivation has spread on to the
more fertile lands of lower elevation. Here and on the coastal strip,
Mediterranean polyculture on small, intensively utilised holdings has
been extended to selected parts, especially west-facing hillsides which
benefit from a somewhat heavier rainfall and greater atmospheric
humidity.

(III) The Algarve highlands consist of two dissimilar upthrust blocks.
The larger one to the east, the Serra de Calderão, is an upthrust of
schists falling away steeply on the south along a series of faults — a
western outlier of the Sierra Morena. Most of it is semi-arid and nearly
useless, though it contains some irrigated valleys. The Serra de
Monchique to the west is composed of syenite which weathers freely
in the comparatively humid climate of this area washed by seas on two
sides. The upper parts are clothed with woods of sweet chestnuts and
cork oaks, below which the hillsides are terraced down to the valley
floors, both used for the Mediterranean type of polyculture with the
help of irrigation.

(IV) The Algarve coastland is formed mainly of folded Jurassic and
Cretaceous beds dipping towards the coast under a narrow Tertiary
belt. This coastal strip, well supplied with underground waters tapped
from countless wells, is highly productive and densely populated; it
produces all manner of crops including the entire supplies of primeurs
for Lisbon. The limestone country behind, on to which sporadic
settlement has spread from the fully occupied coastal belt, is by comparison poor; secano cultivation is the rule, and water for ordinary
purposes has to be drawn from deep wells, from which it is commonly
carried in casks loaded on donkeys. The greater part of the Algarve
coastland is by no means a 'garden of Eden' as it has been

called. Much of it is rather barren limestone country on the whole.

The climate of this sub-region is almost sub-tropical. The high lands behind it ward off any northern climatic influence, and the predominant maritime influences maintain equability of temperatures; though it suffers from excessive Mediterranean characteristics in the marked seasonal distribution of scanty rainfall. Given the needful supplies of water, whether from wells or from streams (as in the Serra de Monchique), selected parts of this area are able to produce an amazing variety of crops: bananas and oranges; figs, almonds and olives; and all kinds of temperate and warm temperate cereals and garden produce.

The eastern half of the Algarve coast is low and sandy, the western half rocky with headlands at intervals, the westernmost of which, Cape S. Vincent, was designated by Strabo as the 'end not only of Europe, but of all inhabited lands'. This Atlantic promontory has also given its Arabic name Algarve (=the West) to the whole southern region. Geological structure and geographical situation have ordained that this coastal strip should be most of what counts in Algarve. Its six towns, the largest of which are Faro, Tavira, Portimão and Lagos, contain one-third of the population of the whole province, and the strip itself fully two-thirds, supported not only by the productivity of the soil, but also by the extensive fishing of sardines and tunny and fish preserving industries.

The Portuguese Economy

Though Portugal is one with the rest of Iberia in structure and situation, it has turned its back on Spain and developed a maritime outlook in its external relations. Spain and Portugal have in fact little to offer each other in the form of specialised products to exchange, and Portugal has perforce had to look elsewhere for trading partners, mainly with Great Britain, the United States and the Portuguese colonial territories, which together account for over half of both its exports and its imports.

Portugal is a comparatively poor country, somewhat backward in its economy and largely dependent upon agriculture which employs 40 per cent of its active population and (including arboriculture) supplies 50 per cent of its exports. It is notably deficient in mineral fuels and iron ore deposits; its total output of coal and lignite amounts to little over half a million tons per annum, and that of iron ore to not much more than 100,000 tons metal content. Some compensation for the fuel shortage is afforded by the considerable, hitherto largely unused, hydro-electric power potential of the northern rivers, notably the Douro and the Zezere, some of which has been developed increasingly in recent years (p. 364). Unfortunately the ores of copper and of wolfram, the two chief minerals, are not much use to a country which has little heavy industry, and they are accordingly exported.

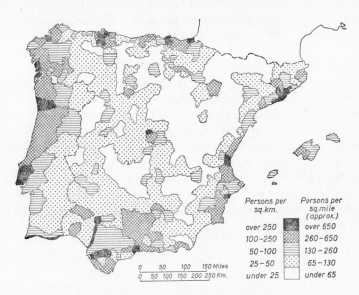

Fig. 111. The distribution of population in Iberia. After *Atlas Geográfico de España*. Aguilar Ediciones, 1954.

The dependence of the Portuguese economy upon exports of primary products to pay for necessary imports appears in the trade figures. Forestal products (including cork), wines, sardines and mineral ores are the chief export items, while iron and steel ingots, foodstuffs, vehicles and raw cotton head the list of imports. Except for fishing and forestry, Portugal is essentially an agricultural country, but the average cereal yields are low, and the home production even of wheat and maize needs to be supplemented by considerable imported supplies. The overall food shortage is indicated by the fact that in the densely populated northern rural districts the staple food is a kind of bread (borõa) made of maize meal mixed with a little rye or wheat flour. Were it not for emigrants' remittances, even the existing modest standards of living could hardly be maintained.

Whatever the causes, Portugal has long suffered from economic stagnation and apparent over-population; as a Portuguese geographer has observed, 'only one product has been continuously exported for five centuries, namely men,' and this draining away of active male elements may have had undesirable cumulative effects. However, in recent years the country has roused itself in some measure from lethargy; positive expressions of revival appear in the rapid development of hydro-electric power resources and of drainage works on a national scale, and a considerable expansion of manufactures.

THE DISTRIBUTION OF POPULATION IN IBERIA

In the Peninsula as a whole there is a striking concentration of population in the peripheral zones where the density in a number of districts exceeds 500 per sq. mile (Fig. 111). With the exception of the Madrid nucleus, an artificial creation, the interior plateau block covering nearly two-thirds of the total area is thinly populated, averaging not more than 100 persons per sq. mile; like the Massif Central of France, the Meseta is largely a negative area. In Iberia indeed, a land of sharp physical contrasts, the population map effectively epitomises the close relationships between the geographical factors and the human geography.

Chapter 32

ITALY: I
STRUCTURAL REGIONS AND CLIMATE

LYING astride the Central Mediterranean Sea, Italy including Sicily almost divides that sea into two parts; were it not for the comparatively shallow Sicilian Straits and the geologically recent break at the Straits of Messina, the Italian land bridge connecting Central Europe with North Africa would be complete. Though it seems that in a past geological age Europe and Africa may have been connected across Italy, in point of fact much of the land now above the sea in that country is the result of late Tertiary uplift whereby great thicknesses of Pliocene beds were added to the former skeleton (see p. 430). In contrast with the Aegean area where wholesale foundering has taken place, leaving only the mountain heights as islands, Italy owes its present form largely to accretions resulting from late Tertiary uplift and to the outward extension of the coastlands built up with the waste products of intensified erosion.

Except for parts of the high Alpine core along the inland border, and for several detached blocks in Calabria and Sicily, Peninsular Italy and Sicily contain only a few trifling remnants of the old crystalline rocks associated with the Hercynian orogeny, so abundant in the Iberian Peninsula. Excluding Sardinia and the crystalline Alps just mentioned, Italy comprises the following structural sub-divisions: the high predominantly limestone Alps and the Pre-Alps east of Lago Maggiore; the infilled northern plain; the Apennines proper; the outer (eastern and south-eastern) arc of coastlands comprising (*a*) the central Adriatic strip; (*b*) the Gargano-Murge limestone platforms, (*c*) the Tavoliere-Murge depression, (*d*) the Sicilian Tertiary formations; and lastly the complex hill and valley western zone (Fig. 112).

(I) The crystalline Alps incorporating various Hercynian remnants, e.g. the Aar-St. Gotthard, the Mt. Blanc and the Pelvoux massifs, are the root zone of the Alps in which granites and metamorphosed sedimentary rocks have been squeezed up under intense pressures. The

main watershed which naturally lies along the axis of this core zone
has been followed in the main, but with some deviations as in the region of the Swiss Ticino, by the inter-national boundaries. Though
too elevated to be of any agricultural value except in some deeply-cut
valleys such as the Val d'Aosta, the crystalline Alps have been turned
to account in Italy as in the adjoining countries in two ways: for
building up a limited tourist industry, and what is much more impor-

Fig. 112. The structural regions of Italy. I. High crystalline Alps.
II. Sedimentary Alpine zone. a. High Calcareous Alps. b. Pre-Alps.
III. Infilled syncline. IV. Apennines and Pre-Apennines. Va, b, c, d. Outer
arc of coastlands. VI. Western hill and valley zone. VII. Sardinia.

tant in Italy, for the development of hydro-electric power using the
heads of water derived from their ice and snow fields.

(II) The sedimentary zone begins just east of Lago Maggiore whence it
widens out to a breadth of over 80 miles beyond the River Adige, but
narrows again eastwards in Italian territory to 30 or 40 miles. It consists of two formations, the high Calcareous Alps and the Pre-Alps.
The former occupy extensive areas east and west of the Adige, notably
in the region of the Dolomites where they are composed of gaily
coloured Triassic magnesian limestones. This region, known as the
Trentino and famous for its beautiful, fantastic scenery, is readily

accessible from the south by the deeply trenched valleys of the Adige system, and from the north by the Brenner Pass.

The Pre-Alps extend in a comparatively narrow band along the front of the high Calcareous Alps, from which they differ in being composed mainly of the later and less resistant Lias and Cretaceous rocks of the Mesozoic series. As the innermost members of the sharply upthrust Alpine arc (Fig. 55), they rise somewhat steeply from the

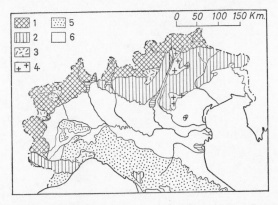

Fig. 113. The geological structure of Northern Italy (generalised). 1. Metamorphic rocks (schists etc). 2. Mainly Permian and Triassic, except on the southern (Pre-Alp) margin. 3. Granites. 4. Igneous rocks. 5. Tertiary. 6. Quaternary.

lowlands wherever they have escaped intersection by powerful valley glaciers. Some of the deep clefts so formed are now occupied by lakes. (III) The North Italian Plain (Pianura Padana) is structurally a synclinal trough filled with hundreds of metres of waste materials swept down from the Alps and the Apennines — a process still in progress, as appears notably in the extension of the deltaic marshes into the Adriatic at an average of 40 feet a year. During the late Pliocene almost the whole of this North Italian trough was occupied by a western arm of the Adriatic Sea (Fig. 115); later, at the time of the maximum Quaternary glaciation and the corresponding lowering of the general sea-level, both the present plain and the Adriatic basin as far south as the Gargano Peninsula were dry land. Later the sea, rising here as elsewhere in level by about 300 feet, regained possession of the land to well within the present shore line of the Plain, from which it is being pushed out once more as described above.

(IV) The Apennines, the almost continuous spine of the Italian peninsula, with a broken extension in northern Sicily, are the product of two distinct orogenic movements. The first occurred in the middle Tertiary, when Cretaceous limestones and later marine clays were uplifted by folding to form the spinal and the subsidiary chains from the region of Genoa through Calabria into Sicily. The pronounced curves seem to have been caused by the resistant influence of, or

Fig. 114. The geological structure of Central and Southern Italy and Sicily (generalised). 1. Recent volcanics. 2. Crystalline rocks (granite, schists). 3. Limestones. 4. Tertiary beds (soft sandstones, clays, marls). 5. Recent marine and alluvial deposits. 6. Ragusa petroleum field and pipe line. 7. Tuscan lignite deposits. 8. Lardarello thermal district.

possibly eastward pressures exerted by, the old Corsica-Sardinia block. Vigorous erosion followed, and the seas crept back on what had been land till all that remained by the late Pliocene was a skeleton highland extending from the Maritime Alps to a little beyond Rome, and south of that a string of islands (Fig. 115). The final phase of uplift, which came in the early Quaternary period, differed from the earlier one in being epeirogenic, i.e. of general uplift instead of folding. In this a varied assortment of marine deposits was raised together with, and on the flanks of, the surviving earlier formations, in particular the Cretaceous limestones which now form some of the highest parts, e.g. in the Abruzzi Apennines; while in Calabria and north-east Sicily granitic intrusions and metamorphic rocks of an earlier period of mountain-building, and subsequently exposed by erosion, were raised as detached blocks. The Calabrian horsts of Sila, Serre and

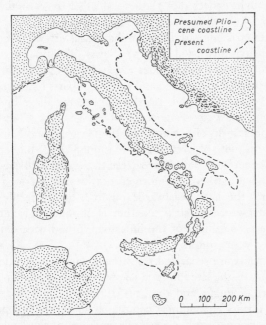

Fig. 115. Italy and neighbouring lands in the Pliocene.
Note. The Cadibona and Giovi Passes marked were apparently overflow channels of the Padane Gulf into the Ligurian Sea.

Aspromonte are apparently exhumed remnants of the still earlier Hercynian folding.

This sequence of events all points to the youthfulness of Italian land forms south of the Alps except those of Calabria just mentioned. The consequent softness of the prevailing uppermost strata has given the forces of erosion full play, notably on the unconsolidated friable beds of the outer northern and eastern flanks of the Apennines. These have been dissected and deformed by numerous streams large and small, so much so that in a long stretch from Bologna southwards there are typical 'bad lands', gullied by countless ravines[1] separated by knife-like edges. In central and southern Sicily the older Tertiary beds have likewise suffered considerable, though less severe dissection. On the inner western flanks of the Apennines on the other hand, these destructive processes have not been so much in evidence, partly because permeable limestones in the river catchment areas regularise run-off, and partly because the Pre-Apennine ranges cause much of the mountain drainage to be collected by the several larger rivers on their longitudinal courses before they break through to the sea.

(V) The outer coastland arc from Emilia to western Sicily comprises the four sub-divisions listed earlier (p. 427). The first of these, the narrow coastal belt, is an exiguous extension of the Northern Plain south-east from Rimini, backed and broken in parts by projections of the inland Tertiary foreland, up the numerous valleys of which it extends greater or shorter distances.

The second sub-division comprises the Gargano and Murge limestone platforms, both of Cretaceous limestone like the higher parts of the central Apennines. Both have shared in the general Post-Pliocene elevation, and are tilted, the former northwards on to a lagoon-fringed shore, the latter eastwards on to a highly fertile, though generally narrow coastal strip. Neither is of much agricultural use owing to the permeability of the limestone, pitted with dolinas and honeycombed with grottoes.

These plateaux are separated from the Apennines by a depression covered earlier by the late Pliocene sea, which comprises two sections, the Tavoliere di Puglia and the Pre-Murge trough (Fossa Premurgiana). The former is an almost completely level, uplifted portion of the sea-bed, floored with clays and sands, a region of uncertain drainage in which the streams often dry up in summer and which ends south of Gargano in a succession of lagoons. The latter is more elevated; it begins with the saddle south of the transverse Ofanto River, from which it slopes away into the Gulf of Taranto, its Pliocene surface beds being intersected by the shallow valleys of the Bradano and several smaller parallel seasonal rivers. Both the Tavoliere and the Pre-Murge depressions present monotonous landscapes of semi-arid, steppe-like character.

Much of Sicily, apart from the remnant 'Apennine' highlands in the

---

[1] These V-shaped ravines known as *calanchi* are commonest in the upper basins of the consequent rivers, where numerous tributary valleys converge fan-wise upon the main valleys.

north-east and north and the conical mass of Etna, is covered with uplifted late Tertiary clays and sands averaging 1,200 to 1,500 feet in elevation. Being readily eroded, these have been dissected into tabular forms by the numerous streams which tend to widen their valleys at the expense of the upland plains by gullying and through landslips, especially where the underlying beds are of clay. These Tertiary platforms and likewise the northern highlands commonly extend near to, or actually on to the coasts, so that coastal lowlands are few and comparatively small.

(VI) The Western hill and valley and coastal region, extending from the Arno Valley to well beyond Naples on the mainland, has a complicated geological history, reflected in the confused variety of its structural and relief forms. In late Pliocene times the greater part of this area was covered by a Tyrrhenian Sea embayment dotted with island remnants of an earlier uplift. The accumulation of waste from the re-elevated Apennines, together with the general epeirogenic uplift, gradually extended the shore to include outlying Pre-Apennine ridges and most of the islands in the newly-formed land — a process still in progress as shown by the immature, marshy belt of the Tuscan Maremma. Some of the inland depressions also are incompletely filled up, and one of them is still occupied by the shallow Lake Trasimeno.

South of the Tuscan hill and valley country lies the volcanic belt associated with the Tyrrhenian foundering. There the considerable crustal disturbance of Quaternary to Recent times has resulted in extensive outpourings of lavas and tuffs (now more or less weathered on the surface) and the still active Mt. Vesuvius, and Stromboli in the Lipari Islands. Both the jointed lava flows and the loosely compacted tuffs are readily dissected by rivers and streams, so that this volcanic belt, like Tuscany but for a different reason, has a considerable variety of low and moderately low relief forms. Here also as on the Tuscan coastland, there is a belt of recently-formed lowlands in the Pontine marshes and the Neapolitan Campania.

(VII) Sardinia differs essentially in origin and build from the youthful body of Italy and its extension into Sicily. This Hercynian remnant, composed basically of ancient crystalline rocks, has been subject to immense stresses that have contributed to its present distinctive structural and relief forms, and these may be most conveniently outlined together with those of the geologically related island of Corsica in the following chapter.

P

CLIMATE

It is evident from the general account of Western Mediterranean climatic conditions (pp. 365–9) that Italy lies in a zone of transition. Thus within its territory, extending over 10 degrees of latitude, three varieties of climate can be distinguished: a modified Central European climate in the northern parts, approximately as far south as the latitude

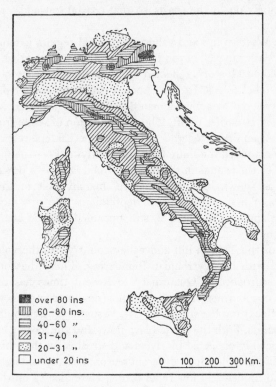

over 80 ins
60–80 ins.
40–60 ”
31–40 ”
20–31 ”
under 20 ins

0   100   200   300 Km.

Fig. 116. The mean annual rainfall of Italy and Corsica.

of Florence; a definitely Mediterranean type from Rome southwards; and an intermediate variety in the central section of the Peninsula.

In the northern region the rainfall, averaging about 30 inches on the Plain and rising to over 40 inches on the mountain slopes, is generally well distributed, though with a distinct summer-autumn maximum.[1]

[1] Of the yearly totals, 62·5 per cent falls in the six months May-November at Padua, 62·0 per cent at Piacenza and 63·8 per cent at Milan.

The mean monthly temperatures there show a considerable range, 42·1° F. (23·4° C.) at Milan for example, compared with 22° F. at London. The summers are as hot as those of Sicily, while the winters are as cold as those of central Germany, the average January temperatures being near freezing point. In respect therefore of both rainfall and temperature distributions, the climate of northern Italy has distinct Central European affinities.

In southern Italy from Rome southwards, the climate becomes progressively more Mediterranean in its essential features. The rainfall averaging 32·7 ins. at Rome already shows the typical Mediterranean distribution of a late autumn and winter maximum, about half the total falling in the four months from October to January, and little more than one-tenth in the three high summer months. At Palermo, while about 56 per cent of the lower total of 29·4 ins. comes also in the same four cooler months, the rainfall of the three summer months is down to 1½ ins. At Agrigento in southern Sicily two-thirds of the yearly 20·2 ins. falls in the four months October to January, while that of the three summer months is insignificant — little more than half an inch. The range of temperature between the hottest and the coolest months, which is 32·6° F. at Rome, falls to 25·7° F. at Palermo owing to its distinctly milder winter, but rises to 29·5° at Agrigento where African influences reduce the winter temperatures and, combined with the negligible summer rainfall, raise the temperatures at that season.

The area covered by the transitional type of climate shows considerable local variety according to physical conditions. Siena, about 50 kilometres south of Florence, which may be taken as representative, has the north Italian feature of the fairly low January temperature of 40·3° F. (London 41° F.), but has the Mediterranean characteristic of winter maximum rainfall — 45 per cent of the total in the four winter months.

Taking into account the total amount and the seasonal incidence of the rainfall, in combination with all the conditions that cause loss of moisture, (i.e. evaporation, seepage or run-off) maps may be constructed to show the scale of aridity (or the reverse), determined by the net amounts of moisture available for the cultivation of characteristic crops. Such a map is Fig. 117, based on the work of De Martonne and Italian investigators; in the areas marked sub-arid, irrigation is required for most summer-growing crops other than those which are distinctly drought-resisting, and also for humid-region crops in the areas marked as marginal sub-arid.

Because of pressure of population on the available agricultural resources in Italy, especially in the south, extension of the margin of cultivation there is of first importance. As shown on the map the largest area of sub-arid lands is in the south-east where, in order to increase the surface water supplies for crops, an elaborate system of aqueducts has been constructed, the main supply conduit of which,

Indices of aridity
☐ Definitely arid
▨ Sub-arid
▨ Marginal sub-arid
▨ Sufficient precipitation

Aqueducts and branches

Fig. 117. The arid and sub-arid regions of Southern Italy and Sicily. The Apulian aqueducts.

the Apulian aqueduct 150 miles in length, draws water from numerous reservoirs fed by rivers and springs in the Apennine catchment area to the west (Fig. 117).

In Sicily, on the other hand, where there is another considerable sub-arid area, very little can be done owing to the absence of any useful catchment area from which waters can be drawn for irrigation purposes.

FORESTRY

For a mountainous country in warm temperate latitudes Italy has a small proportion of its area classed as forest land, only 19 per cent in all, including open woodlands. Fully two-thirds of the whole country is more or less mountainous, of very limited use for agriculture except for summer pastures; the Alps and the Apennines alone cover nearly half the total area, but of the original high forest, even at higher elevations, only remnants still exist.

Deforestation, which has continued from Roman times, especially in the Peninsula and Sicily, with little replanting till recently, has not only depleted the supplies of useful timbers, but also led to disastrous erosion of the unconsolidated beds that cover much of the Apennines and their outer flanks into Sicily (p. 431). More than in any other West European country, there has been pressure in Italy from the dense population in the limited productive parts to make inroads on the forests for supplies of timber and fuel, and still more to increase the areas of farm land.

Less than one-tenth of the present-day forests are purely coniferous (pines, cypresses, cedars), and those mostly on the Alps and northern Apennines. Elsewhere the predominant form is open woodlands consisting of mixed or more commonly broad-leafed species in which evergreen oak, wild olive and myrtle are characteristic, these woodlands being generally very scattered except in parts of Calabria and Sardinia; large areas of woodland which have been cut over in the past are covered with degenerate secondary growth of myrtle, xerophytic shrubs and creeping plants often forming dense thickets (macchia).

THE ITALIAN ECONOMY

It will be apparent from the above survey that, except in parts of the northern plain, Italy as a whole has been poorly endowed with naturally fertile lands receiving a reliable rainfall. Of the total area of 320,700 sq. kilometers (123,800 sq. miles), the Alps, Pre-Alps and Apennines Proper cover over half (52·3 per cent), and of the rest by no means all parts are productive. Yet with only one-third, at the most, of its lands suitable for intensive agriculture, Italy supports a population of 50 millions, with an unusually high proportion (40 per cent of the active persons in 1951) engaged in agriculture and related industries. There are 3 million holdings under 5 hectares (12 acres) and the pressure of peasant population is such that much marginal land is under cultivation. Thus the need is great to reclaim unused, potentially productive lands wherever possible — by draining the coastal marshes and by irrigation works both in the northern plain and in the semi-arid parts of the South. Upwards of 4½ million acres have been reclaimed to date, and a still larger area of lands supplied with irrigation; but further progress may well be slow owing to the inevitably high costs of other less feasible projects.

Unfortunately also Italy is deficient in mineral resources, having little else than the comparatively small deposits of mercury in Tuscany and of zinc-lead in Sardinia, and the recently exploited stores of natural gas in the Northern Plain (Fig. 119) and of petroleum in Sicily. The deposits of both coal and iron ore are of small account, and the hydro-electric power resources, though great, are not capable of much further development without an excessively costly national grid to remedy the winter shortages in the North and the summer shortages in the South. Some contribution to the supplies of electrical energy is

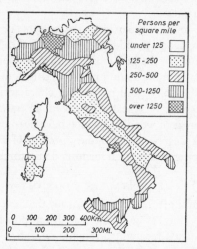

Fig. 118. The distribution of population in Italy. Based on population figures by Departments 1957.

made by utilising the natural gas vents of the Lardarello district in Tuscany (Fig. 114), the output from which in 1960 was 1,914 million kWh., about 3·9 per cent of the total power supplies.

With a natural increase of over 400,000 per annum and no comparable unused natural resources, Italy is faced with a population problem. The relief formerly afforded by extensive emigration, chiefly to Latin America and the United States, has diminished owing to the imposition of restrictions on immigration; and with that there has been a decline in the invisible item of exports by way of emigrants' remittances to their home land. The pressure on staple food supplies has led to a 'battle for grain', one of the spear-heads of which has been the break-up of latifundia, especially in the south-east[1] for the

[1] In the dry belt of the Taviolere di Puglia and the Pre-Murge trough; but also in the Tuscan Maremma and Lazio, in eastern Calabria and in the Po delta. Under the agrarian reform of 1950 over 4 million acres were scheduled to be expropriated and

cultivation of cereals on lands formerly used simply as sheep-runs.

In recent years manufactures have expanded notably; the index of industrial production rose from 100 in 1958 to 153 in 1962, and the proportion of the active population employed in industry from 27 per cent in 1931 to over 36 per cent in 1962. The greatest expansion has been achieved in iron and steel manufactures, in the engineering

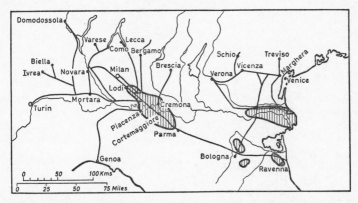

Fig. 119. Methane fields and pipe lines in Northern Italy.

group and in chemicals. The growth of these and other industries located mainly in the relatively prosperous North is helpful in redressing the inequality of incomes by attracting unemployed agricultural workers from the overpopulated South where standards of living are unduly low. Yet though Italian industry has the advantage of comparatively cheap supplies of labour, it is questionable whether, in view of the limited internal mineral and other resources, manufactures can continue to expand enough to cover the increased imports of commodities which are needed to improve the standards of life in the South and the islands, where the rates of natural increase of population are unusually high.

Italy is faced with peculiar difficulties in her external trade, arising from the essential and inelastic nature of the chief imports (fuels and primary raw materials) and the non-essential nature of much of the exports for which the markets are apt to be capricious. More than most countries Italy must welcome any steps towards the liberation of

distributed to peasant farmers. By the end of 1957 nearly 1½ million acres had been re-settled.

trade that may enable her to exchange the products of her labour resources in the forms of manufactured goods and of citrus fruits,
primeurs and other climatic specialities, for indispensable raw materials and supplementary foodstuffs. Hence Italy's adherence to the
European Common Market as one of its prime and principal members.

Chapter 33

ITALY: II. NORTHERN ITALY

THE general features of the structure and climate of Italy have been outlined in the previous chapter. In this and the following specifically regional chapters, further details of the physical geography are given as required, to supply the background of the natural settings in which human life and activities have developed in these long-settled lands, account being taken both of man's response to the physical conditions and of the ways in which human intervention has modified these.

Northern Italy may be taken as comprising the whole basin of the Po, the Adige and the smaller rivers that drain into the Adriatic between Rimini and Trieste; the Ligurian coastland as far east as La Spezia which is bound up with the interior Plain in its economic development; and inasmuch as the Apennine watershed (and with it the boundaries of all the provinces) lies well to the south, most of the northern Apennines is also to be included. The international frontiers also follow the Alpine watershed in the main, the only exceptions being that of the Swiss Ticino wedge (Fig. 57) and the artificial N.–S. boundary with Yugoslavia in the north-east.

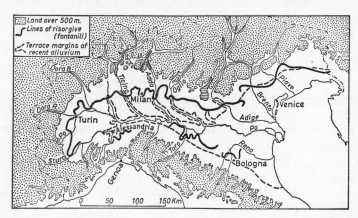

Fig. 120. Selected features of the relief and drainage of Northern Italy.

The so-called Northern Plain is an elongated trough extending about 240 miles from the foothills behind Turin to the delta coast, with a further 60 odd miles in the limb at the head of the Adriatic. With an average breadth of about 60 miles in the Po Valley, it covers some 16,000 sq. miles in all, an area considerably larger than the Netherlands and almost exactly the same size as Switzerland. Its population, well over 16 millions in 1957, gave an average density of over 1,000 per sq. mile — one of the highest for a comparable area anywhere, and exceeded only by those of the great river plains of Monsoon Asia. This remarkable and still rising density of population is the result of widespread industrial expansion superimposed on the overall intensive agriculture, in both of which the human element has made the fullest use of the physical endowments and economic opportunities.

A notable feature of the infilling of the Plain is the lines of junction between the upper coarser and porous materials, largely of fluvio-glacial origin, and the lower finer and more compact alluvial deposits. The numerous springs[1] along the edges of the former are valuable in supplying water for irrigating the rice fields (notably in Lombardy) and the meadows on the rich lands lower down. It will be observed from Fig. 120 that these spring lines are much more continuous for obvious reasons on the Alpine than on the Apennine side of the whole valley plain. The only marked break in the former is that of the vol-canic stumps of the Euganei and Berici hills west of Venice.

Except in the flood plain region below Mantua, this trough area is neither level nor symmetrical in cross-section profile. It has in fact sagged in the medial zone under the weight of the enormous masses of sediments derived from the vigorous erosion of the Alps and the re-elevated Apennines. On the northern side there are two terrace steps: an upper one 600 to 1,000 feet above sea-level, built up mainly with coarse morainic glacial deposits (especially round the lower ends of the lakes) and semi-porous fluvio-glacial materials; and a lower one be-tween 300 and 600 feet in elevation composed of finer fluvio-glacial deposits, below which lies the alluvial valley proper which, from a height of about 300 feet at Alessandria, falls away gradually eastwards to the sea in the 200-mile course of the axial river. The powerful Alpine tributaries of the Po have cut trenches covered with alluvium in the lower terrace (Fig. 120), and have pushed the main river with their loads of deposited sediments well towards the Apennines in the

[1] Italian *resorgive* (*fontanili* in Lombardy).

upper half of the basin, so that although terraces can be distinguished also on the south, they are both narrower and more broken than on the northern flank.

The surface of the infilled depression as just described is broken by two emergent hilly areas of different origins, namely the Monferrat uplands in the bend of the Po east of Turin, and the Euganei and Berici hills some 40 miles west of Venice. The former, composed of Tertiary (mainly Eocene) calcareous rocks, rise to heights of over 2,000 feet near the Po, from which they fall away south-east to less than 1,000 feet along the Tanaro River. They are simply a detached section of the Apennine-Ligurian system, separated from the main uplift by the incised valley of the Tanaro. The Euganei and Berici hills consist of the stumps of denuded Eocene volcanoes, rising more or less sharply from the surrounding plain; they appear to be southern outliers of the more extensive volcanic outpourings in the Alpine region east of the Adige.

In the flood plain of the Po-Adige river systems, especially in the lower region where the rivers are charged with more sediment than their slackening currents can carry through to the sea, the risks of inundations are serious. The levées, constructed to prevent the rivers wandering freely as they did in prehistoric times as their channels became partially choked, have to be raised periodically; but since the level of the river waters cannot be raised indefinitely above that of the surrounding country, some of the rivers have been straightened here and there to expedite their flow, and networks of canals have been constructed (similar to those in the Netherlands), a small section of which is shown in Fig. 127. In view of these conditions it is not surprising that the larger towns in the lower valley are situated well away from the rivers; only two leading towns, Cremona and Piacenza, are actually on the Po, and those in its middle, not its lower course.

AGRICULTURE

The rainfall varies considerably in amount from place to place, though it is in general fairly well distributed throughout the year; Milan gets nearly 40 inches, Turin 35·1, Padua 33·3, but Mantua and Verona get only 25·7 and 25·3 respectively. All these stations have May-June and October-November maxima, and no month without appreciable rainfall. While these amounts, in view of their seasonal spread, seem generous on the whole compared with conditions in much of the south and the islands, supplementary irrigation is helpful for intensive agriculture in the areas receiving smaller rainfalls, and is essential for the widespread cultivation of rice. Hence the importance of the *resorgive* (spring) lines at the junction of the upper permeable terrace with the lower one more retentive of moisture.

The upper terrace at the foot of the mountains is naturally indifferent agricultural land, too stony and porous for general arable farming. Parts of it are, in fact, covered with heath vegetation and,

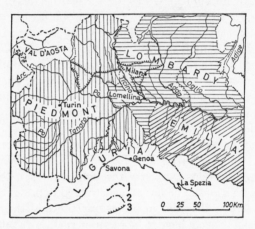

Fig. 121. The north-western provinces, the heart region of modern Italy. 1. International boundaries. 2. Provincial boundaries. 3. Canals.

apart from vineyards which extend well into the eastern drier part of this zone, cultivation is scattered. Thus the lowlands below about 600 feet account for much the greater proportion of the field crops and dairy products of the whole northern region which produces 98 per cent of the total Italian rice crop of nearly 600,000 tons, over three-quarters of the maize, beet sugar and cows' milk, and 43 per cent of the wheat. The two provinces, Piedmont and Lombardy (Fig. 121), alone produce 90 per cent of the Italian rice,[1] over 40 per cent of the maize, and contain over one-third of the dairy cattle. The distribution of various leading crops in Italy is shown in Figs. 122 and 123, from which it will be seen that the only important forms of cultivation in

[1] The area of most intensive cultivation of rice is in the upper section of the Plain, in the Lomellina and adjoining parts west of the Adda, intersected by rivers and canals (Fig. 121) because the supplies of water can be more readily regulated there for the growth and the proper ripening of the crop, than in the lower flood plain.

which the North (excepting Liguria) does not share are tree crops, olives and citrus fruits.

Some of the general features of the alluvial riverine and deltaic lands which require protection from flooding have been described above (p. 443). These, owing to the high water table, are eminently suited, as are similar areas of the Netherlands, for use as meadows, with the special advantages in Italy that the climate is warmer and

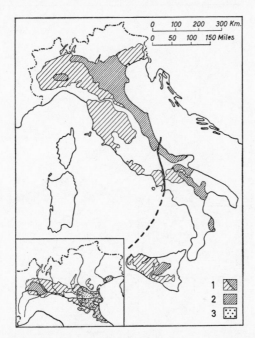

Fig. 122. The chief wheat lands (main map) and rice lands (inset map) of Italy. 1. The more important areas of cultivation. 2. Areas of most intensive cultivation. 3. The main area of beet sugar production (inset map). The heavy line marks the generalised boundary between soft and hard wheats.

there is abundant water for irrigation, thus enabling six or more cuttings of grass for hay or silage. Sugar beet, linked with the dairy industry in supplying valuable by-product fodders (see p. 54), are also grown extensively in these parts, which account for nearly all the half million acres given to this crop in Italy; the areas of most intensive cultivation are the deltaic lands of the Po, Adige and Piave Rivers (Fig. 122, Inset).

It is not surprising therefore that the northern provinces, having all these fodders available for the maintenance of cattle, are the leading source of dairy products in Italy. They hold nearly 6 million out of the total 8½ million cattle in the country, and a still larger proportion of the milk cows, since many of the stocks listed as cattle in other parts are primarily draught animals. Much of the milk supply is made into cheeses including such well-known kinds as Gorgonzola and Par-

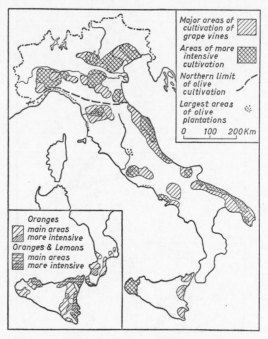

Fig. 123. The principal areas of cultivation of grape vines and olives, and of citrus fruits (inset map) in Italy.

mesan; owing to the relative shortage of meat in Italy, cheese is a popular staple protein article of diet.

It may seem abnormal that grape-vines are widely cultivated in the North where most rain comes in early summer and late autumn. Grape-vines, however, are not native of the Mediterranean lands but of Western Asia, apparently the Caspian region of Persia, whence they were introduced into Sicily as far back as 1500 B.C. Being deep-rooted they can tolerate summer drought, a condition which may be imposed by their need for sunny weather during the ripening period, although drought is not essential for the quality of the wines; hence they do best on fairly dry, south-facing slopes which are often terraced for the vineyards in Italy as in other parts of Western Europe, e.g. the Rhineland. In Northern Italy, which produces just over half the Italian wines, the chief centres are the hilly southern Piedmont (noted for its Asti Spumante) and the comparatively dry eastern foothills in Lombardy and Venetia, though large quantities are also produced on the Apennine slopes and the Po Valley in Emilia-Romagna (Fig. 123).

Maize, used mainly in the North to feed cattle and pigs, is grown extensively on the northern lowlands, the yield of grain being nearly equal to that of wheat, though considerably less land is given to maize than to wheat (owing to the normal higher yield per acre). Cultivation of this crop is spread mainly over the arc of country north of the Po which extends from Piedmont through Lombardy to the head of the Adriatic. Thanks largely to the supplies from this maize belt which contributes over 70 per cent of the Italian total, Italy produces more maize than any other country of Peninsular Europe except Yugoslavia. Though this same belt together with Emilia-Romagna is also a highly important wheat-growing area, it is relatively less important for this crop than for those others described above, more wheat — and all the hard wheat — being produced in the Peninsula and Sicily than in the Po Basin (Fig. 121).

MANUFACTURES

Industry plays a highly important and increasing role in the Italian economy. Over 70 per cent of the total exports by values consist of manufactured goods, though the receipts from these are largely offset by the cost of imported raw materials and fuels. What it all amounts to is that Italy, after providing the greater part of her own requirements of industrial products, is able, with the proceeds of exports of the balance, to purchase the necessary imports of raw materials and fuels with some margin to spare. The proportion of the active population engaged in industry, which in 1951 was 33·5 per cent compared with 42·5 per cent employed in agriculture, is considerably larger now.

The leading branches of industry are the heavy metallurgical together with shipbuilding and engineering of all kinds, cotton, woollen and other textiles, and the chemical group. All these, but for some exceptions in iron and steel manufactures, are located mainly in the North which, with its abundant supplies of hydro-electric power and facilities for trade both overland by the trans-Alpine railways and by sea through the ports of Genoa and Venice, is far more advanced in industry as well as in agriculture than the rest of the country. Here manufactures are more widely distributed than generally in North-Western and Central Europe where the coalfields have attracted industrial agglomerations; though there is one large constellation of

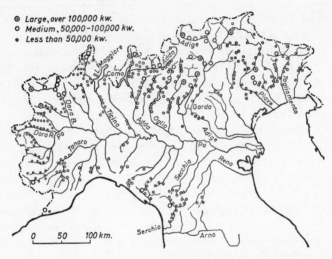

Fig. 124. Hydro-electric power stations in Northern Italy.

manufacturing towns in an elliptical area 120 by 50 miles of which Milan is the geographical centre (Fig. 125). It should be noted that the towns in this large group, together with those in the four smaller groups shown on the map, are only a selection of the more important ones that are associated with manufactures and commerce. Others, some quite large, which are mainly regional centres without special function, are naturally omitted. The concentration of population in urban knots, helped in a number of instances by the growth of industry, is an even more marked feature of the agriculturally rich northern plain than of the rest of Italy and the Mediterranean world in general.

In the metallurgical and engineering group the variety of products is extraordinary — from iron and steel and ocean-going ships to delicate precision instruments such as calculating machines. The varied forms of these manufactures and their distribution can be given only in broad outline.

The full-scale iron and steel works and likewise the larger shipbuilding yards are mainly on the Ligurian coast, where the bulky materials required can be assembled from foreign sources by sea, e.g., coal from the United States and iron ore from North Africa. The chief iron and steel works·are at Cornigliano (near Genoa) and Savona, and there are shipyards at Genoa, Savona and La Spezia, though some

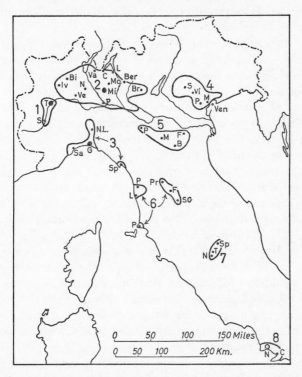

Fig. 125. The major industrial areas and centres in Italy. 1. *Piedmont*: Turin, Savigliano. 2. *Lombardy–Piedmont*: Biella (Bi), Ivrea, Novara, Vercelli (Ve), Varese (Va), Como, Lecco, Monza (Mo), Milan (Mi), Bergamo (Ber), Brescia (Br), Pavia. 3. *Liguria*: Genoa, Savona (Sa), Novo Ligure, La Spezia. 4. *Venezia*: Venice, Marghera–Mestre, Padua, Schio, Vicenza. 5. *Emilia*: Parma, Modena, Ferrara, Bologna. 6. *Tuscany*: Pisa, Leghorn, Piombino, Prato, Florence, S. Giovanni. 7. *Umbria*: Spoleto, Terni, Narni. 8. *Campania*: Naples, Castellamare.

smaller ones exist at Trieste, Monfalcone and Venice on the Adriatic coast. Some heavy metallurgical plants are in operation also at inland places, e.g. at Aosta, using local ores and electric smelting, and at Turin, Milan, Bergamo and Brescia, depending largely upon scrap imported from Germany and elsewhere. These and a few other minor centres in the North produce 70 to 80 per cent of the Italian output of about 7 million tons of crude steel. It is noteworthy that the total production of foundry iron is little more than 2 million tons — an indication of the marked dependence of the Italian steel industry upon domestic and imported scrap. Thanks to these supplies and to the increasing use of electric current in lieu of solid fuel, steel output more than doubled in the period 1951–9.

Of the widespread mechanical engineering industries two forms are outstanding — manufactures of motor vehicles of all kinds, and of lighter more intricate mechanical appliances, in both of which the Italians excel. The production of motor cars is dominated by Fiat and other firms at Turin, though some are produced also at Milan and Modena, while motor cycles are manufactured near Como and motor lorries at Brescia. The wide range of mechanical appliances includes such items as electrical apparatus, radio sets, sewing machines and typewriters, for the last two of which Olivettis of Ivrea are foremost.

Though the traditional textile group has not expanded recently on the same scale as the metal-working group — some branches in fact having suffered depression — it is still of great importance, including as it does manufactures of cottons, woollens, silks, artificial silks and linens. The largest branch is that of cottons where, however, unemployment has been greatest, partly owing to the competition of the rapidly expanding production of synthetic materials; and much the same has happened in the textiles using locally grown hemp and flax. The woollen manufactures are holding their own, though like the cotton textiles they depend primarily on imported raw materials.

These textile manufactures are distributed widely over the more or less continuous industrial belt which extends in an arc from Savigliano south of Turin to Padua near Venice (Fig. 125); cottons more especially in Piedmont and upper Lombardy, woollens also in upper Lombardy and east of the Adige in Venetia, and artificial fabrics in an area north-west of a line from Turin to Milan, i.e. in the upper section of the Plain where hydro-electric power is readily available. The Bologna-Parma group of towns south of the Po in Emilia has scarcely any share in the textile group, but has extensive manufactures of engineering products and chemicals especially of agricultural machinery and fertilisers, and highly important food-processing industries.[1]

[1] Especially flour-milling, cheese-making (Parmesan named after Parma) and processed meats (Bologna sausages — polony).

Leading Towns

In the succession of towns from end to end of the Plain and along the adjacent coasts three are outstanding in economic importance and population, Milan over $1\frac{1}{4}$ million inhabitants, Turin 730,000 and Genoa nearly 700,000. Next to these come Bologna and Venice, each with less than half the population of Genoa. Some others such as Savona, Verona and Trieste owe their rise primarily to transport connections (now largely lost by Trieste); yet others comprising an array of medium-sized towns, of which Padua, Brescia, Ferrara and Parma are the largest, owe as much to the development of manufactures for their importance as to their functions as agricultural market centres.

Milan is the undisputed commercial and industrial capital not only of the North, but of all Italy. It is the geographical centre of the fertile densely populated Lombardy Plain, highly developed in both agriculture and industry. It is moreover a focus of E.–W. routes across the upper Plain and the meeting place of the main trans-Alpine international railways through the St. Gotthard and Simplon-Lötschberg tunnels (Fig. 58), with direct connections to the port of Genoa by the Bocchetta Pass, and from that city, or via Parma, to Rome. In and around Milan almost all the manufactures referred to above are represented, many on a considerable scale, by reason of which and because of its transport connections it has become the leading financial centre of Italy.

Turin, at the confluence of the Dora Riparia with the Po in the uppermost section of the Plain, is obviously less favourably situated than Milan as a leading commercial centre; though it too is served by major traffic routes — by those running east along the Po Valley and south to the ports of Genoa and Savona, by the international railway across the Alps through the Mt. Cenis tunnel, and by the line up the Dora Baltea valley to beyond Aosta whence the new motor highways through tunnels under the Mt. Blanc Massif and the Great St. Bernard Pass (the former completed 1962) will give connections with Switzerland and the Rhine Valley (Fig. 126). Turin has specialised in manufactures of all kinds of transport equipment, not only of motor vehicles for which it is famous, but also of railway rolling stock, marine engines and aircraft.

Genoa is of course first and foremost a major port serving not only Piedmont and much of Lombardy, but also Switzerland and southern

Germany for their East-of-Suez and South Atlantic trade. It is in fact the great seaport terminal, the apex point of the four international trans-Alpine routes which converge on the industrial hub-region Milan-Turin. The Ligurian foundering (p. 359) has provided Genoa with a deep water harbour, but has at the same time caused it to be hemmed in by steep hills behind, so that it has been forced to expand

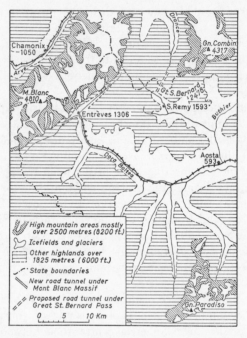

Fig. 126. The Val d'Aosta-Mont Blanc Alpine region: Communications. Heights in metres.

along the water front westward for a distance of ten miles. Some of the extensive storage accommodation and the larger industrial installations, e.g. shipyards, and iron and steel and chemical works, have been built on reclaimed land in the 'suburbs' of Cornigliano and Sestri Ponente. These industrial developments are the result of Genoa's large shipping and transport trade, in which it handles huge quantities of bulky imported materials, most conveniently processed in or near the port itself.

Savona, with only one-tenth of the population of Greater Genoa, is in many respects a small-scale replica of that city both as a port and in the development of similar forms of primary industry. Though Genoa is overcrowded, Savona is not likely to become a serious rival owing partly to its more limited hinterland, and partly to the great capital cost of extensions.[1]

Venice, unlike other ports on the delta coast, has preserved its facilities for shipping by river diversions and similar rectifications

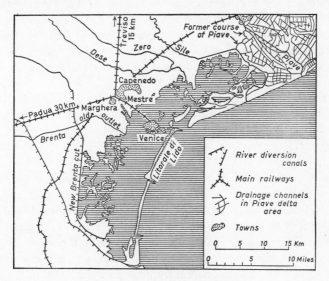

Fig. 127. The Venetian Lagoon area.
Note. Other less numerous drainage channels (not shown)
intersect the rest of the land area.

(Fig. 127). It depends in part on its tourist attractions, but more solidly upon its services as a port for the wide eastern part of the Plain, and for places farther afield by its connection through Verona and the Brenner Pass with the Upper Danube region. It has long been noted for its artistic glass-making industry,[2] and now has in its mainland offshoots of Mestre-Marghera iron-smelting, steel-manufacturing and chemical works.

With the conspicuous exceptions of Milan and Turin, Bologna (350,000) is much the largest of the inland towns, larger even than Venice. Its pre-eminence over its fellows on the Via Emilia is the

---

[1] 'To him that hath shall more be given' holds of ports and cities, as of persons, in respect of material things.

[2] For which Murano on a small nearby island has been famous.

outcome of several inter-related factors: its central situation in Emilia-Romagna and its functions as capital of that province; its nodal position in the railway system; and the development of a variety of manufactures helped recently by nearby deposits of natural gas. In Bologna the main-line railway from Venice meets the Via Emilia trunk system, and then branches off across the Apennines to Pistoia and Prato, continuing from the latter to Florence and Rome. The exploitation of the deposits of methane in the neighbourhood and in the Po delta (the richest hitherto discovered), already under way, will doubtless further benefit its already considerable manufacturing activities which include large railway workshops in addition to those directly connected with agriculture (See Fig. 119).

In the sitings of many of the towns in the northern lowlands five distinct alignments can be recognised: (I) on or near the *resorgive* line north of the Po, good examples being Vercelli, Novara, Milan and Vicenza; (II) at the exits of the Alpine valleys, e.g. Ivrea, Como, Bergamo and Verona; (III) along the Via Emilia where the Apennine slopes meet the Plain, e.g. Parma, Reggio, Modena and Bologna; (IV) on or near the Adriatic coast, namely Venice, Ravenna and Rimini; (V) on the banks of the Po where for understandable reasons there are only two important towns apart from Turin — Piacenza and Cremona. The majority of the noteworthy towns in the whole area are situated in the first two alignments, favoured by special geographical conditions which will be apparent from the preceding account.

Chapter 34

ITALY: III. PENINSULAR ITALY

THE line previously assigned as the southern limit of Northern Italy, that from La Spezia to Rimini, may be taken as the northern boundary of the Peninsula. In general structure this is the complete reverse of Northern Italy. Whereas the latter consists of a synclinal trough filled with the waste of the mountain systems that frame it, the latter is essentially an anticlinal uplift bordered for the most part by recently emerged lowlands covered in parts prior to or since emergence with deposits derived from the dorsal range.

THE APENNINES

The Apennines, the master structural element of the Peninsula, average four to five thousand feet in height; yet they are far from being entirely negative either for human settlement or as a barrier to communications. Though the elevated limestone plateaux and heavily eroded steeper Tertiary slopes are of little use, numerous longitudinal and some transverse depressions separate the block upthrusts of the post-Tertiary re-elevation; and these, situated in the mountainous zone of fairly generous precipitation, escape the disadvantage of insufficient supplies of ground water common enough in the populated parts of the southern half of Italy. The most striking of the depressions are the Pleistocene lake basins (Fig. 128), now commonly followed by the major rivers, the Arno, the Tiber and its tributary the Salto, and the Garigliano in their upper courses. With the gradual infilling of the lakes, marshes and peat bogs were formed, long avoided by men who kept to the higher and more wholesome margins. Many of them have been drained for settlement, at least in parts, fertile lands being scarce in Italy in proportion to the population.

Throughout the central Apennines the principal rivers commonly flow through the longitudinal valleys in their extended upper courses before breaking through the outer ranges to reach the coasts. Notable examples are the Tiber itself and its tributaries the Salto and the Chiana, the two headstreams of the Garigliano and also of the Volturno, and the upper Sele River. Even the Arno, which has a long transverse main course, repeats this pattern above Florence. All these rivers drain west into the Tyrrhenian Sea; only one Adriatic river, the Pescara, has a lengthy upper course, the others being comparatively short consequent streams.

Fig. 128. The Pleistocene lake basins of the Apennines. After R. Amalgiá and O. Maull.

The drainage pattern is a direct response to the build of the Apennines, in which the dorsal nearly continuous range and consequently the main watershed lie well to the east as far south as the Volturno River, giving a relatively steep fall and a narrow coastal lowland on the Adriatic side. In the western Sub-Apennine zone block upthrusts predominate, hence the somewhat chaotic relief and trellis drainage pattern, especially in Umbria and eastern Tuscany. These structural features of the Apennines and their consequential drainage present two advantages: the more broken relief on the western side open to the rain-bearing westerly winds enables them to penetrate well into the mountain valleys; and the larger western rivers fed by the considerable run-off in their long upper courses can be used to generate hydro-electric power in places (see below p. 457). Even if the interior longitudinal valley floors have been damp and unwholesome in places, the adjoining hillsides have been cultivated from Roman times, and historic towns arose at intervals generally on defensive sites, some of which, e.g. Perugia, Terni, have by now grown to considerable size; others, particularly Assisi, are noted more for their historical associations than for modern developments.

Though the continuous range of the northern and central Apennines presents difficulties for railway construction, and with the exception of the trunk lines Florence-Bologna is crossed only by minor single-track railways, farther south where the mountains become lower and broken by gaps here and there, several lines thread their ways through from Naples and Salerno, to the Apulian towns. Numerous roads, on the other hand, not only penetrate the recesses of the Apennine zone, but boldly cross over to the Adriatic coast. Several of these follow more or less the same routes as those built by the Romans over 2,000 years ago, notably those of the Via Flaminia up the Tiber Valley, of the Viae Salaria and Claudia Valeria eastwards from Rome, and of the Via Latina-Appia through Capua to Tarentum and Brundisium.

The Apennines provide only modest supplies of hydro-electric power compared with the Alps. The chief stations are on the Serchio River north of the Arno in Tuscany, on the Salto-Nera tributaries of the Tiber, on the Liri headstream of the Garigliano, and also on the Neto and Moccone Rivers in Calabria which have lakes in their upper courses. The overall output is restricted by the summer drought which becomes more prolonged towards the south, necessitating the creation of large storage reservoirs (in the absence of natural ones). An outstanding example is that on the Salto, 5 miles in length and averaging a mile in width, the supplies of current available there being used in the large steel works at Terni.

For ages past the central Apennines in Marche, Abruzzi and Molise have been used as summer pastures for transhumant sheep from Latium (Lazio) and Campania as well as from the semi-arid southeast region. The practice was associated in particular with the large estates (latifondi) traditionally common in those parts of the Peninsula; but there may be less of it from now on following the break-up of a number of the estates for closer settlement, and also the provision of waters for irrigation and the watering of live-stock in the southeast.

CALABRIA

Near the administrative boundary of Calabria (which crosses the Monte Pollino) the Apennines change distinctly in character; the NW.–SE. series of mainly folded ranges of the body of Italy give way, but for the Catena Costera, to a succession of crystalline horsts separated by transverse depressions and lowland embayments. In order from north to south these are the granitic Sila Grande and Sila Piccola between 5,000 and 6,000 feet in their highest points; the Serre Massif of lower elevation, also granitic, and the schistose Aspromonte, which again rises to nearly 6,000 feet. The block upthrusts have been accompanied by downward displacements in the form of rift valleys, e.g. the Crati trench west of Sila Grande and the Straits of Messina. In this greatly disturbed area continued crustal instability causes frequent and sometimes destructive earthquakes.

The Tertiary deposits which once apparently covered the crystalline rocks having been removed, the erosion surfaces now exposed consist of undulating plateaux with projecting heights similar to those of Dartmoor in Devon. On them numerous radial rivers rise and plunge down the steep slopes carrying with them masses of debris. Only two or three of the larger ones such as those mentioned above, which are fairly regular in flow, have been utilised for the development of hydro-electric power.

Though some forests of beech, chestnuts and Corsican pines remain on the upper slopes, widespread deforestation through the centuries has led to serious erosion and the piling of waste on the lower valley tracts — the more so because of the torrential winter flow of the rivers and streams often dry in summer — to the detriment of agriculture which, in the absence of minerals and of any considerable manufactures, must be the mainstay of the population numbering $2\frac{1}{2}$ millions and still increasing above the average rate. But except in the Tertiary country east of the Silas, agricultural production is hardly likely to expand; the available lands on the Crati depression, round the margin of the horsts and up the mountain sides, are fully occupied, and the marked summer drought sets limits to more intensive utilisation.

The prevailing forms of land use are typically southern: the extensive cultivation of cereals, mainly autumn-sown wheat; plantations of fruit trees and the like, especially of olives, vines and citrus fruits; small-scale mixed tillage including horticulture; and the production of food crops for the peasant occupiers' requirements. The chief commercial crops are citrus fruits, the distribution of which is shown in Fig. 123 (inset), next to which come olives, grown widely on the lower slopes of the massifs, and then tomatoes. Except for the latifondi that remain after sub-division in the land reform in the country east of the Silas, most of the land under cultivation is worked by small peasant farmers, in scattered groups owing to the broken physical build of the peninsula. Towns are few and generally small; the largest are Catanzaro and Reggio, the latter having grown as the chief port and food-processing and fruit-packing centre.

Calabria is often quoted as an over-populated region, as it certainly is by North-West European standards of living, now that the traditional relief to overcrowding by emigration overseas has diminished. The establishment of manufactures which, but for some textiles at Reggio, are poorly developed, may well expand under Government encouragement with the help of hydro-electric power supplies now available. At all events Italian authorities are hopeful rather than pessimistic about the prospects for the future.

THE EASTERN COASTLANDS

Of the three types of recently uplifted formations of the mainland outer Apennine zone (p. 432), the coastal strips north and south of the Gargano peninsula and the lower Apennine slopes and valleys, composed of mingled marine and alluvial deposits, are unusually productive and fully cultivated. Thanks to their fertility the whole coast and foreland belt carries a fairly dense population, in spite of the relative poverty of the karstic limestone platforms and of the sub-arid trough, hitherto domains of latifondi.

Though the rainfall is marginal throughout, it can be supplemented on the coastal strip north of Gargano by waters from the numerous Apennine rivers, and in the Apulian coastland by supplies from springs issuing from the Murge limestone, as well as by those now available from the Apennines via the Apulian aqueduct (Fig. 117). The climatic conditions are well suited to the cultivation of vines (for wine), olives and wheat, especially the hard macaroni variety, all of which this Adriatic coastal belt produces in considerable quantities.

Both the limestone platforms and the Pre-Murge trough have remained till recently comparatively backward areas given largely to extensive pastoralism, because of their unattractive features, notably their insufficient and unreliable rainfall and extremes of temperature, as well as their physical characteristics previously noted (p. 432).

Whether the projects of closer settlement now under way in selected parts will prove successful seems to depend very much on the provision of adequate supplies of irrigation waters. So far the whole area has given rise to only one considerable inland town, namely Foggia, and that mainly as a railway and agricultural market centre.

The general regularity of the coasts here as elsewhere on the recently elevated lowland shores of Italy renders it necessary to create partly artificial harbours as at Ancona and Bari where headlands are helpful in providing shelter for shipping. Brindisi and Taranto are exceptional in being situated on land-locked bays, but Brindisi has lost some of its former importance for express transit traffic between North-Western Europe and the Levant and the East, with the development of air services. Taranto, besides being a naval base, has become in fact the chief port of south-east Italy, its hinterland covering the whole Peninsula south of Naples for trade with countries lying to the east.

THE WESTERN HILL AND VALLEY ZONE

The western coastal region between the Apennines and the Tyrrhenian Sea is of particular interest in its physical build and land forms as well as in its past and present human importance. Covering rather more than one-sixth of the area of the whole country it contains nearly 12 million out of the total 50 million inhabitants and two of the three greatest cities.

The distinctive relief forms consist for the greater part of Tertiary hills and valleys and volcanic extrusions of recent age which repeat in their general alignment the NW.–SE. Apennine trend; but they include also some outcrops of Mesozoic rocks which appear as ridges here and there, as in the Permo-Triassic Alpi Apuane north of the Arno and the Cretaceous limestone Monti Lepini south of the Tiber. All these uplifted relief forms together with the interspersed valleys, depressions and coastal flats combine to give the whole region extremely varied, but nowhere greatly elevated topography, except in the outliers of the Pre-Pliocene Apennines east and south of Naples.

In the general Quaternary re-elevation of the Peninsula various subsidiary chains, e.g., the Chianti and the Volterra Hills, were uplifted. These, forming the series known as the Anti-Apennines, were at first separated by arms of the sea which with subsequent infilling and further general elevation became lagoons and were finally converted into alluvial depressions, such as the Val de Chiana for example.

Along the coast, on the other hand, the former islands appear as isolated summits rising out of the recent deposits or as promontories, e.g., Piombino and Monte Argentario. In the volcanic areas either side of the lower Tiber and south to beyond the Sorrento Peninsula the Apennine trend again appears following the line of the old volcanoes and fissures, and as the ashes, tuffs and lavas are readily attacked by the agents of erosion and are much dissected by rivers and streams, here also there is a considerable variety of relief.

This volcanic belt is simply one of the manifestations of crustal instability associated with the recent uplift of the Apennines and of subsidence in the Tyrrhenian area. The major activity which produced the extensive sheets of ejecta dotted with old craters and crater lakes has left aftermaths in the still active Vesuvius and the thermal gas vents in Tuscany (p. 438). The former is locally destructive at intervals, the latter have been exploited to useful purpose. Beyond Naples the volcanic belt turns sharply south following the Calabrian alignment, to reappear in the Lipari Islands, where Stromboli and Vulcano are still active, and thence into eastern Sicily.

Another manifestation of crustal instability and continued adjustments is the occurrence of earthquakes. Some associated with the spasmodic outbursts of Vesuvius are mostly local. The more serious majority are the results of deep-seated disturbances in the central and southern Apennines and their continuation into Sicily, where they are often intense and sometimes destructive. Fortunately for the west coast region north of Naples, whatever shocks occur there are for the most part only light.

Having a generally sufficient rainfall, a mild climate and no high mountains, this Tyrrhenian belt can for the most part be utilised for one form or another of agriculture, arboriculture or animal husbandry, though a large proportion of it is hilly and the overall yields are not at all high. Such as it is, the most is made of it. The three provinces, Tuscany, Latium (Lazio) and Campania contain nearly a quarter of all the sheep in Italy and produce almost one-fifth of the wheat and over one-sixth of the wine, but much smaller proportions of the maize and olive oil.

The whole region is overwhelmingly agricultural, but with marked concentrations in the more fertile districts, especially the basins and valleys of the Arno and its tributaries round Florence, the Alban Hills and the neighbouring districts south-east of Rome, and the Campania coastland, notably the Phlegraean Fields west of Naples. The most productive parts are the leading wheat and wine-producing areas shown in Figs. 122 and 123. The least attractive have been the swampy coastal flats of the Tuscan Maremma and the Pontine Marshes and of a few inland depressions, e.g., the Val de Chiana, all of which, however, have been drained, or are being gradually drained for settlement. Yet despite these improvements and the generally intensive agricultural utilisation, this region cannot provide from its own resources enough produce for its population numbering nearly a quarter of the total in the country.

MINERALS AND MANUFACTURES

The west coast region including Elba Island has been a little better endowed with minerals used in industry than the rest of youthful Peninsular Italy; at all events, in the past, when iron and other metals were exploited first by the Etruscans and then by the Romans, their metal-using arts having been in fact one of the tokens of their advancement in civilisation.

Whatever deposits of iron and non-ferrous metal ores (copper, lead, zinc) formerly existed, mainly in Tuscany — meagre enough compared with those elsewhere in the world — they have been depleted after more than two millennia of exploitation; and all that is of any real importance now on the mainland is the mercury associated with igneous intrusions in the volcanic area of Mt. Amiata. The Colline Metallifere, a source of various metals in the past, now produce nothing much except a little iron ore, of which the old rocks of Elba contribute the greater part of the present Italian production amounting to about 650,000 tons (metal equivalent); the rest is mined almost entirely in Sardinia and Val d'Aosta.

On the other hand, the whole region is rich in limestones suitable for building purposes and cement manufacture, and Tuscany in particular in the ornamental altered forms of the calcium group — marbles in the Alpi Apuane and alabaster near Volterra.[1] The abundance of these materials in Western Italy, together with the heritage of the Greek arts of shaping them, gave rise to the great architectural achievements of Rome in her prime — a tradition that has lasted till the present day.

These mineral resources constitute only a slender base for modern

---

[1] The Alpi Apuane marbles, including the white statuary marbles of Carrara, are metamorphosed Triassic limestones. Alabaster is a solid translucent form of gypsum, a hydrated sulphate of lime.

forms of industry, and the region is not much better endowed with fuel and power resources. The Apennine rivers provide comparatively small supplies of hydro-electricity, and some moreover is used on the spot in the mountain zone as at Terni. The production of lignite in various small fields in the upper Valdarno (Fig. 114) forms only a trifling contribution to the power requirements; and but for the thermal generation of electricity from gas vents in the Lardarello district (p. 438) there are as yet no other significant sources of energy, so that industry in general, and especially the iron and steel works, have to rely largely on imported fuels.

Four leading centres of industry can be distinguished within the region: those of the upper and the lower Arno Valley, that of the Piombino-Fallonica district opposite Elba, and a fourth, a highly important one, round the shores of the Gulf of Naples (Fig. 125). The first is dominated by Florence which has added to its traditional craft industries of metal work and glassware and woollen manufactures the modern forms producing chemicals (e.g. fertilisers) and electrical machinery. Some 20 kilometres to the north-west on the main line to Bologna lies Prato which has long-established woollen manufactures, and about 35 kilometres up the Arno Valley is S. Giovanni where there are steel works. Pistoia at the exit of another trans-Apennine railway, which specialises in cotton textiles, may be regarded as an outlier of the Florentine nucleus.

Of the two leading towns on or near the coast in the Arno Valley, Leghorn has quite outdistanced Pisa in population and economic importance.[1] Leghorn on its artificial harbour is now a major port, and has besides developed a whole range of modern port industries such as engineering, shipbuilding, oil-refining and chemical works, whereas Pisa as a focus of railways and an important market town has specialised in those connected with agriculture.

The third industrial district is a distinctly modern creation in the form of large iron and steel works at Piombino (on the south side of the headland) and at Fallonica, which get supplies of ore from Elba nearby, and use imported fuel.

Naples, together with the almost continuously built-up waterfront on either side extending 40 kilometres from Castellamare on the south to beyond Pozzuoli in the west and containing more than $1\frac{1}{2}$ million inhabitants, engages in almost every type of industry now that

[1] See pp. 383 for the rise of Leghorn and the eclipse of Pisa in the 16th century. Pisa is now 6 miles inland.

Northern firms have established branch factories there. Among the older manufactures are soap and chemical works, textiles, especially of jute, general engineering and shipbuilding (at Castellamare); among the newer are manufactures of machine parts and of radio and electrical equipment, and also more especially of iron and steel in the large modern full-scale plant at Bagnoli. In the constellation of small outlying towns of the densely populated suburban districts to the north of the city, the processing of food products, especially of tomatoes for export, is the leading industry.

Towns, Mainly Tourist Centres

The western hill and valley region is one of the richest in the world for historic towns and stone-work monuments, paintings and similar works of art, the legacies of gifted people of the past. Because of this cultural heritage and the pleasant climate, the region attracts streams of tourists from all over the Western World, whose disbursements help to redress Italy's adverse balance of ordinary import and export trade. A number of the places mentioned above as being engaged in manufactures are far more interesting on account of their historical associations, remains of the past, and art treasures. Among such towns are Florence, Pistoia, and Pisa; and Naples, itself the centre of a district full of Roman associations as at Capua, Capri and Pompeii.

Some other towns, notably Siena and Arezzo in Tuscany and Viterbo in Latium, which owe their continued existence to their functions as agricultural market centres, contain reminders of their distinction as cultural centres in the past, or of the historical events associated with them.

Rome is in a class by itself among the cities of Western Europe. Apart from its printing and fashion trades and the making of certain artistic products (mainly for tourists) it has few industries other than those which serve local requirements. Yet its population of one and three-quarter millions exceeds that of its rival, Milan, by half a million.

It owes much to its situation at a focus of natural routeways midway in the Peninsula; and that it has long been the largest city in the Mediterranean lands has been fostered by three related historical developments: the growth of the highly centralised Roman Empire with Rome as the nucleus; the establishment there of the headquarters of Western Christendom, and the choice of the city as the capital of United Italy.

Although the Roman Empire has passed long since, its tradition has persisted and in a measure been assumed by the Catholic Church, which has made Rome, in spite of vicissitudes, the spiritual home and administrative centre of a leading religion of the Western World. This and the status of Rome as the capital of United Italy have combined to make the city a great administrative centre, which because of its traditions and associations and its architectural remains also attracts immense numbers of visitors, those from abroad alone being estimated at half a million per annum. It is these special functions, the main sources of income for the people of Rome, that distinguish it from other large cities.

The mainly accretionary Tyrrhenian coast of Italy, like the Adriatic coast, has few good natural harbours. Even Naples and Salerno, situated in places where promontories provide some shelter for shipping, have had to build elaborate breakwaters. Both Rome and the Arno valley region are served by almost entirely artificial ports — the former by Civitavecchia some 40 miles to the north-west, and the latter by Leghorn mentioned above — owing to the constant silting of the mouths of the Tiber and the Arno.

Chapter 35

THE ITALIAN ISLANDS AND CORSICA

SICILY

SICILY, named after its primitive inhabitants the Sicani, and also known as Trinacrium by the ancients because of its triangular shape, is essentially a recently severed western extension of the Apennine system, with the mountainous zone in the north flanked on the south by the Tertiary rocks of the uplifted outer Apennine arc (Fig. 114). The Sicilian Apennines are a composite and somewhat broken series, hardly to be called a range, of three geologically diverse sections: the crystalline Peloritani Mountains similar in structure to the Aspromonte horst; the Nebrodi Mountains composed in the main of early Tertiary sandstones and conglomerates; and the upthrust blocks of Triassic and Jurassic limestones south and west of Palermo (known under various local names) which are separated by depressions composed of soft Quaternary beds partly eroded away by the sea as in the wide Castellamare Gulf.

The succession of dissected residual blocks of this Sicilian Apennine zone, three to five thousand feet in elevation, forms the main watershed but for the Torti and one or two other northern rivers east of Palermo that rise well inland. From this watershed short streams, torrential in winter and more or less dry in summer, flow into the Tyrrhenian Sea, and some longer ones such as the Salso from the Nebrodi Mountains and the Simeto from the Peloritani Mountains find their ways across the Tertiary plateau south or south-east. The remaining rivers are mostly short and seasonally fluctuating in volume, and neither they nor for that matter those just mentioned are of much use either for the development of hydro-electric power or for irrigation without the construction of large storage reservoirs.

The Tertiary beds of the southern dip slope, raised several thousand feet in the general Post-Pliocene uplift, now form a much dissected plateau cut by rivers and streams into broad valleys, ridges and ravined slopes. These weak Tertiary sands, clays and calcareous beds are interrupted in the west by a projecting area of Triassic limestones and in the east by the Lauro volcanics of the Iblei Mountains and the massive outpourings of the still active Mt. Etna. Thus in general Sicily is composed of frayed upland and dissected mountain formations, often ending in cliffs along the shores, which leave few comparatively small coastal plains, of which the largest and most productive are the Catania 'bay' between Etna and the Lauro volcanics, the Palermo Conca d'Oro, and the south-west Marsala coastland.

As seen in the rainfall map (Fig. 116), the only considerable parts of the island that receive at all generous precipitation are the northeastern mountains including Etna; the marginal amounts elsewhere are attenuated by the marked summer drought and the visitations of the scorching sirocco, hence the relatively high proportions of lands defined as arid or sub-arid. Unfortunately too, the run-off is generally rapid owing to the common occurrence of impermeable clays, and, as noted above, large-scale irrigation is hardly feasible.

Yet the majority of the 5 million people of Sicily depend on agriculture and derived industries for their livelihood. The mineral deposits — sulphur in the Caltanisetta area and petroleum in the south-east between Ragusa and Gela — the products of which are mostly exported to the mainland industrial centres, do not add much to the resources of the Sicilians either directly or indirectly. True, there is a considerable tourist industry, but this is concentrated mainly in a limited area in the east where Mt. Etna and the remains of Greek and Roman civilisations are features of interest. Altogether the means of livelihood are rather scanty for supporting at a reasonable standard the mainly agricultural population, averaging 550 per sq. mile in density, in a land where barren mountains and ravined hillsides occupy fully a quarter of the total area.

The chief crops are cereals, mostly hard wheat, citrus fruits, grapes for wine and the characteristic dry zone types, olives and almonds, the three latter being often grown on terraced slopes. The leading areas of production of most of these are indicated in Figs. 122 and 123 (Inset).

Since early Roman times, wheat has been grown, as a rule, by extensive prairie-like cultivation on large holdings; Sicily was one of Rome's main sources of this cereal. At the present time nearly $1\frac{3}{4}$ million acres are given to wheat, much more than in any mainland province, but the average yield of about 12 bushels per acre is low by West European standards — an expression of none too favourable soil and climatic conditions.

Citrus fruits, of which Sicily is a major producer, especially of lemons, are confined mainly to areas where some additional supplies of water are available either from rivers and streams or from springs on the margins of the limestone platforms, that is to say, mainly in the east round Mt. Etna and the Nebrodi and Iblei Mountains, and in the Palermo district. Grape-vines are widely cultivated as a terrace crop, but with special concentration in the Trapani-Marsala area in the west, noted for its strong wine. Olives and almonds are also widely grown, mostly on hill-sides as means of utilising land unsuitable for other crops. Huerta cultivation (market-gardening) is practised wherever fertile alluvial tracts or plots are to be found, all along the north and east coasts from Palermo to Syracuse, where the heavier rainfall, the early arrival of spring weather, the numerous mountain streams and ready access to ports for shipment of the perishable produce are favourable conditions.

For a mainly agricultural region, Sicily has now as from early times an unusual concentration of population in urban centres. The three largest, Palermo, Catania and Messina, with populations of half a million, over 300,000, and 230,000 respectively, are all ports serving the districts of most intensive land use and largest export trade. Of the other considerable towns three, namely Caltanisetta, Enna and Ragusa, are inland market centres; and the rest including Syracuse, Trapani and Marsala are, like the three largest towns, also ports. Sicily has a fairly large import and export trade, chiefly with mainland Italy and North-Western Europe.

As a coveted strategic base controlling the passages between the Western and the Eastern Mediterannean, Sicily has had a troubled history under its successive foreign rulers since its golden age from A.D. 850 to 1250, the period of its control by the enlightened Arabs and Normans. When it was incorporated in United Italy in 1860 it was in a sorry state from which it has not yet properly recovered. Over-population of lands of impoverished fertility has led to poverty, to provide remedies for which the authorities of the more prosperous mainland have only quite recently concerned themselves. The best hopes, apart from irrigation works, seem to lie in training schemes for skills in industry, and in the active development of manufactures of which there are as yet few except in Palermo.

SARDINIA

Sardinia differs in its structural framework from Peninsular Italy and Sicily; together with Corsica it is a land apart, in which Hercy-

nian elements trending NNW.–SSE. dominate the build and relief
forms (Fig. 129). Almost the whole eastern half of Sardinia and the
western two-thirds of Corsica are composed of granites and schistose

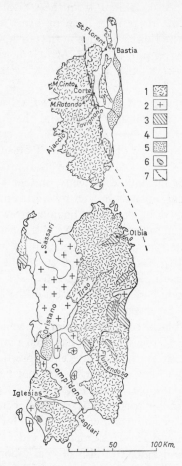

Fig. 129. The structural elements of Sardinia and Corsica (generalised).
1. Granites, schists etc. 2. Volcanic rocks. 3. Mesozoic limestones.
4. Tertiary beds (in Sardinia), Triassic to Eocene (in Corsica). 5. Alluvial
marsh (partly drained). 6. Carbonia coalfield. 7. Major fault line.

crystalline rocks, bounded on the east in Corsica by a fracture line
which continues as a down-throw into the Tyrrhenian Sea off the
north-east coast of Sardinia. These crystalline massifs in both islands
have been tilted downwards to the west from their uplifted eastern

tectonic boundaries, and in Sardinia have been subjected to considerable fracturing and vertical displacements in the past, which account for the scattered basins and cappings of Mesozoic limestones from Olbia southwards. Also resulting from these displacements, sections of the old crystalline rocks have been upthrust as blocks rising to over 4,000 feet in the Limbara Ridge in the north, and to well above 6,000 feet in the central core, in M. Gennargentu, where the Flumendosa and several other rivers rise and form a radial drainage pattern.

Along a line running roughly north from Cagliari, the massif dips beneath the extensive volcanic sheets and the Mesozoic and later deposits of the central depression, but similar crystalline rocks reappear in the south-west in the Iglesiente Plateau, and again in the north-west in the Nurra Peninsula and its continuation in Asinara Island. The larger crystalline plateaux present typical peneplaned landscapes of rolling uplands broken by worn upthrusts and jagged residual projections of harder rocks, boulder-strewn slopes (a feature of the Gallura region in the north-east) and trenched river valleys. Of the original Mediterranean forest vegetation, at lower elevations on these uplands, much has gone leaving steppe-like expanses with a broken cover of heath plants and coarse herbage. Though there are patches of cultivation here and there, most of the land is used simply as rough pasturage for sheep and goats.[1]

The Iglesiente block, composed mainly of schists uplifted with a distinct NW.–SE. Hercynian trend, has been rent by an E.–W. depression floored with Tertiary and Recent deposits, which is followed by the eastward-flowing Cixerri River. The northern section exceeds 5,000 feet in its highest part, and the southern 3,000 feet. This south-western region is of importance to Italy both for its intrusive mineral deposits of lead, zinc and iron pyrites and also for the Tertiary coalfield in the Carbonia Basin. It is in fact, the chief source in the whole country of lead and zinc, and also of coal (about a million tons), although this is not of smelter quality and is used mainly for the generation of electricity. The granite and early Palaeozoic rocks of the Nurra Peninsula in the north-west also contain some lead and zinc ores, but apart from these minerals this remote corner is of no economic importance.

The medial depression was covered by the sea prior to slight uplift

[1] Sardinia contains nearly a third of the 8¼ million sheep in all Italy, and almost a quarter of the goats.

and to infilling in the northern parts with volcanic materials, and in the Sassari Basin and in the Campidano with waste derived from erosion of the uplands — a process still in progress in the lagoon-swamp areas west of Cagliari and south of Oristano. The lavas and tuffs are covered largely with macchia and garigue and are of little use except as winter quarters for sheep brought down from the uplands. The Sassari depression with a cover of Tertiary and Quaternary beds is moderately fertile and is noted for its extensive olive plantations. Of greater agricultural value, however, are the Campidano and the adjoining eastern Tertiary slopes known as the Sarcidano. The most potentially productive sections here are the formerly swampy alluvial areas; one bordering the Gulf of Oristano is now systematically drained, and the other is a similar belt in the south round the Cagliari lagoon. Between these alluvial tracts extends the rolling Tertiary plain, now used extensively for mechanised wheat cultivation.

In recent years ambitious projects have been taken in hand to regulate the Tirso and the Flumendosa and some of their main tributaries for the threefold purposes of flood control and of providing supplies of water for irrigation and for the generation of hydro-electric power. The authorities, provided with funds from the Central Government, have been taking steps to rehabilitate the backward economy of the island, hitherto dominated by a rather primitive form of pastoralism. They are using all the means that may promote the cultivation of crops suited to the marked Mediterranean climate of the lowlands where the rainfall is none too plentiful (Cagliari 16·6 ins.) — especially hard wheat, grape-vines, olives, and delta crops such as rice on the reclaimed lands.

The total population, barely $1\frac{1}{2}$ million, is less than a third of that of Sicily which is only a slightly larger island. The relatively low density of about 150 per sq. mile is a natural reflection of the large proportion of the island which is more or less waste land and has scarcely any permanent inhabitants. As is to be expected, most of the Sardinians are concentrated on the Campidano and Sassari depressions and in the mineralised section of Iglesiente. Cagliari, the capital, is the largest town; yet, although its population has nearly doubled since 1931, it still has less than one-tenth of that of Milan. Oristano, at the northwest end of the Campidano corridor, is also a growing town, but is smaller than Sassari, the second largest centre of population, and than Carbonia in the south-west which has grown remarkably in recent years. One other town, namely Olbia on a ria inlet in the north-east, has some importance as a 'packet station', linked by railway with Oristano and Cagliari, and with Naples by shipping services.

ELBA

Separated from the Tuscan mainland by the narrow Piombino Strait five miles wide, the island of Elba has importance out of all proportion to its size owing to its deposits of iron ore. First worked by the Etruscans and then by the Romans, both using wood charcoal as smelting fuel, these deposits have throughout been the leading domestic source of the metal for the people of Italy.

The island consists of three distinct parts separated by narrow necks of low elevation, corresponding probably to fracture zones; a rise of 70 metres in the sea-level would divide Elba into three islands. The easternmost section is composed of granite, schists and Palaeozoic rocks which contain the deposits of ore, the middle one of Eocene sandstones and calcareous rocks, and the westernmost simply of the granite dome of Monte Capanne which rises to 3,300 feet.

On a sheltered harbour of the northern coast lies Portoferraio which, as the name indicates, is the port for shipments of iron ore to the mainland. Smelting works have been in operation at Portoferraio for some time past, but these have become inefficient compared with the modern full-scale plants at Piombino, Fallonica and Bagnoli which now take most of the ore (p. 463). For the rest as the build of Elba does not lend itself much to agriculture, the majority of the islanders are settled round the indented coasts where fishing is their main source of livelihood.

CORSICA

The similar geological history and the close structural affinities of the French island of Corsica with Sardinia noted above (pp. 468–70), makes its treatment more appropriate here than as an appendage to the survey of France in Part I; more especially so, because the two islands were joined as one until a geologically recent time and also because the physical geography of Corsica is of greater interest than its human geography.

The large western section of the island (Fig. 129), composed mainly of granites, was uplifted to heights averaging well over 6,000 feet in the east. There, owing to headward erosion by the rivers flowing down the fracture slope, notably the several headstreams of the Tavignano and the Golo, the main watershed has receded to the line of the surviving highest points, M. Cinto and M. Rotondo, both exceeding 8,500 feet. From this summit ridge the western rivers, fed with the abundant precipitation of between 50 and 60 inches per annum, tumble down their deeply cut valleys into ria-type inlets separated by the promontories of the residual ribs of the massif.

This whole granitic region, of dissected broken relief in the west and of bleak plateaux inland covered with snow in winter, is clearly of little use for agriculture except for alluvial patches in the lower sections of the valleys and for summer pastures above the tree line; and the original forests of evergreen and cork oaks and chestnuts and of Corsican and umbrella pines (at higher elevations) have been sadly depleted after ages of cutting without replanting by the succession of alien rulers. As in other parts of the Mediterranean regions, the deforested lands have become commonly covered with scrub and maquis, especially the *macchia* characteristic of Corsica comprising various aromatic plants.

East of the main fracture line Alpine structures predominate; though here, too, there are upthrusts of ancient crystalline rocks, mainly schists and gabbro, the longitudinal depressions between which are floored with later sedimentary rocks in parts, while the coastland south of Bastia is covered with recent deposits and alluvium. This eastern and north-eastern region accounts for most of the limited cultivation in Corsica — on less than 2 per cent of the total area, thus necessitating substantial supplementary imports of food products. The Corsicans, in fact, are not an agricultural people in the ordinary sense, nor are they interested in fishing; their economy is based on a traditional simple form of pastoralism in which sheep and goats constitute most of the live-stock.

The population of Corsica, numbering about 275,000 in all, is mainly of mixed Italian stock speaking an old Italian dialect. These people have in the past kept much to themselves in the inland parts away from the coasts where the various foreign rulers have established themselves. The last people to occupy the island for an extended period before the French, were the Genoese, who after 400 years of unpopular domination sold the islands to France in 1760. In spite of their Italian affinities, the Corsicans have shown no serious desire to disassociate themselves from France, of which Corsica is one of the Departments.

The low average density of population, about 80 per sq. mile, is understandable in view of the mountainous build and generally infertile nature of the soils of the island. At the present time fully one-third of all the inhabitants live in three ports, Ajaccio the capital, Bastia and St. Florent, which derive some support from a considerable tourist traffic. The only inland centre of population of any size is Corte, on the railway connecting Bastia and St. Florent with Ajaccio, via a col below 1,200 metres south of M. Rotondo.

BIBLIOGRAPHY

MUCH informative material in book form is available on the physical, the human, the general economic and the regional geography of North-Western and Central Europe and the separate countries that compose it. For up-to-date information on the changing scene this book material is supplemented by the numerous articles and notes scattered throughout later numbers of periodical journals, and by the data contained in official and semi-official statistical publications. The following selection of reference books including some specialised works in French and German, and summary lists of periodical publications may give some guidance for further study.

Note. The dates given below for some of the works are for 2nd or later available editions.

NORTH-WESTERN AND CENTRAL EUROPE

I. GENERAL WORKS

The Human Geography of Western Europe, H. G. Fleure, 1918.
The Peoples of Europe, H. G. Fleure, 1922.
Principles of Human Geography, P. Vidal de la Blanche, compiled by E. de Martonne, 1926.
Race in Europe, Julian Huxley, 1939.
L'Homme et le Sol, Henri Plat, 1949.
An Historical Geography of Europe, W. G. East, 1950.
London Essays in Geography, L. D. Stamp and S. W. Woolridge (Editors), 1951.
A Geography of Europe, G. W. Hoffmann (Editor), 1953.
Europe and the Mediterranean. N. J. G. Pounds, 1953.
Les Migrations des Peuples, Max Sorre, 1955.
Europe and its Borderlands, A. G. Ogilvie, 1957.

II. THE PHYSICAL FRAMEWORK, MINERALS

The Geological Growth of Europe, Grenville Cole, first published 1914.
The Quaternary Ice Age, W. B. Wright, 1937.
Das Eiszeitalter, P. Woldstedt, 1954.
The Earth Beneath us, A. Swinnerton, 1955.
Das Relief der Erde, Vol. I, *Europe and Asia*, F. Machatschek, 1955.
The Quaternary Era, J. K. Charlesworth, 1957.

Welt Atlas. Die Staaten der Erde und Ihre Wirtschaft, 1957. [Especially useful on Central Europe.]

The Geography of Iron and Steel, N. J. G. Pounds, 1959.

III. CLIMATE, VEGETATION, AGRICULTURE

The Geography of Plants, M. E. Hardy, 1920.

Plant and Animal Geography, M. I. Newbigin. Completed by H. J. Fleure and others, 1936.

The Agricultural Geography of Europe and the Near East, U.S. Dept. of Agriculture, 1948.

The Climates of the Continents, W. G. Kendrew, 4th edition, 1953.

Climatology, A. A. Miller, 8th edition, 1953.

Everyday Meteorology, A. A. Miller and M. Parry, 1958.

IV. THE BRITISH ISLES

The Physiographical Evolution of Great Britain, L. J. Wills, 1929.

Great Britain: Essays in Regional Geography, A. G. Ogilvie (Editor), 1930.

The British Isles, L. D. Stamp and S. H. Beaver, 1933 and later editions.

An Economic Geography of Great Britain, Wilfred Smith, 1949.

Britain's Structure and Scenery, L. D. Stamp, 1946.

The Coalfields of Great Britain, Sir Arthur Trueman (Editor), 1954.

The English Climate, C. E. P. Brooks, 1954.

Ireland, T. W. Freeman, 1960.

Wales. A Physical, Historical and Regional Geography, E. G. Bowen (Editor), 1957.

The Siting of British Steelworks, British Iron and Steel Federation, 1958.

The World's Iron Ore Supplies, British Iron and Steel Federation, 1959.

V. FRANCE AND THE LOW COUNTRIES

Les Régions Géographiques de la France, E. de Martonne, 1924. English translation from latest edition by H. C. Brentnall, 1949.

La Personalité Géographique de la France, P. Vidal de la Blanche, 1941.

The Netherlands, B. Landheer (Editor), United Nations series, 1944.

La Répartition de la Population sur le Territoire Belge, C. Mertens, 1947.

The Belgian Kempenland, F. J. Monkhouse, 1949.

Physical Planning in the Netherlands, Netherlands Government Information Service, 1955.

Géographie Universelle Larousse, Vol. I, 1958. [Contains some useful details of French manufactures.]

La Sidérugie Française, Roger Biard, 1958.

La Région du Nord et du Nord-Est, R. Nistri and C. Prêcheur, 1959.

Western Europe (France and the Low Countries), F. J. Monkhouse, 1959.

VI. CENTRAL EUROPE

Swiss Life and Landscape, Emil Egli. English translation by Paul Elek, 1949.
The Regions of Germany, R. E. Dickinson, 1945.
Switzerland: a democratic way of life, A. Siegfried. English translation by Edward Fitzgerald, 1950.
The Ruhr. A Study in Historical and Economic Geography, N. J. G. Pounds, 1952.
Germany, R. E. Dickinson, 1953.
Switzerland, Foder's Modern Guides, 1955. [Contains good accounts of manufactures.]
Czechoslovakia: a geographical and historical study, H. G. Wanklyn (Mrs. J. A. Steers), 1954.
Ökonomische Geographie der Tschechoslovakischen Republik, M. Blazek, German translation by H. Langer, Berlin, 1959. [Contains useful maps and accounts of industrial distributions]

VII. SCANDINAVIA AND NORTH ATLANTIC

The Baltic Region, E. G. Woods, 1932.
Industry in Norway, Norges Industriforbund, 1951.
Swedish Agriculture, H. Oswald and others, Swedish Institute, 1951.
Industries of Norway, O. J. Adamson, 1952.
Farming in Finland, W. R. Mead, 1953.
Atlas over Sverige (Swedish Atlas), 1953–6.
The Economic Geography of the Scandinavian States and Finland, W. R. Mead, 1958.
Background to Sweden, T. Heywood, 1950. [Especially useful on forests and forestry.]
The Scandinavian World, A. C. O'Dell, 1957.
World Sea Fisheries, R. Morgan, 1956.
The Open Sea, Vol. II, *Fish and Fisheries*, Sir Alister Hardy, 1959.

THE WESTERN MEDITERRANEAN

GENERAL WORKS

An Historical Geography of Europe, W. G. East, 1935 and later editions.
The Mediterranean, A. Siegfried. English translation by D. Hemming, 1948.
Southern Europe, M. Newbigin, 3rd edition revised, 1949.
Géographie Universelle, Vol. VII, *La Méditerranée*, 1934.

IBERIA

Le Portugal, P. Birot, 1950.
Géográfia de España y Portugal, Vols. I and II, *Land forms, climate and vegetation*, L. Solé, Sibaris, 1955, Vol. V, *Portugal*, O. Ribeiro, 1955.

Atlas Medio Universal de España, Aguilar, 1956.
Spain. A Geographical Background, W. B. Fisher and H. Bowen-Jones, 1958.
The Individuality of Portugal, D. Stanislawski, 1959.

ITALY

Handbuch der Geographischen Wissenschaft. Italien, H. Kanter, 1935.
Atlante fisico-economico d'Italia, G. Danielli, 1940.
A Geography of Italy, D. S. Walker, 1958.
L'Italia, 2 Vols, R. Amalgiá, 1959.

For Iberia the several volumes of the *Géográfia de España y Portugal* and for Italy R. Amalgiá's monumental work *L'Italia* are exceptionally authoritative and comprehensive and reasonably up to date.

JOURNALS AND PERIODICALS

The Times Review of Industry.
The Economist (weekly publication).
Transactions of the Institute of British Geographers.
Geography.
     These four contain numerous original articles and notes on current developments in industry and agriculture.

The Geographical Journal.
The Geographical Review.
Annales de Géographie.
Petermann's Geographische Mitteilungen.
Annals of the Association of American Geographers.
United Nations Commission for Europe, *Economic Surveys.*
Board of Trade, *Overseas Economic Surveys.*
     Very informative on all aspects of economic activity, though the statistical matter is more or less back-dated.
     France 1953; Belgium and Luxembourg 1953; Netherlands 1949; Switzerland 1954; Denmark 1955; Norway 1949; Sweden 1953; Finland 1952.

OFFICIAL AND SEMI-OFFICIAL MAINLY STATISTICAL REPORTS

The Statesman's Year-Book, S. H. Steinberg (Editor), published annually by Macmillan & Co. Ltd.
United Nations, *Annual Statistical Abstract; Demographic Yearbook; Statistical Annual of Food and Agricultural Organisation.*
U.K. Statistical Abstract; Statistical Digest of Ministry of Power; Agricultural Statistics (Ministry of Agriculture and Fisheries).

Statistisches Jahrbuch der Bundesrepublik Deutschland. [Includes some international statistics as well as West German.]

Statistisches Jahrbuch der Schweiz.

Annuaire Statistique de la France.

High Authority of European Coal and Steel Community. (C.E.C.A.). Reports and Statistics.

British National Coal Board. Statistical Publications (and Maps).

British Iron and Steel Federation. Statistical Reports.

These last two series include some comparative European statistics.

INDEX

Cross references are commonly given, so that passages in the text relating to particular places, features or topics can the more readily be found from one or another of the entries. In a number of instances where several page references appear, the more important of these is in heavy type. A few conventional abbreviations are used, e.g. mt(s). for mountains, penins. for peninsula and (n) following page number for footnote.

PRINTED IN GREAT BRITAIN
BY ROBERT MACLEHOSE AND CO. LTD
THE UNIVERSITY PRESS, GLASGOW